BENEATH A CRESCENT MOON

AN OTTOMAN EMPIRE NOVEL

MARK MACEDONIA

BENEATH A CRESCENT MOON

AN OTTOMAN EMPIRE NOVEL

MARK MACEDONIA

CHRISTOPHER MATTHEWS PUBLISHING

Beneath a Crescent Moon, *An Ottoman Empire Novel*
by Mark Macedonia

Copyright © 2022 by Mark Macedonia
All rights reserved
First Edition © 2023

Published by

Christopher Matthews Publishing
an imprint of First Steps Publishing (Oregon)
FirstStepsPublishing.com

Interior formatting, cover design by Suzanne Parrott
Cover Art, *"Beneath A Crescent Moon,"* @ davrab / Fiverr.com

Library of Congress Control Number: 2022917013
Historical Fiction | Ottoman Empire | Middle Eastern fiction
Suleyman the Magnificent | action adventure | war & military | romance

ISBN: 978-1-945146-55-8 (hb)
       978-1-944072-74-2 (pb)
       978-1-944072-75-9 (epub)

10 9 8 7 6 5 4 3 2 1

Printed in the
United States of America.

DEDICATION

To the thousands of high school students
that I've had the pleasure to teach for over three
decades, whose energy and enthusiasm
fueled my passion for imparting history,
while inspiring my writing.

To my wonderful wife, Sandy,
who continues to inspire me
with her love.

the OTTOMAN EMPIRE
from 1453 - 1566 A.D.

TRANSYLVANIA

MOLDAVIA

WALLACHIA

Belgrade

Black Sea

OTTOMAN

Constantinople
(Istanbul)

EMPIRE

Manisa

Izmir

ANATOLIA

Adana

Sicily

Crete

Rhodes

Cyprus

Mediterranean Sea

Jerusalem

Cairo

LIBYA

EGYPT

Nile River

■ Ottoman Empire, 1453
■ Ottoman gains, 1481
▨ Ottoman gains, 1521
▤ Ottoman gains, 1566

0   250   500   750 Kilometers

0   250   500 Miles

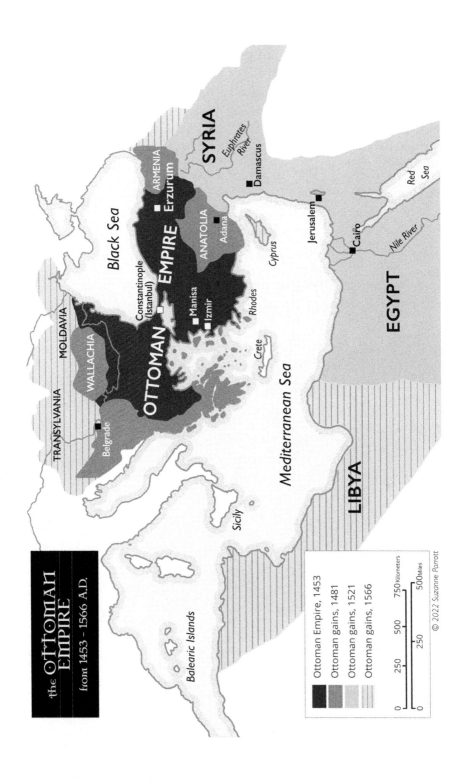

the **OTTOMAN EMPIRE**
from 1453 - 1566 A.D.

Black Sea

MOLDAVIA

TRANSYLVANIA

WALLACHIA

Belgrade

Constantinople
(Istanbul)

OTTOMAN EMPIRE

Manisa
Izmir

ANATOLIA

Adana

ARMENIA
Erzurum

SYRIA

Euphrates
River

Damascus

Jerusalem

Cairo

Nile River

Red
Sea

EGYPT

Cyprus

Rhodes

Crete

Mediterranean Sea

LIBYA

Sicily

Balearic Islands

Ottoman Empire, 1453
Ottoman gains, 1481
Ottoman gains, 1521
Ottoman gains, 1566

0   250   500   750 Kilometers
0   250   500 Miles

© 2022 Suzanne Parrott

"Thou shouldst not have been old
till thou hadst been wise."
–William Shakespeare, *King Lear*

PROLOGUE

Within the 16th century of the Common Era, Europe was a continent in search of an identity—a quest with its beginning forged three centuries earlier, launching the phenomenon that became known as the European Renaissance. This extraordinary event reawakened an interest in the classical period of ancient Greece and Rome, transforming medieval Europe into a society eager to explore a means toward reclaiming ownership of eminence bygone.

The most dramatic revolution of the century erupted within the area of religion after Martin Luther, a German Catholic monk, challenged the power and traditions of the Catholic Church with accusations of corruption and his proclamation of *justification by faith*. As the most powerful and influential institution within Western Europe, the Catholic Church was rattled to the core by the *Protestant Reformation*—a splintering of Catholicism that afforded monarchs and their subjects a choice of which Christian Denomination they deemed held the true path toward salvation. This contemplative road was paved with much bloodshed, evidenced by an eruption of battles between European Christians beginning as early as the third decade of the century, spawning a period of crisis that culminated in a restructuring of the religious, as well as the political map of the continent.

Despite the explosion of Christian conflicts raging across the continent, coupled with the prospect of further instability as England and France strive to compete on a level with Spain economically and militarily, the more pressing concern for the fate of Europe in the 16th century loomed in the southeastern corner of the continent. Supported by a population of Turkish peoples inhabiting the Anatolian Peninsula, the Islamic empire of the Ottomans had been on the warpath. With a capitol based in the former Byzantine capitol of Constantinople, which the Turks often referred to informally as Istanbul, the banners of the Ottoman sultanate—symbolized by a white crescent moon and a white five-pointed star—had already been unfurled over territory on three continents. The domain of their impressive empire included the Balkan peninsula in southeastern Europe which had been given the name *Rumelia* by the Turks, persuading the Ottoman sultan—known to the Europeans as *Suleyman the Magnificent*—to set his sights on penetrating deeper into European territory.

It is here where the story begins, as Suleyman has led his impressive war machine of over one hundred thousand men—composed of archers, artillery, cavalry, infantry, and the fabled elite troops known as the *Janissary corps*—to the outskirts of Vienna, Austria, in the autumn of 1529. Defending the Austrian capitol against the mighty Ottoman force would prove to be a formidable task, presenting the realistic possibility that before the onset of winter, the surviving population of Vienna could very well awaken as Ottoman subjects *beneath a crescent moon . . .*

CHAPTER ONE

Vienna, Austria – October 14, 1529

It had already been a very wet autumn, and although the elderly Nicholas Graf von Salm had seen more than his share of cold, rainy days over the course of seven decades, he welcomed the inclement weather slowing the Ottoman assault on the city he protected. But on this day, the German commander was greatly unnerved by a two-day cessation in the rainfall. He pondered the change in the weather, while strolling inside the twenty-foot high stone wall near to the Carinthian Gate—one of four main entrances located within the wall encircling the Austrian capitol. Carrying his silver helmet with its long, pointed tail, he stepped boldly with erect posture and confident demeanor, trying hard to mask his concern while in the presence of one of the Austrian militia officers.

"It seems the Ottoman cannon fire has stopped?" the young militia leader noted, keeping pace with the surprisingly robust von Salm.

Von Salm pulled on his ragged, hoary beard. "Only temporarily I'm afraid, for it is midday and time for their Saracen prayers. I believe that before too long the heathens will be at it again, trying to weaken the city's wall."

The two men scattered a brood of chickens as they walked, while dodging Austrian men of all shapes and sizes moving to and fro with wheelbarrows full of cobblestone.

Von Salm paused beneath the overhanging eaves of a small home built near the wall. "Fortunately, the Turks seem to have only the use of their smaller cannon—weapons designed to shoot at men and not at walls." He cupped his bare hands to his mouth, blowing into his palms. "It grows colder." He viewed the dark gray clouds forming overhead. "Such cold temperatures are unusual for this time of year. We may see snow today."

"Where have the Ottomans placed their larger cannon?" the militia officer asked.

"Nowhere," von Salm replied. "Captured Turks who have been put to the question have revealed how the wet weather has transformed the main dirt roads into quagmires, delaying and perhaps even preventing Suleyman from moving his larger, heavier siege cannons closer to Vienna. The Lord has blessed our city with its location." He adjusted the brigandine he wore made of leather lined with oblong plates of steel fastened to the fabric, protecting his midsection from the neck to the waistline. "I'm sure all Viennese know the story of how almost three hundred years ago the Mongols rode from out of the east to lay siege to Europe, quickly conquering all the peoples east of the Danube, before preparing to lay waste to Vienna."

The officer hesitated with his response. "I can remember my grandfather telling such a story, but I was very young."

Von Salm took a deep breath, slightly disappointed by the officer's historical deficiency, before resuming his steps. "Vienna was on the front line of the Mongol onslaught, for were the city to fall, the Asian brutes may have expanded their empire westward to the Atlantic coastline. Suddenly, the demon horde retreated upon learning of the death of their Khan Ogodei. Mongol custom decreed all must return to Mongolia for the funeral of a khan. The great distance between Ulaanbaatar and Vienna discouraged the Mongols from ever again returning to Central Europe, and Vienna was spared. We find ourselves in a similar situation today."

"Vienna was fortunate then," the officer said. "But Constantinople is much closer to Vienna than to Ulaanbaatar."

"Yes—but Suleyman relies greatly on his heavy artillery," von Salm replied. "And it takes time to move such equipment this far north over dry roads let alone wet ones, especially when his objective must be met before the onset of winter. If the Lord gives us a late wet spring, as well as a wet autumn, the sultan has fewer days in which to move his army. The fact that the Ottoman siege of Vienna has now dragged on for weeks is only by the grace of God. We owe our good fortune to the Lord's provision of rainfall. Without it, I fear the city would have fallen."

The men stopped to inspect the Carinthian Gate towering before them, permitting the militia officer to examine his boots, prying one foot at a time from the grasp of thick mud. "According to your orders, the men are tearing up the cobblestone streets inside the city."

"The absence of stone roads is certainly a nuisance with this weather," von Salm remarked. "But digging up the roads will prevent the cannon balls passing over the wall from exploding upon impact against the stone streets. Now their deadly barrage will sink harmlessly into the mud."

The officer frowned beneath his thin black mustache. "I must admit, it angers me to know how one can see the sultan's tent from the spire of St. Stephen's, while Ferdinand has run off to hide in Bohemia."

"It is not for us to question the actions of a king," von Salm said. "In all my many years of military service, I have never fought a battle for the preservation of a king. Rather it has been for the preservation of a kingdom."

"What kingdom?" the officer mocked. "Vienna has been reduced to a military camp with thousands of foreign soldiers. This city of twenty thousand now numbers barely four hundred of the original inhabitants, who—like me—have not fled. Are we fools?"

"You are still breathing, is it not true?" von Salm replied. "Who would have thought our small numbers could have lasted this long against an army of over one hundred thousand? God is with us, my friend." He gazed upon the large gateway now sealed with bricks, set several rods from where they stood. "The Turks failed to gain entrance at the Schotten Gate to the north of the city four days ago. Since the bulk of their army is encamped to the southwest of the city, I suspect here, at the Carinthian Gate will be their next target. Give me your report."

"The larders are restocked and the wells refilled. The villages outside of the city wall have been destroyed to prevent the Turks from using the structures for cover. We have sealed all four main city gates with brick, and have completed the construction of earthen bastions at intervals along the wall. The bastions will provide each tercio opportunity to use their arquebuses effectively against the Turks."

"Yes, the Spanish musketeers and their long guns were instrumental in our success at repelling the Ottoman assault on Monday."

"At least the Emperor Charles has not abandoned us by sending his Spanish troops for assistance, while his brother hides," the officer groaned.

Von Salm frowned, deciding to offer an opinion on the sore subject. "Ferdinand is a puppet of his brother Charles. Vienna's fight is Charles' fight. Were it not for Spain's war with France, I believe Charles would have been here with us. And now with Hungary's betrayal by forming an alliance with the devil

Suleyman, and many dissenters growing restless across the Holy Roman Empire persuaded by Luther's heresy, Charles cannot afford to lose Austria. Now, what else?"

"The Turks continue to dig from their position in an effort to detonate explosives beneath the city's wall. In response, our men have launched surprise attacks beyond the wall, to disrupt the Ottoman sappers in their attempt at tunnel building," the officer described. "We are using their own tunnels against them with hit and run strikes, having much success. However, it has been very dangerous for our men. Thus, our side is not without its share of losses as well."

"Such brave men have we in our ranks," von Salm said. "Aside from the Spanish musketeers, who are here in Vienna on loan from Charles, and the German pike men—the landsknecht— whose desire to fight has its roots in obtaining wine, women, and wages, the Viennese are not a professional army, but rather composed of peasant farmers and craftsmen fighting for their very existence!" He paused before turning to look the officer in the eyes. "And yet, our resilience continues to frustrate the Turks!"

"Maybe the silence of Ottoman cannon is a sign that Suleyman has given up the fight?" the officer guessed. "He boasted about having breakfast inside of St. Stephen's Cathedral by Monday last, and today it is Thursday. Perhaps he realizes that capturing Vienna is not worth the great loss of life his army has endured?"

"I wish it were true," von Salm replied. "However, I sense the sultan is a man void of compassion. I'm guessing right now he is probably seething at the message I sent him, in response to his boast about breakfast."

"What was your reply?"

"Your breakfast is getting cold." Von Salm flashed a wide grin, before gazing up in the distance at the spire of St. Stephen's from its position rising above the center of the city, dwarfed only by the majestic snow-capped Alps.

The officer returned the grin. "Why do you think they waste cannon fire against our wall with their smaller cannon?"

"I'm not sure," von Salm said. "Perhaps it is to soften us before the next attack."

They directed their attention to a group of five men crossing the street some distance before them, whose identity as landsknechts was unmistakable; for they were dressed in flamboyant garb of vivid colors, feathered wide-brimmed hats, and boastful codpieces.

The militia officer stared at them with a snobbish gaze, before turning toward von Salm. "Their clothing expresses contempt for our way of life."

"Yes, their manners are coarse. But they can fight," von Salm replied. "How is Vienna paying for their services?"

"We've been forced to melt down gold objects from within the church."

"The Lord certainly works in mysterious ways."

Suddenly, a few rods from where they stood, a woman stepped from out of her home located near to the wall, shaking a cowbell violently. Immediately, von Salm and the officer rushed to her doorway.

"What it is, Frau Steiner?" von Salm asked, instinctively bringing his right hand to the handle of the sword sheathed at his side.

"It is the basin of water you instructed us to keep watch over in our cellar!" she replied. "My sons have reported the water . . . the water—it moves!"

Both men rushed past the woman and inside the small dwelling, easily locating the door to the cellar. Hurriedly, they descended a wooden staircase until arriving in the small, cold, damp, subterranean room dimly lit by a few candles. Two boys stood in the far side of the room standing beside a basin of water set near the outer wall. The boys stared at the basin with the devoutness of pilgrims, only breaking from their hypnotic gaze in turning toward the stairs upon the arrival of von Salm and the officer—both men pacing briskly toward them without saying a word. At the circular basin, all four focused on the container of liquid, waiting only momentarily, before witnessing the appearance of ripples upon the surface of the water.

"They're digging!" von Salm exclaimed. "We must sound the alarm! They're digging beneath the Carinthian Gate!"

Quickly emerging from the cellar, both men began to shout as they rushed into the street. Soon a chorus of voices relayed the distress call, until the bells of St. Stephen's began to clang, chasing multitudes of men—young and old—from out of their homes and into the streets of Vienna, charging in the direction of all four main gates.

Within moments at the Carinthian Gate, scores of men having become accustomed to the routine arrived carrying picks and spades. Sternly, von Salm directed a group to enter the Steiner home, ordering them to begin digging through the outer cellar wall. He directed a second group to dig outside of the house, in the city street near to the Carinthian Gate.

From off in the distance, the sound of crashing cymbals, pounding drums, and blaring horns could be heard originating from within the Ottoman ranks. Suddenly, as if the curtain had been raised on the final act of a play, the characters began to assemble in preparation of another assault on the battle-worn Austrian capitol.

Behind the wall that protected the city, the tercios took formation hustling into placement on the bastions constructed near the four gates. These infantry units, composed of Spanish musketeers clad in short-stuffed breeches and padded doublets, moved systematically into position, easily identified by the turtle-shaped helmets fashioned with flat brim and crest extending from front to back. Each musketeer fell into rows carrying his arquebus—the impressive long barreled firearm that had become the unit's trademark.

As the Spanish musketeers assembled into position, countless numbers of German landsknecht, carrying their fourteen-foot spear-tipped pikes, scurried up wooden ladders placed against the city wall. Dressed in ruff doublets beneath leather jerkins of vivid bright colors, the mercenaries wore open-faced bowl-shaped helmets with metallic neck collars, and carried straight, broad, flat swords, sheathed at their belts.

From their vantage point atop the wall, the landsknecht and cannoneers could see how weeks of the Ottoman presence in the countryside had transformed the landscape. With a feverish work ethic reminiscent of an ant colony, thousands of Ottoman troops had labored incessantly at moving closer to the city, converting both the fallow and green fields beyond the capitol into a myriad of trenches running parallel to the city wall, like church pews set before an altar. Hidden within these trenches, Ottoman sappers worked steadily with spades and picks to burrow beneath the earth in the direction of Vienna; while positioned at the edge of the forest just beyond those earthworks dug farthest from the city, appeared a great many Ottoman soldiers.

"They are advancing!" cried out several cannoneers.

Despite the anticipated hell and fury that was certain to be unleashed by the Ottoman war machine, and the wave of hysteria the sight of its movement generated, not lost among the defenders of Vienna was the poignant beauty on display with the Ottoman approach. Advancing toward each of Vienna's four main gates, thousands of the sultan's elite infantry—the Janissary corps—marched in quick-step time, carrying their matchlock arquebuses pressed against their right shoulders, with its barrel pointed to the sky. Their ranks were interspersed with men dressed in brightly colored woolen *dolama* coats of red, blue, or green, punctuated by a *bork*—elongated headgear composed of red felt rising to a twelve-inch fold, featuring a gold-plated spoon on its front, before forming a twenty-four-inch tail falling at the back. The colorful military procession gradually blanketed the terrain, as if a vivid tapestry was being spread outside the city's wall. Situated well behind the advancing army were the *sipahis*—Janissary cavalry remaining stationary, waiting patiently for the order to charge at the moment the infantry might breach the gates.

Suddenly, staggered bursts from Ottoman artillery, fired from the nearly three hundred cannons interspersed among the sipahis, peppered the city's wall with cannon balls from every direction. In response, the cannoneers atop the wall returned the artillery fire, although their cannon numbered less than one third of the Ottoman total. Soon it became apparent that because of the great size of the city, the weapons had been dispersed too far apart from one another to be effective.

It wasn't long before the Ottoman troops reached the first trenches farthest from the wall, resulting in the cessation of the music, bringing an abrupt halt to the orderly Janissary march. Spreading like autumn leaves shuffled by the wind, the elite corps broke ranks and hurried into positions within the trenches.

Behind the city's wall near to the Carinthian Gate, von Salm expressed more concern with the digging than with the Ottoman advance. Returning inside the Steiner home, he rejoined the first team of diggers within the cellar, and with a fretful glare set beneath a face crisscrossed with lines of age, he waited patiently for news from within the sizable hole that had been unearthed through the cellar wall. He didn't have to wait very long.

"We've found it!" cried out a muffled voice from inside the hole. Soon the perspiring, dirty face of a digger appeared from out of the opening. "There's a tunnel here, but no charges!" the man described, breathing heavily. "We found it just in time, as I saw the back of one of those devilish sappers running away from me down the tunnel like a frightened rat!"

Von Salm breathed a sigh of relief, before quickly finding his way out of the cellar, approaching the second team of diggers. "Anything?" he inquired of the group.

"We found a tunnel!" revealed one of the men.

"A second tunnel?" von Salm repeated with surprise. "The sultan plays his final hand today! Have you found any charges?"

"None as of yet! We are still searching! There appears to be a large chamber just beyond the tunnel! It's as if they have been digging in this location for some time!"

The commander's lips parted and his eyelids grew wider. "The tunnel in the cellar is a diversion!" von Salm yelled. "We need buckets of water here quickly! The black powder will be in this tunnel beneath the gate! We must work fast to find the charges and douse them with water before they can be lit!"

Suddenly, with a deafening roar, from beneath the Carinthian Gate the earth exploded into a maelstrom of fire thrown upward among chunks of soil and stone sent airborne. Instantly the gate and portions of the wall on either side crumbled into a pile of debris, consuming a dozen cannoneers and landsknecht who had been placed on top of the wall, while burying many of the diggers below it. Von Salm was among those buried beneath the bricks, until a group of men pulled him from underneath the rubble, finding him breathing, but unconscious. As Ottoman cannon balls rained down around them, the men carried von Salm's broken body off to St. Stephen's Church; for it was evident by his condition that they had nothing in which to treat his mortal injuries, save an attempt at the power of prayer.

CHAPTER TWO

The sight of the ninety-foot breach in the wall where the Carinthian Gate had stood only moments before, produced a wave of euphoria that rippled through the lines of the battle weary Janissary. Months of campaigning, which involved a repetitive routine of marching, setting camp, and fighting, made more troublesome by a topography converted into a watery obstacle course by a seemingly endless deluge of rain, had taken its toll on the Ottoman army. Now the sudden appearance of the breach was viewed as a sign from heaven that the siege of Vienna was coming to a close. Infused by the sudden turn of events, in unison—without an order given—Janissary troops found the surge of energy to burst out from under the cover of the trenches. Leaving their arquebuses behind, they unsheathed their curved swords, holding them to the sky, and rushed the opening with a maddening cry.

Despite the confusion ensuing as a result of the explosion at the gate, the tercio held its position steadfast on the bastion nearest the breach, forming two lines facing the trenches. At the sight of scores of Janissaries charging toward them, the first line of musketeers, with arquebuses cocked and loaded, blew on the end of their slow burning match cords, before setting the fuse within the serpentine. They braced their weapon's stock against their right shoulder, and aimed its barrel in the direction of the charging Janissaries. When given the order to fire, the Spaniards pulled the trigger of their weapons, and in a cloud of smoke unleashed a barrage of balls that cut down many of the brave Ottoman troops. Quickly, the first line of musketeers stepped behind the second line and worked at the tedious task of reloading their arquebuses. Still, Janissaries who had survived the first line of firing surged forward, emboldened by the return gunfire from those men remaining in the trenches, only to be met by a second deadly volley of musket fire from the second line of the tercio. Once again, scores of Janissaries fell where they were hit; however, by now the remaining corps had moved within only a few rods of the breach. Their close proximity to the bastion rendered the Spanish arquebuses ineffective because of the time it took to reload the weapons, forcing the musketeers in resorting to close combat, using their firearms as clubs.

As expert swordsmen, the Janissaries held the upper hand against the musketeers; however, if the breach in the Vienna wall had been viewed as a sign from heaven for the sultan's elite troops, the sudden appearance of great numbers of landsknecht filling in the breach appeared as demons from hell. The swift arrival of the pike men caught the Janissaries by surprise, and the charging Ottoman troops found themselves virtually running into the landsknecht's spear-tipped pikes, which inflicted mortal stab wounds on those Janissaries who were not immediately impaled.

The fighting at the Carinthian Gate lasted for two hours before the exhausted Janissaries decided to abandon the siege at the breach without a command to do so. As does a contagious disease, the defiant action swept quickly throughout the Janissary *ortas*—the Ottoman battalions which were engaged in separate battles with the city's defenders at locations all around the outside of the city wall. The rumor of retreat dispirited the battle-weary troops, while confusing the orta's *corbacis*—these commanding officers suddenly finding themselves amid a whirlwind of disorganization. The engagement's ensuing chaos resulted in an asymmetrical withdrawal, resembling the remnants of a retreating wave after breaking violently against the shoreline.

Suddenly, the heavens opened, unleashing a heavy snowfall that converted the theater of war into a sea of white. The victorious defenders immediately viewed the flurries as a sign that the Lord consecrated the battlefield, while the fleeing Ottoman ranks interpreted the changing weather conditions as frozen tears from Allah.

Janissary troops stationed to the north of Vienna were members of the last ortas to get word of the retreat at the Carinthian Gate, and upon hearing of it, scattered like a swarm of bees taking flight from a fallen hive. Moving away from Vienna, thousands of men dotted the footholds of the Alps near to the capitol, haphazardly trudging through the blinding flurries and freshly fallen snow.

With their heads drooped as they marched straight into a cold, blustering wind, two of the Janissary lost sight of a group of fellow corps members. They raised their heads to find how together they were following the snowy footprints of a lone man who moved briskly, several rods ahead of them. Their trek brought them from off the open battlefield into a thick forest of tall spruce trees, which the snowfall had converted into a wilderness land-scape encased in white.

"Parshan, your match cord is still lit!" one soldier alerted the other, speaking in Turkish.

Both men stopped so that the soldier could remove the arquebus slung over his shoulder, quickly locating the slowly burning cord. Pinching the end of it, he extinguished the fuse, before reaching down to rub his fingers in the cold, wet snow. "Damn this wretched weather!"

The other Janissary turned, staring straight ahead through the maze of spruce and lofty oaks with trunks rising majestically to great heights above them. He watched as the stocky, short man whom they followed continued to move farther ahead of them.

Parshan returned the arquebus to his shoulder. "Haris, why doesn't he stop?"

Haris shrugged his shoulders. "Does he know the way back to camp? Who is this man, and why do we follow him?"

"He is filthy, covered with dirt. I think he's a sapper," Parshan guessed. "When the corps scattered, I looked up to see him ahead of us. He moves with confidence, so I assumed he knew the way back to camp."

"He moves quickly, but not with confidence," Haris said. "Didn't you notice how he keeps turning around to gauge our progress as though he is trying to place distance between us and him? Look how far away he is now!"

"Hey there!" Parshan yelled out. "Do you know where you are going?" He waited for the figure to turn around, but the man ignored him. "Perhaps he's deaf from working so close to the explosives in the mines!"

"He was certainly an ugly one," Haris described, before resuming his pace through the forest, crunching the virgin snow beneath his feet. "There is a large scar on the left side of his face running from the corner of his eye to below his lower lip."

Parshan scoffed. "Perhaps it's an indication that he failed at sword play? It would explain why he ended up a sapper, forced to dig in those underground deathtraps!"

"I think he may be deserting! Shall we go after him?"

"No, Haris. Let him go," Parshan said. "If he is deserting, the Austrians or Germans will probably capture him. When they pull his breeches down to find his cock has been cut as our faith requires, they will realize he is not one of their own and hang him!"

Haris halted his advance. "I'm sure he moves in the opposite direction of our camp. Something is not right."

Parshan stopped, exhibiting a heavy sigh. "This is my first experience with defeat. I did not think it to be possible!"

"What? Did you think the Janissaries to be invincible?" Haris asked.

"Yes—yes I did! I heard no call to retreat! Why did our orta fall back from the siege?"

"Our troops failed at the Carinthian Gate, and took it upon themselves to retreat. There were no orders given from anyone in command—not the corbacis, not the *yeniceri agasi*, or even the *serasker*!"

"Those commanders take their orders directly from the sultan!" Parshan proclaimed. "The Janissaries—all of us—have failed our leader!"

"Save your breath, Parshan." Haris continued onward, negotiating the trunks of trees, while treading through the rapid accumulation of snow. "We have not failed the sultan or his commanders! If anything, they have failed us! This siege has gone on long enough! The foul weather has destroyed the willpower of the troops! Months of marching in torrential rain, through flooded plains, and over muddy terrain has brought illness, starvation, and much death to our corps! And now we have this bone chilling cold and snow to deal with! Without the large cannon, the siege was doomed from the beginning!"

Parshan followed close behind. "What you say is dangerous!"

"The sultan is better off with his Janissaries alive, would you not agree?" Haris pressed. "We are the heart and soul of his army! The sultan will forgive us! His power depends on us, and we are of no use to him if we are dead!"

Suddenly, an explosion echoed throughout the forest, and

Haris watched as Parshan collapsed face down into the snow. Instinctively, he took cover behind a massive tree trunk. "Parshan! Parshan!" he called to his companion, but the fallen Janissary did not move. It was then that Haris noticed a growing stain of blood begin to saturate the snow near to Parshan's head.

Pressing his back firmly against the tree trunk, Haris took a deep breath and pulled the arquebus from off of his shoulder. *I have no fire to ignite the cord! How many of the enemy can there be? Am I surrounded? Has the shooter reloaded his arquebus? I need to force him to shoot again to determine his location! It may give me time to attack while he reloads!* Haris grabbed his arquebus and flung the firearm high into the air. The movement of the weapon broke the branches of saplings, resulting in a second shot being fired in the direction of the flying arquebus. *The shot came from behind me, from out of the north!* Haris had made his decision and unsheathed his curved sword, bursting out from behind the tree. With his hand holding the sword pointed to the sky, he ran blindly in serpentine fashion, scanning the terrain for any movement. Suddenly, another shot rang out and Haris stopped in his tracks, falling backward onto the snow covered forest floor.

Minutes passed as Haris lie motionless, while snowflakes gradually began to blanket him. Finally, two landsknechts emerged slowly from behind trees, each carrying their own arquebus. Without uttering a word, one of the Germans paced directly toward Haris, while the other proceeded in the direction of Parshan. "Be careful!" called out a third landsknecht, appearing from behind a clump of trees where the shots had originated. He remained stationary along with a fourth man who poked his head out from behind a fallen tree trunk.

"This one looks to be dead!" the landsknecht nearest to Parshan called out.

"And the other?" one of the men who lingered in the distance inquired.

The second landsknecht stepped up to Haris, whose body remained motionless on its back with eyes shut. "This one's skin is as white as the snow that buries him!"

The other man rolled Parshan's body over on its back. "As is this one! Poor, wretched souls! They are the lost ones—Christian boys from the land of the Greeks who have been kidnapped, enslaved, and placed under the demonic spell of the Turks! By killing them, we have freed them! God is left to judge them now!"

The landsknecht standing over the body of Haris grinned. "Well, if God is busy judging them, then no one will mind if I take this fine looking sword. The blade will fit nicely above the mantel of my hearth." He bent over to pry the handle from within Haris' grasp. Suddenly, Haris opened his eyes, bringing his hand out from beneath his thigh, clutching a curved dagger. Before the landsknecht could respond, Haris slashed his blade at the man with the speed of a striking serpent, slitting his throat. Blood drained from the wound like red wine pouring from a bottle, causing the landsknecht to slump forward, falling face first to the ground.

The landsknecht closest to Parshan's body watched the grisly fate that had befallen his comrade, and quickly poured gunpowder from a bandolier into the pan of his arquebus. Haris rose hastily, clutching his sword, and rushed toward the man, who worked frantically at stuffing a ball down the barrel with his ramrod. But Haris was on top of him before he could raise the firearm to apply the burning cord to the powder. With a powerful swing, Haris severed the landsknecht's arm, before finishing him off by severing his head.

Haris did an about face to find the third landsknecht sprinting toward him wielding a long, straight, flat sword. Setting his feet in motion, he charged the German. They engaged one another, colliding with the ferocity of two elks butting antlers as their meeting of swords produced the harsh clashing of steel. With their weapons locked together, and their bodies pushing against one another, Haris used the strength in his sword hand to lift both blades in the direction of the sky, locking each against one another. Suddenly, he pulled his sword away from the other, and in one swift motion, brought the weapon down, slicing off the immodest codpiece of the landsknecht's costume that had projected outwards from the groin. At first, the quickness of the action appeared to stun the German, before Haris could see a grimace laced with rage fill the landsknecht's face. Suddenly, the German took the offensive and began to swing his sword indiscriminately. As he pushed forward, Haris blocked the landsknecht's slashing sword with his own blade, while matching the attacker's steps with backward steps of his own. The violent dance continued for a few rods, as Haris defended the strikes, waiting for his opponent to overextend his reach. When the landsknecht lunged forward with a stabbing motion, Haris dodged to his right, spun completely around, slicing his sword deep into the German's left side. The landsknecht gasped, spitting blood from his mouth, and collapsed face down into the snow.

Breathing heavily, Haris wasted no time identifying the fourth person who had made the decision to take flight. He gave chase for a dozen rods or so, before seeing his prey stumble over a log, falling to the ground on his stomach. As he closed in, the individual attempted to hurry to his feet, but slipped again and had rolled over on his back, only to find Haris standing above him. As he moved to strike him, Haris noticed the youthful face and bright blonde hair of his captive. He hesitated, slowly bringing his weapon down to his side.

"How old are you?" Haris asked, breathing heavily.

The young man stared upward. "You speak German?" he uttered with a trembling voice.

"How old are you?" Haris repeated.

"I am sixteen!"

"You are younger than the others!"

The young man swallowed hard. "I can see that you are not very old yourself."

Haris raised his sword in an aggressive posture. "Do not underestimate me!"

The young man huffed. "If you are going to kill me, do it quickly!"

"One should not be in such a hurry to welcome death! Were there just the four of you?"

The young man nodded.

"On your feet!" Haris commanded. "What is your name?"

He quickly rose. "Ademir."

Haris slowly lowered his sword. "I am surprised to find a landsknecht so young. I thought them all to be seasoned professionals."

"I am a new recruit. They did not discriminate when it came to lack of experience. Every able bodied man was hired to protect against the siege." Ademir unintentionally rested his hand on top of the handle to his sheathed sword.

Haris raised his sword. "Don't be foolish, young landsknecht!"

Ademir gasped when he realized his mistake, quickly removing his hand from the weapon.

"You defended Vienna," Haris said. "How did you find your first taste of battle?"

"Frightful!"

Haris grinned, slowly lowering his blade. "You will become

used to it." He could see a quizzical expression overtake Ademir's frightful glare. "What is it?"

"Your skin is fair. I had imagined all Turks to be darker skinned, and you speak my language."

Haris produced an exasperated frown, recognizing Ademir's ignorance. "I speak five languages, and I'm not Turkish."

Ademir glanced back in the direction where the lifeless body of Parshan lay. "I am sorry about your friend."

"He was a warrior," Haris replied without remorse. "The breath of life is fleeting for such men."

Ademir lowered his head. "I fear I am a coward."

"I learned this day that there is nothing cowardly about running from a fight that you cannot win."

"And you—I saw you fall when you were shot?"

"Your eyes deceived you," Haris said. "The arquebus is deadly, but unreliable in the hands of amateurs. I feigned my death to draw your accomplices out in the open."

"You're not going to kill me?"

Haris studied Ademir with a perplexing stare, as if he were making an effort to commit his face to memory. "Turn away from me, and drop to your knees!"

Ademir hesitated.

"Do as I say!"

Ademir turned, dropping into a kneeling position with his knees sinking beneath the deep snow.

"Are you Christian?" Haris inquired.

"Yes—"

"Roman, Greek, or one of Luther's renegades?"

"Roman."

Haris surveyed the area, planning his exit. "Do not turn around until I tell you to do so! Is this understood?"

31

"Yes—"

"I am not going to kill you . . . Ademir. My advice for you is to leave this place, end your novel career as a landsknecht, and go back from whence you came. And when you get there, be sure to thank God that your fate has fared far better this day than did your accomplices."

Ademir swallowed hard, continuing to kneel motionless in the cold wet snow. He waited patiently, unsure of what actions Haris took behind him.

Haris slowly backed away from the landsknecht, until he was far enough away from his prisoner to turn his back on him. Returning to the area where the body of Parshan lay, he found it almost completely covered by the unyielding snowfall. Reaching down, he slid the arquebus from off of the dead Janissary's shoulder, placing the firearm around his own, and then retrieved the bork, as well as the sword. "Goodbye, my friend," he whispered.

After nearly thirty minutes had passed, Ademir—whose hearing had been magnified tenfold out of fear—could only distinguish the sound of a whispering wind rattling dead leaves that failed to escape their branches before the sudden snowfall. He shivered as the bitter wind passed through him, and looked down upon his hands, which were turning blue from the cold. Finally, his frigid situation forced him to break his silence. "Valiant warrior!" he called out, but received no answer. "Valiant warrior?" he called again. Still nothing. Turning his head slowly, he scanned the area around him, unable to locate any sign of his captor with the exception of footsteps in the snow. Like a phantom, Haris was gone.

CHAPTER THREE

Within the Ottoman camp outside of Vienna, the arrival of dusk coincided with the return of the last members of the Janissary corps who were still among the living. For several hours, the disorganized advent of troops had trickled in like despondent refugees fleeing a war zone, appearing haggard, exhausted, vanquished.

The camp they returned to was a village of colorful Turkish tents, positioned to surround the largest centralized tent belonging to the sultan. It was here that Suleyman could be found, standing outside of the entrance to the royal shelter flanked by two bodyguards, observing the return of his beleaguered corps in silence and with solemnity. The tall leader, with thin mustache and closely shaven beard skirting his protruding chin, stood clearly recognizable by the large, white, cylindrical crowned, fluted woolen headgear he wore, trimmed in gold and adorned with four peacock feathers. He watched with mixed feelings the reappearance of his army, aching with great disappointment in how his esteemed Janissaries failed to take Vienna, but such emotions were tempered by heavy sadness; for the chosen men of the corps were to him as sons are to a father—a subservient relationship forged with loyalty and veneration. It was then that the sultan noticed his commanding officer, the Serasker Pargali Ibrahim Pasha, wearing conical headgear with three feathers, moving briskly toward him with a hurried gait. As he drew closer, the Ottoman leader could distinguish the stern, but somber expression in his friend's face; for the sultan already anticipated how the news his most decorated officer bore would be more painful for Ibrahim to deliver, than it would be for Suleyman to hear.

Ibrahim approached Suleyman with his head bowed, slowly lifting his eyes to the sultan. "Sultan, Vienna remains unconquered," he said boldly.

Suleyman noticed the stubble on his commander's usually clean shaven face, and stared back into the dark brown eyes of his highest ranking military leader. "Did you order the retreat?"

"No, Sultan," Ibrahim replied quickly. "The Janissaries at the Carinthian Gate had been repelled with heavy losses. Their ortas fell back without the signal to retreat."

Suleyman said nothing, but Ibrahim had known him long enough to recognize that the Ottoman leader's silence warranted an opinion from his commander.

"But I believe it to have been the correct decision," Ibrahim added.

Suleyman turned away, slipping through the tent's entrance with Ibrahim and the sultan's bodyguards following close behind.

Inside the spacious oval-shaped royal shelter, a half dozen tree poles supported a crimson canvas. Beneath the canvas, the interior of the tent featured a small wooden table set aside hanging sheer curtains organized in the shape of a rectangle concealing the sultan's canopied bed. The only other furniture was sofas set upon several large decorative rugs covering every square inch of earth inside the shelter. Positioned within the center of the tent were two dozen large, soft, colorful cushions arranged in a large circle around a cast iron vase that produced a flame from its contents of burning oil.

Within the circle of pillows, the sultan dropped to the ground into a fetal position. Suleyman nodded to Ibrahim, who responded by taking a seat on the carpet directly opposite the sultan.

"Have you come directly from the battlefield?" Suleyman asked.

Ibrahim studied the sultan's dark brownish-green broadcloth worn over a second red one with v-neckline that covered his upper body. "Yes, Sultan."

"You must be cold." Suleyman turned toward one of the bodyguards positioned in the shadows of the tent. He clapped his hands, and immediately the guard approached the sultan with his head bowed. "Bring me Cahil."

Quickly the bodyguard exited the tent and within minutes returned with a servant.

"Cahil, coffee to warm my serasker," Suleyman commanded. The servant bowed his head, backing his way out of the tent's opening.

"You are too generous, Sultan," Ibrahim said.

"Are they coming?"

"Yes. I expect them here soon."

Suleyman played with the sable fur cuffs sewn to the bottom of his sleeves. "I wish the subject of the conversation that lies ahead would have had us discussing how to divide the spoils of Vienna."

"As do I, Sultan."

"But who are we to question the designs of Allah."

"You are very wise, Sultan."

The servant returned and moved toward the sultan, holding a ceramic tray containing a small pot with two pewter cups of steaming coffee, filling the tent with its earthy fragrance.

"Give them both to the serasker," Suleyman said, waving his hand in Ibrahim's direction. The servant bowed and did as the sultan ordered.

As the servant exited the royal tent, a dozen Janissary officers, led by their supreme commander—the yeniceri agasi—filed inside, immediately approaching the sultan. One by one, each officer prostrated himself before Suleyman, before scurrying into a sitting position cross-legged on the carpet within the circle of pillows.

After all, had been seated, Ibrahim rose to his feet to address the group. "Our Sultan Suleyman Khan, Sovereign of the Sublime House of Osman, Sultan of Sultans, Khan of Khans, Commander of the Faithful, and Successor of the Prophet of the Lord of the Universe, has called upon his officers at this hour so that you may present your thoughts, while offering advice as to what course of action may lie ahead with knowledge that the Christians remain in control of Vienna. Our sultan assures you that you need not fear to speak the truth." Ibrahim bowed toward Suleyman, before recoiling into a sitting position.

The tent remained silent for a few minutes as the officers gathered their thoughts, and summoned the courage to speak their minds. Suddenly, one brave soul broke the uneasy silence with a description of the day's events at the Carinthian Gate, followed quickly by another and another, and so on. Not once did any of the officers look in the direction of the sultan, instead addressing all of their comments directly at Ibrahim. Over the next hour, there were those who lamented about the lack of siege cannons, and those detailing problems with the sapper's inability to blow up all of the city gates, while others blamed the wet and now frigid weather conditions for contributing in the failure to take Vienna. In contrast, several officers—in a display of pride designed to impress the sultan—maintained their belief that the capitulation of the city was only a matter of time, and encouraged Ibrahim to order another assault with guarantees of victory. Still others bravely expounded upon how the length of the military operation had taken its toll on men, resources, and supplies—pointing out how food provisions were dangerously scarce for both men and animals, and claiming how several thousand camels had already been lost because of the horrid conditions. Finally, it was suggested that the most telling warning sign against the idea of promoting the continuation of the siege, could be found among the disillusioned faces and dismal morale of the troops themselves.

Suleyman sat silently throughout the entire session without so much the slightest movement, as if he were a mannequin. Demonstrating internal vigilance and constraint, he listened carefully to all of the comments from his officers with a dignified elegance, failing to reveal any hint of emotion.

When all conversation had fallen silent, Ibrahim addressed the sultan. "Your Royal Majesty, your loyal servants have spoken."

All eyes in the tent followed Ibrahim's acknowledgment of Suleyman, and like the revolving beams from a lighthouse, each face in turn rotated in the direction of the sultan. The limber Ottoman leader—weeks shy of his thirty-fifth birthday—displayed his agility by springing to his feet effortlessly. Glancing back at the circle of faces, Suleyman slowly brought his palms together in a gesture of prayer. "In the name of God, most merciful and most compassionate!"

"Allah Hu Akbar!" his officers responded with zeal.

Suleyman lowered his hands. "As I was listening, I began to think about the literature of our faith." He paused to take a breath. "The great mystery of the Quran is how passages within the holy book bring different meaning to each individual." He commanded his audience with a slow, calming voice. "Allah does not reveal His intentions easily, but rather places trust in the faith and logic of His subjects, leaving it to them to unravel His message." He could see how his statement elicited nods of agreement from among his subjects. "As your sultan and your caliph, I have thought deeply about why Allah has brought us to the gates of Vienna, but have yet to permit us entry. It is frustrating, I know—for I can hear it in your voices. But take solace, my Janissaries, that in spite of our setbacks, each day has been victorious, for we have continued to weaken our enemy. Sometimes victory is not always easy to discern.

"It has occurred to me that often when I write poetry, I am easily inspired, and words flow effortlessly as do our ships sailing on the calm waters of the Bosporus," Suleyman continued. "But then there are times when finding the right verse is troublesome, causing me to walk away from the prose until I am stimulated again." The sultan brought his hand to his beard, stroking it gently. "I believe this is such a time. The story of our conquest of Vienna remains incomplete—stalled like the frustrated poet. But it is not the end of the story. We and not the Christians are the authors! How the story ends will be on our terms!" Suleyman brought both hands to his broadcloth, and tugged on the garment as to modestly suggest his words were prophetic. After a long pause had produced an unnerving silence, the sultan gathered in a deep breath. "You will have my decision, along with your orders, within the hour. God's peace, be upon you!"

"And God's peace be upon you!" the officers replied with enthusiasm, before rising to their feet. Each man offered a solitary bow to the sultan, holding their heads low and backing themselves out of the tent.

After all the officers had gone, Suleyman dismissed his bodyguards, so that he could be alone with Ibrahim.

When it became evident they were the last two inside of the

tent, Ibrahim spoke. "The officers, they are good men—all of them."

Suleyman frowned. "Yet, I am irritated by the failure of those at the Carinthian Gate. Such cowardice can be contagious. Perhaps for those ortas that retreated at the gate, I shall execute each of their corbaci's to set an example!"

"Then why not execute me instead, for I am their commander," Ibrahim suggested with callousness—the sudden informality between he and Suleyman implying the depth of their friendship.

Suleyman gave Ibrahim a stern look, before his frown twisted into a grin of contentment. "You are correct. You are my serasker in time of war, and yet you are also my grand vizier in time of peace! But most importantly, you remind me that you and I are like brothers." Suleyman's tone grew softer. "I am frustrated—you are frustrated. It is better to resort to patience in such matters, for as our Prophet says: 'If you punish, then punish with the like of that wherewith you were afflicted. But if you endure patiently, indeed it is better for the patient'."

Suleyman approached Ibrahim slowly, now with a gentle smile splashed across his face, and placed his hands on Ibrahim's biceps. "If ever a time there was to become lost in the sweet sounds of your musical talent, then I wish it could be now. Do you remember when first we met as boys, how I was drawn to the sound of your violin?"

"Yes, Sultan. Unfortunately, I did not bring my violin on this campaign—only my sword, courage, and loyalty to you."

Suleyman took a deep breath as his smile widened. "Ibrahim, my brother, I once promised you that I would never harm you."

"I remember."

Suleyman pulled his friend closer to him. "Then as Allah is my witness, I remind you of my promise." The two men shared a firm hug, exchanging a small kiss on each cheek.

The sultan released his hold on Ibrahim. "Tell me Ibrahim, if we should continue the siege, do you believe Charles will come?"

"No. The Christian king may fear your army, but his greater fear is the embarrassment he may suffer in losing to you on the battlefield."

Suleyman clenched both fists. "He is the main reason I have brought my army to this place. My wish was to defeat his forces in combat to show Europe that I, Suleyman, and not the pretender Charles, am the most powerful leader on the continent!"

"Charles uses the excuse of his conflict with France as a reason not to challenge you."

"Yes—but there will be a time when he will have to face me." Suleyman paced the width of the tent before stopping and spinning toward Ibrahim. "If Allah wishes this not to be that time, then we are wasting our energy here, especially now that the winter grows closer."

"Then your decision is to abandon the siege?"

"Not abandon, but rather delay," Suleyman stated. "You will declare our siege a victory! We have achieved our goal of weakening the city's wall. Give the order to my army that tomorrow at dawn we shall begin our triumphant return to Constantinople."

CHAPTER FOUR

Haris found his way back through the forest alone just as dusk prepared to extinguish the final sunlight of the day. Tired and cold, he lumbered in the direction of his own tent, passing the grisly sight and strong stench of the bloated carcasses of camels and horses, while other Ottoman troops meandered about, wandering aimlessly under a pall of confusion.

"Haris!" a voice called out from behind.

Haris stopped, turning to find his orta's corbaci, identified by the heron-feathered crest headgear that he wore, as well as the gold soup ladle insignia sewn to the breast pocket of his dolama coat. He took a moment to ponder his commander's age, which he believed to be at least ten years older than his own, and studied his deep olive complexion that made him appear not only younger, but Turkish as well. Haris realized how rare it was to actually find a person of Turkish descent among the Janissaries, guessing that perhaps his corbaci's roots were probably Greek. His name was Kamil, and he moved briskly toward Haris with a serious yet consoling expression—a look more befitting that of a friendly Constantinople merchant than that of a military officer. With what little energy he had left, Haris summoned the ability to stand at attention for his commander.

"Relax, Haris," the corbaci ordered.

Haris took a breath and eased the posture of his lanky stature, which exhibited a height taller than that of his commanding officer. The corbaci gave Haris a once over, closely examining his blood stained dolama, noticing how he carried an extra sword in one hand, and a second bork in the other.

"Allah challenges us this day," the corbaci remarked. "Too many obstacles for us to overcome I'm afraid, and the greatest one is that we fight far from home."

Haris did not reply, but stood shivering with frozen strands of his brown hair protruding from beneath his bork.

"Are you wounded?" the officer pried, his upper lip buried beneath a thick dark mustache.

"No, sir," Haris responded with a strained voice, barely above a whisper. He looked down upon his shirt. "This blood is not my own."

The corbaci's thick eyebrows turned upward. "I pity the man who confronted you."

"Men, sir. There were four—" Haris paused, remembering the young landsknecht. "Three—there were three of them. Parshan is dead." He extended the sword and bork toward his commander.

The corbaci took the bork from Haris. "Keep the sword. I think Parshan would have wanted you to have it. He was a good soldier, as are you."

Just then, several Ottoman soldiers passed Haris and his commander, herding a number of civilian prisoners of both sexes clad in tattered, dirty clothing. He noticed how the prisoner's hands were bound at the wrists, fastened to a longer rope pulled by the soldiers, as though they were a group of pack animals. As Haris watched them pass, suddenly one of the prisoners—a young woman—slipped and fell to the ground bringing the procession to a halt. He stepped toward her, bent down and grabbed the woman by the arm, pulling her into a standing position. The young maiden with long, blonde hair glared at him with swollen, sympathetic, emerald eyes that seemed to speak to him. Haris felt the urge to say something to her, but before his tongue could form the letters, the line of prisoners moved away. He turned back toward his commander, clenching his free right hand with a grimace.

"What ails you?" the corbaci asked.

"It's my hands, sir. They ache from the cold."

"Show me them."

Haris held out his hands, which exhibited a deep redness.

"You're dehydrated and bitten by the cold. Go directly to a Janissary medical tent and have your hands looked after. That is an order."

"Yes, sir."

Haris altered the direction of his footsteps away from the area where his tent was pitched, on a course now to the most northern point of the camp where medical tents had been set up. Each of these shelters appeared ten times the size of a soldier's shelter, containing doctors, medical supplies, and the many wounded and dying. He searched for a grouping of tents with green flags tapered to a point, flying above the canvass, which identified the enclosures as medical shelters exclusive to the Janissaries; for as the sultan's elite corps, these troops received the best medical care from the finest physicians within the Ottoman war machine.

Haris had been fortunate as a young warrior, having never set foot inside a medical tent on the battlefield, but he remembered Parshan telling him how should that day come, be sure to see the bald Jewish doctor, for he was known to have the most success with his patients. However, realizing his affliction was not life threatening, he decided to settle for any doctor. Haris dragged himself over to the first tent, stepping inside the entranceway to find bodies of the wounded stretched out on blankets covering the ground, many of them twitching and groaning with pain. He grimaced from the overwhelming stench, before noticing a man glancing in his direction. The man wore a turban, was dressed in a cloth apron, and clutched a sickle-shaped surgical saw with its teeth dripping blood. "I am full in here!" the man announced. "Try Jucef in the next tent!"

Haris backed out of the tent, and entered an adjacent shelter to find a scene identical to that of the previous one. The main difference was the appearance of the short, middle-aged man in a blood-stained apron who did not wear a hat. The man revealed a head of shoulder-length salt and pepper hair that fell from the sides and back, but with the top of his head hairless, displaying the smoothness of an egg shell. Haris guessed he could be Parshan's Jew.

With skin the color of honey, the man turned toward Haris. "What is it that ails you?"

"Are you Jewish?" Haris asked him.

The man frowned. "If you would rather see a Turkish physician—"

"No—no, it is you I would like to see," Haris interrupted quickly.

The physician sighed. "What ails you?"

"My hands ache from the cold. It is not as serious as what I see around me, but my corbaci ordered me to see a doctor."

"Hold out your hands," the doctor ordered. Haris extended both arms, as the physician leaned in closer to examine them.

Haris winced. "You smell like olive oil."

The doctor raised his eyes to Haris. "It is a concoction of olive oil and wine. I rub it over me to prevent infection of my patients," he explained. "You have been bitten by the frost and despite what you may think, it is serious. Sit down and place each hand under your armpits. Hold the position until I tell you otherwise."

Haris dropped into a sitting position, folding his arms across his chest. He placed his hands underneath opposite armpits, watching as the physician was approached by a young male assistant. "The doctor within the next tent reports they have run out of oil to boil for application to wounds," the assistant said.

The doctor stared at the ground in a moment of thought. "Tell them to mix egg yolks, and oil of roses, with turpentine. Then give it to the patients to drink. It will prevent gunpowder poisoning. And when you return, bring me a bucket of warm water—not hot, but warm."

The assistant nodded and left the tent. The doctor spun away from Haris, disappearing from view as he moved to tend to other patients located deeper within the shelter. A short time later he reappeared, carrying a bucket of water, setting it at his feet. "What is your name?"

"Haris."

"Either this is your first battle, or you are very good at soldiering. I have not seen you in my tent before."

"I fought at Mohacs, three years ago."

The doctor reached for the bucket's handle. "Ah—the sultan's greatest victory to date. Then you are a good soldier. It was a bloody battle, with many casualties." He set the bucket closer to Haris. "Soak your hands in the warm water for a while."

Haris freed his hands, and plunged them into the soothing water. "Where are you from, Doctor?"

The physician flashed a cynical smile. "You care about my history? That is a rare quality to find among the Janissaries—young men so focused on performing their duty for the sultan. Haris, why don't you tell where you come from. I am sure yours is a more interesting story."

Haris took a breath. "I was raised in Lezhe."

"Ah, you are Albanian?"

"No. My parents are Croatian. My family left Nin and settled in Lezhe when I was very young."

"What is your age?" the doctor asked.

"Twenty-four."

The doctor studied Haris' face with great interest. "You have interesting blue eyes, even for a Croat. They are like the color of the sea."

"My birth name is Jadran—it means, from the Adriatic."

"I was also born near the sea as well—the island of Majorca in the Mediterranean," the doctor explained. "But I make my home in Constantinople now. My name is Jucef ben Ezmael."

"How did you get here?"

The doctor chuckled, implying how the story of his journey was a peculiar one. "When I was thirteen, Ferdinand and Isabella, the Catholic Monarchs of Spain, attempted to rid the Iberian Peninsula of my kind—Sephardi Jews—by expelling the entire Jewish population from their kingdom."

"Why?"

"Why?" the doctor scoffed. "Because we are Jews! We are the scourge of the earth!" he exclaimed, mockingly. "Ah, but not all peoples are so unwelcoming. Where the kingdom of Spain cast us away, the Ottoman Empire offered us refuge. My family travelled east across the Mediterranean and settled in Izmir. When I grew into a man, I moved to Thessaloniki, where I began to study medicine. It was there that I studied under a physician named Moses Hamon. It changed my life."

"You learned much medicine from him?"

Jucef chuckled. "Yes, but sometimes in life, it is more about whom you may know, than what you may know. My connection and friendship with Moses afforded me the opportunity to follow him to Constantinople when he became the sultan's physician. And now here I am tending to the Janissaries. You may remove your hands from the water now. I think you're going to live." He smiled, before tossing Haris a piece of dry cloth.

"You are satisfied in the role of a physician for the sultan's army?"

Jucef pointed to his stained apron. "Do I look satisfied? I have the blood of young men splattered over my clothing. I work amid conditions where the mindless carnage of war forces me to butcher men with amputations. My goal is always to keep men alive, but sadly I am often faced with the grim reality that many in my care will die." He frowned. "No, I am not satisfied. But, what can I do? Unfortunately, war is a way of life, and the battlefield needs physicians. I wish there were no wars, because it would mean I was back in Constantinople, tending to my private practice."

The doctor turned away from Haris, approaching a wooden table set on the opposite side of the tent, before returning with a steaming cup.

"And now for the final medicinal requirement, a cup of Turkish coffee!" Jucef declared. "As I see it, coffee is the greatest gift our Arab brethren have contributed to the empire." With a grin, he handed the cup to Haris.

As Haris brought the steaming cup to his lips, a Janissary burst in through the tent's entrance. "The sultan has ordered for all to break camp tomorrow at sunrise!"

Jucef turned toward Haris with raised eyebrows. "Man plans and God laughs! Finally, this madness is coming to an end!"

* * *

Much later that evening, when the camp had fallen silent with sleep—the exception being the soldiers assigned to the night watch, as well as the faint cries of the wounded from inside the medical tents—Haris awakened within his tent from a bad dream, calling out to Parshan. Pulling himself into a sitting position, he looked over at the empty blanket set a few rods from where he lay, recalling how the day's events had taken his friend's life. With a sigh, he swallowed hard, deciding to take the opportunity to relieve himself. Throwing off the fur blanket that covered him, Haris pulled himself into a standing position, slipped into his boots, and exited the tent. Although the snowfall had ceased, he shivered in the bitter cold air, and hurriedly plodded through the snow in the direction of a large tree located behind the camp at the edge of the forest. There he began to urinate at the base of the trunk, while scanning outward into the darkness.

Despite the absence of moonlight, his eyes adjusted quickly to the blackness of night, aided by the snowy white topography, which allowed him to distinguish shapes. He recognized a number of stationary shapes common to the forest, before suddenly catching movement off to his left. He continued to stare in the direction of the shifting shadows, before suddenly recognizing the silhouette of a hooded figure, followed by another, and then a third—fourth—fifth—sixth . . . *Austrians!* Quickly he returned inside his tent, retrieving his bow and quiver full of arrows, before returning to the forest.

Taking cover behind a large oak, Haris slung his quiver over his right shoulder, and with the patience of a hunter, searched for a target. Suddenly, he saw a small flame materialize, appearing to dance in mid-air, before ascending rapidly on a flying course toward the camp. He watched the flame reach its zenith, before descending upon an Ottoman tent which exploded into a fireball. Haris pulled an arrow from the quiver, and fixed it to the bow-string. He pulled the string back with great force until the bow bent at both ends, aimed, and fired. Within seconds the arrow found its mark, as one of the hooded figures fell violently forward onto the ground.

With a burning tent and deadly assailants lurking in the wood, the quiet evening had quickly erupted into chaos within the Ottoman camp. Still, Haris noticed how the shadowy figures seemed undeterred, shifting their location from where their fellow attacker had fallen. He believed their movement had been accomplished to feign a retreat, and decided to shift his position as well, keeping a steady eye on their location.

Haris kept the figures in view, while applying an arrow to his bow. As the assailants worked at igniting another hand-held incendiary device, he let fly an arrow which pierced the neck of one attacker, and quickly followed the shot with another arrow striking an assailant through the chest. At the sight of their fallen compatriots, the remaining attackers began to flee; but their decision had come too late, as Haris' skilled marksmanship permitted him to find each of his targets in rapid succession, rendering the wood tranquil once again.

CHAPTER FIVE

Constantinople – April, 1530

On a warm spring evening, Haris slumbered deeply, immersed within a recurring dream that harkened back to what seemed another lifetime . . .

The boy tilted his head upward, gazing out into a clear blue horizon before shielding his eyes from the bright rays of the sun. He wondered why his father had assembled the family outside of the front of their small home, situated on a hillside with the rear of their house offering a stunning view of the azure waters of the Adriatic. Only a few days shy of his eleventh birthday, the boy's first thoughts were that his father was preparing to reveal an early gift for him—perhaps something crafted from his skillful carpenter's hands; but within a household known to erupt regularly with conversation and laughter, the morning unfolded with his parents moving about in unusual silence, quickly putting to rest any assumptions of a birthday surprise. No—there was something different about this day, and the boy harbored a sickening feeling that whatever it was, would not be good.

The boy stood silently with his younger brother and sister in the shadow of their parents, when suddenly, in the distance from a point where the long main dirt road of the village began, a group of men appeared on horseback. They were dressed in kaftans draped with chainmail, carrying swords sheathed at their sides; but what did the most to reveal themselves as Turkish soldiers, were their metal helmets that rose to a steep point in the center of the crown. As they drew closer, mounted atop their barded equines, the boy counted nearly three dozen soldiers, followed by three horse-drawn wagons covered with red canvass.

His father glanced at him with a somber expression. "Turks— they are here, just as we were warned!" The patriarch cast a serious glare at wife, whose eyes began to well with tears.

The boy noticed how his father clutched a small burlap bag, sagging from the weight of its contents. "Father, what is in the bag?"

His father turned to the boy with a heavy sigh. "It is your future."

The family watched as the group of horsemen separated from one another, and began canvassing each village home. Suddenly, one of the soldiers brought his horse to a halt before the boy's house. Immediately, his father approached the horseman as the boy viewed the soldier carefully, surprised to find that the warrior did not resemble a red-skinned tailed demon—characteristics that others in the village had often used in their description of the Turks.

"We are here to collect the tax!" the soldier announced to the boy's father. "One child for the Sultan's devshirme—the annual tribute! The village of Lezhe has been selected because it has been five years since its last contribution!" Suddenly, the soldier noticed a pile of lumber setting next to the man's house. "What is your trade?"

The boy's father hesitated. "I am a carpenter."

"You are exempt from the tax." The soldier lifted the reins of his horse, preparing to move on.

"But I'm Christian!"

The soldier eased the reins. "In addition to Muslims and Jews, all craftsmen are exempt from the tax—that includes carpenters, no matter that you are Christian."

The boy's father turned toward his family, throwing a forlorn, indecisive stare, before spinning back toward the soldier. He raised the small burlap sack that he held. "Perhaps you may reconsider?"

The soldier pored over the boy's father with an inquisitive look that quickly transcended into a judgmental scowl, before reaching down and retrieving the bag. He opened it, peering inside at the coinage with a look of approval. The soldier turned to reach inside a bag slung over the back of the horse, and pulled out a bright red tunic, tossing it to the man. "Tell your son to wear this and say your goodbyes. Do it quickly."

The father returned to his family, handing the boy the red tunic, while his mother began to sob heavily.

The boy flashed a frightened glare. "Mother? Father? What is happening?"

The father dropped into a squatting position so that he now looked upward at his son. "I work hard my son, but my wages are barely enough to feed this family. The Ottoman sultan has sent his soldiers to us this day to collect the devshirme tax—Christian children who will serve the sultan. Some of the boys will be given a chance for selection into the sultan's Janissary corps. It is widely known that members of such an elite group receive education, good pay, and the chance for advancement. It is an opportunity that your life here in Lezhe cannot give you."

"But father, I want to be with you and mother! I do not want to leave!"

The father swallowed hard, but maintained his composure. "Unfortunately, my son, it is not your decision to make. Although it may not seem so now, someday you will come to realize that our intentions this day are born out of concern for your future. We believe this is what is best."

The boy turned toward his mother who had ceased her sobbing, struggling to put on a strong face. With tears still lingering on her *cheeks, she stepped up to her son, handing him a burlap sack. "We love you, my son, and shall keep you in our prayers! We will await the day you shall return to us!"*

The boy opened the sack to find a clean tunic, a pair of breeches, and a small wooden crucifix engraved with a bearded face attached to the body of a fish. He flipped the item over to find the name Jadran carved into the back. With deep sadness he raised his eyes to his mother. "I love you mother!"

"Carpenter! Your son!" exclaimed the soldier from atop his steed—his impatience showing by the scowl on his face.

The boy's mother hugged him, kissing his forehead. "You must go now!"

The boy hugged his little brother and sister, realizing they were too young to understand what was happening. Then he approached his father, giving the patriarch a firm embrace, as tears welled up within the boy's eyes.

"Farewell, my son!" the father offered with trembling voice. The boy turned and with a sickening feeling rising in his stomach, looked up at the soldier.

"The red tunic!" the soldier yelled. "Place it on! Do it now!"

The boy did as the soldier demanded.

From his mount, the soldier turned his horse with a pull of the reins, pointing toward the stationary wagons that set a block away. "Proceed to the wagons!"

The boy watched as dozens of young village males, all clad in red tunics, moved toward the vehicles, before he set his wobbling feet in motion. As he stepped, he spun and gave one final look in the direction of his family—a longing stare laced with a sense of bewilderment.

Haris awakened from his dream with the sound of rooster's squawking, and reached under his pillow to feel the small, wooden crucifix he hid. As he rose from his mattress, he watched other Janissaries rise slowly from their beds, positioned side by side in a row extending the length of the long, narrow quarters. After righting himself and stretching, he stepped outside onto the second story veranda perched above the narrow city street. From his vantage point on the balcony overlooking Constantinople proper, Haris viewed several towering obelisks in the distance set in the center of a large open area flanked by a stone serpentine column—the ancient remains of the Byzantine Hippodrome, the site of many chariot races during the height of the Byzantine Empire.

The quiet thoroughfare below suddenly came alive with the sights, sounds, and smells of a blood-dripping convoy composed of horse-drawn carts carrying butchered mutton and beef carcasses. He recognized the shipment to be a common site, and knew its destination was the Janissary barracks—one of the benefits of being stationed within Constantinople's meat square, known as *Et Maydani*.

Haris realized how fortunate he was to be present in the picturesque Ottoman capitol. Since the siege of Vienna, opportunity had become even more prevalent for him after Corbaci Kamil accepted a promotion to lead one of the sixty-one ortas within the *silahdar*—the sultan's personal bodyguard. Haris' heroism with the bow and arrow against the forest night raiders outside of Vienna, established him as a *ghazi*—an Ottoman warrior hero—and Kamil had not forgotten the brave, loyal soldier, recommending him for a position among the silahdar.

For the past six months, Haris' training for the silahdar had unfolded amidst the splendor of historic Constantinople. He became schooled in contingency plans, along with defensive procedures, as well as learning floor plans of the city's intricate, massive palaces, and the proper etiquette required in the presence of the sultan and his family; however, he had not set eyes on the Ottoman leader since seeing him from a distance during the Vienna campaign. But that was about to change, as for reasons unknown to Haris, the sultan had requested the young Janissary's presence at the *Yeni Saray* or New Palace, for later that morning. The promising reality of the new day seemed for him to be a stark contrast from the previous night's troubling dream.

CHAPTER SIX

The morning grew late quickly for Haris, accelerated by his invented scenarios of what the anticipated audience with the sultan might entail. With every activity he completed, his thoughts were punctuated by imaginary conversations between himself and the supreme Ottoman leader, until finally the hour to prepare for his departure had arrived. Haris bathed and groomed, before beginning the walk from Et Maydani through the busy streets of Constantinople proper to the Yeni Saray, which took him only a quarter of an hour to make. His journey guided him past the magnificent mosque, Hagia Sophia—the former Eastern Orthodox Church—with its great central dome rising nearly two hundred feet in the air, cornered by four towering, slender, pointed minarets.

Sprawling atop the highest point of Constantinople, within the shadows of the Hagia Sophia, Haris easily located the Yeni Saray. The impressive compound graces the top of a promontory overlooking a curved strait known as the Golden Horn, situated where the dark blue waters of the Sea of Marmara meet the Bosporus Strait. The expansive palace's numerous splendid white buildings of one and two story structures—many with domed roofs interspersed with a multitude of towering narrow chimneys—appeared to Haris like mushroom caps growing among tree stems. Structured in layers consisting of four consecutive courtyards winding down to the shores of the Bosporus, the massive complex is surrounded by high walls, with gates controlling entry into each section featuring picturesque pavilions and manicured gardens.

Haris gained entry onto the palace grounds through the unguarded Imperial Gate, and once inside witnessed a large, bustling public courtyard alive with pedestrians perusing the workshops of many guilds. With his attention captivated by the spirited sights and sounds within the courtyard, he proceeded past a building with brick façade—the armory—in his movements toward the next gate.

The Gate of Salutation provided entrance into the second courtyard through its great doors decorated with Arabic religious script, and set flanked by two large pointed octagonal towers. For as many times as Haris had been inside the first courtyard since arriving in Constantinople, not once had he ever set foot on the other side of this gate. His Janissary training had given him advanced knowledge of the palace layout through sensitive drawings privy only to the sultan's silahdar. Thus, Haris understood that beyond the gate, the second courtyard was known as Divan Square and it housed the administrative activities of the empire, permitting entry to only official guests and members of the court. The realization that he would be permitted to pass through the Gate of Salutation filled him with a rush of excitement.

Haris' entry was delayed momentarily at the gate by two Janissaries standing guard, until they could confirm his invitation. This did not take very long, and once cleared for entry, he moved through a much quieter and smaller courtyard shared by Janissaries, court officials, and colorful peacocks. His course took him past a hospital, before arriving upon the palace confectioneries and kitchens filling the air with sweet aromas. Beyond the kitchens, Haris passed by the entranceway to a staircase that descended to the imperial stables, before he cast his eyes on the palace's tallest structure rising several stories above the ground—the Tower of Justice—with its high, golden grilled windows set at the base adjacent to the domed chamber building, where the Imperial Council held its meetings.

When Haris reached the domed Gate of Felicity, which led to the third or innermost courtyard, he found this entrance guarded by three times as many soldiers than the numbers present at the previous gate. The fact that each Janissary guard carried a sword at this location, bespoke of just how close Haris had come to the heart of the empire; for he realized that throughout all of Constantinople, Janissaries were forced to abandon firearms and replace their swords with clubs during times of peace—the exception being those assigned to the innermost courtyard because of its proximity to the sultan and his family. None could pass through this gate without the permission of the sultan.

Of the Janissaries guarding the gate, one large black African soldier stood out, not only in his physical appearance, but with the curt, inquisitive verbal interaction he displayed in dealing with Haris. After answering the guard's questions directly, he was once again delayed and subjected to a body search. When the guards were certain Haris had arrived as an unarmed guest, the African Janissary left his post.

Haris waited patiently for nearly twenty minutes, until the Janissary reappeared in the company of a robed man emerging from a doorway to a square building lined with nearly two dozen columns, set adjacent to the gate. Lean, and slight in stature, the robed figure wore a bright red kaftan extending to his knees with conical headgear. Instantly, Haris sensed how this individual's approach had produced a wave of slight anxiety among the troops, as they quickly hustled into a rigid military pose. As the figure drew near, Haris recognized his angular facial features as Pargali

Ibrahim Pasha, the Janissary Serasker in time of war, and more prestigiously, the Ottoman Grand Vizier.

Haris' heart raced as the grand vizier stopped only rods before him. "Lezhe Haris?" he asked with a deep, commanding voice.

Haris bowed his head and stepped forward.

"*Merhaba*," the grand vizier greeted. "I am Pargali Ibrahim Pasha. Please walk with me." The Ottoman leader turned and proceeded in the direction whence he came, as Haris moved quickly to step alongside of him.

"I gather this is your first time inside the Gate of Felicity?" Ibrahim queried, pacing briskly.

"Yes, my lord. Actually, it is my first time beyond the first courtyard."

Both men continued their steps unabated. "And your first impressions?"

"It is very . . . very regal."

The grand vizier turned his head slightly toward Haris with raised eyebrows. "Regal? That is an interesting word to use, but it is correct." Grinning, he pointed off to his left. "Do you see the gate at the far end of the courtyard?"

Haris followed the grand vizier's arm, recognizing a large wooden door carved into a high wall, guarded by an armed black African sentry.

"That is the Royal Gate, and beyond it is located the harem where the sultan's maids in waiting, concubines, and servants reside. And of course, it also houses the apartments of both the sultan and the Queen Mother. The area is guarded by African eunuchs, since the only male permitted within the harem is the sultan. The sultan's chief consorts and their children, reside in the old palace."

"The *Eski Saray*," Haris said.

"Yes. It is located on the other side of Constantinople near the mosque dedicated to Sultan Bayezid the second."

Both men reached the door from which Haris had observed the grand vizier exiting only moments before. Setting to the left of the door, he viewed a small fountain carved with an inscription that described the cascade as *the fountainhead of generosity, justice and the sea of beneficence*. Beyond the door, the two men stepped into a small, but extravagantly decorated room, illuminated with natural light filtering through stained glass windows. The ceiling was painted in deep blue, with golden stars styled to replicate an exaggerated evening sky, while the portraits of ten sultans adorned the room's walls, beginning with the Ottoman Empire's founder, Osman, and running through Suleyman.

A second door inside the room gave the men entrance to a much larger area, and immediately Haris' attention was drawn to a lacquered domed ceiling with foliage patterns, surrounding a colorful drawing of a mythical Persian bird alongside a depiction of a dragon in flight. Set against the walls of the chamber were situated lavish carpets and ornate pillows, while a fountain flowed forth from a wall at the end of the room. At the far end of the chamber, positioned on a raised platform, set the sultan's throne, covered with gold cloth, and behind the throne were intricate mosaic designs speckled with azure and gold, bordering a large, grilled window embedded within the wall.

"This is the throne room of the Audience Chamber," Ibrahim described, stopping in its center. "On most occasions, the sultan would greet his guests in this room. However, today he wishes to meet with you outside in his private garden. Have you been schooled in the proper etiquette when in the presence of the sultan?"

"Yes, my lord."

"You may not make eye contact or speak directly with the sultan," Ibrahim said.

Haris prepared himself for the litany of reminders ready to burst forth from the grand vizier.

"When in the supreme leader's presence, you must keep your head bowed and your eyes cast downward at all times, unless of course it becomes the sultan's wish to allow you to speak directly to him. Should you wish to reply to his royal majesty before he gives you permission to do so, you must speak to me, and I will address him for you. And when the sultan beckons you to approach him, he will extend his left hand toward you. Without touching his hand, you will bend forward and gently kiss it—all the while with your eyes to the floor. Is this understood?"

"Yes, my lord."

"Before we proceed, have you any questions?"

Haris gathered his thoughts, before finding the courage to ask, "Why would the sultan desire to see me?"

Haris noticed how the grand vizier seemed surprised by the question. "Why does it matter? Are you in a position to say no?" he inquired, with a scolding tone. "We are slaves Lezhe Haris— you and me both. The sultan is our master, and we must do as our master wishes."

Haris bowed his head in a gesture of acknowledgment.

The grand vizier sighed. "You will find out soon enough why the sultan has summoned you. Come, we must not keep his royal majesty waiting."

At the opposite end of the chamber was another door, and Haris followed the grand vizier through it out into a small courtyard composed of terraced gardens and pavilions. Together they paced side by side, traversing along a tiled walkway lined with vertical gilt-bronzed posts that supported cross-beams and lattices training woody vines. Upon reaching the end of the walkway, which opened into a square centered by a large circular garden of multi-colored tulips, both men stopped, casting their eyes upon the sultan. The Ottoman leader, with his back to his visitors, stood examining the beautiful arrangement of flowers, wearing conical headgear, and a long, golden, silk gown with designs of the clouds, moon, sun, and stars woven into the fabric.

"God's peace, be upon you, Your Royal Majesty," Ibrahim greeted.

Without turning around, Suleyman replied, "And God's peace, be upon you."

"As you have requested, I present to you, Lezhe Haris."

The sultan continued his scrutiny of the tulips. "It is clear that you hail from Lezhe." Haris noted how Suleyman spoke with a beautiful, clear voice, addressing him as though he had eyes in the back of his head. "Then you are Albanian?"

Haris turned toward the grand vizier who, with a nod of his head, encouraged him to reply. "I . . . I am Croatian—but was raised in Lezhe, Your Royal Majesty."

The sultan finished his inspection of the flowers and slowly turned, causing Haris to bow his head, casting his eyes to the tile foot path. "Croatian, Albanian—they are all beautiful people, yet troublesome at the same time," Suleyman remarked. "Strong people and good fighters are they both, as well as the Macedonians and of course the Greeks. Their homeland is not a peninsula populated by people who take lightly to being conquered. That is why I draw my Janissaries from their kind. They are a proud people with a rich history. Take for example Skanderbeg, the national hero of the Albanians. Are you familiar?"

Haris turned toward the grand vizier with his eyes still fixed to the walkway. "As a boy I had heard his name spoken often. But I do not recall his story."

"Ah—what a pity, for Croatians and Albanians have long memories," Suleyman said. "Of course, Skanderbeg's mark on history occurred before my birth, but I'm aware of him, and how his heroism continues to breathe life into Albanian folklore. Did you know he was a Janissary officer before he betrayed the sultan?" The sultan paused briefly, before resuming his discourse. "I make it a habit to study my people's history. Skanderbeg's resistance against the Ottomans is legendary. Having pride in one's family heritage is the foundation for a people. Diversity is what gives my empire its strength. Would you not agree?"

Haris remained silent, with his head bowed.

"Hmm—it appears I query you with topics you are unprepared to answer. It is good to know when you are challenged with a question you cannot answer, as opposed to creating a foolish response. You are loyal to your own Croatian heritage, are you not Lezhe Haris?"

"I am a Janissary—the corps is my family. My loyalty lies with the sultan."

A long pause by the sultan began to unnerve Haris, before Suleyman spoke again. "So, they tell me you are a ghazi of our siege in Vienna. How does it feel to be honored in this way?"

Haris hesitated, as he gave careful thought to his response. "As we returned to camp, my friend died standing next to me," he recalled, speaking at the grand vizier. "A true hero would have been aware we were being followed, and should have been able to prevent my friend's death. As for the night in the forest, any Janissary would have defended the camp as I did."

Another long pause ensued, before Suleyman announced, "Lezhe Haris, you may approach your sultan."

Haris stepped slowly toward Suleyman with his head bowed, as the sultan extended his left hand toward him. Bending forward,

Haris could see a ring with its gold band smothered by a large, sparkling ruby. He kissed the top of the hand and backed away with eyes fixed to the tile pavement.

"Lezhe Haris, you may raise your head, and address your sultan directly," Suleyman said.

Haris slowly lifted his eyes to behold the sultan's tall stature and gentle looking round face, set beneath a broad forehead. He noticed how the sultan's dark brown eyes exchanged an approving glance with his grand vizier.

"It is time for my grand vizier to leave us alone," Suleyman hinted.

"As you wish, Your Royal Majesty," Ibrahim acknowledged with a bow, backing away, before turning and proceeding down the shaded walkway.

Suleyman waited until the grand vizier had disappeared from view, before gently running his index finger over a tulip petal. "Do you appreciate my garden?"

"It is most beautiful, Your Royal Majesty," Haris remarked.

"This is my sanctuary," Suleyman described. "Later next month, during Ramadan, I will make a habit of breaking my fast out here in the garden at sunset. It seems only fitting to do this, as I can imagine how my garden replicates the tranquility and beauty which must exist in heaven."

"I have no doubt, Your Royal Majesty."

"From here we can see the beauty that surrounds the palace—the abundance of water and the splendor of Constantinople . . . or rather Istanbul, as the locals see fit to call it." Suleyman smiled. "I think Istanbul is more befitting a name for the city. It sounds more congenial and is shorter, rolling off of the tongue with less effort than Constantinople. I believe someday it may become the new name for the capitol. Come, I wish to show you the view."

Suleyman stepped away from Haris, moving around the circular garden of tulips.

Haris followed the sultan until stopping at a stone wall, which revealed a panoramic view overlooking a great body of water, spotted with sailing vessels. "The Sea of Marmara," Suleyman described, facing the dark blue water and exhibiting a side profile that revealed a curved nose.

"It is a stunning view, Your Royal Majesty."

"Stunning, yes, but how else would you describe it, Lezhe Haris?"

Haris thought for moment. "It is not a wine dark sea."

Suleyman turned away from the watery landscape, facing Haris. "You've read Homer—although the great poet's description was of the Mediterranean, and not the Marmara."

Haris gathered in a breath, assembling his words. "The sea appears deceptively pacific. It is as though the great water's ferocious nature lies dormant beneath the surface, biding its time."

Suleyman produced a large smile with his fine lips lifting both his closely shaven beard and his thin mustache. "Very poetic. I too am a lover of words," he professed. "On the subject of bodies of water, do you know I have never seen the Adriatic Sea? Although someday I believe that I will. Ibrahim—the grand vizier—was born and raised in the region of Rumelia, not far from the Adriatic coastline, as it appears were you." The sultan grinned. "He is Greek, so you are in good company."

"It is an honor to be mentioned in the same breath with the grand vizier, Your Royal Majesty."

"I can see the resemblance in the two of you, for you are both handsome men, and although you and I have only just met, I detect a common inner connection shared by both you and my grand vizier. You are alike in carefully choosing your words. It is a skill which serves negotiators well. What do you say of my observation?"

"I do not know the grand vizier personally, Your Royal Majesty. I only know myself. But I respect your judgment."

Haris noted how Suleyman's pronounced Adam's apple called attention to his slender neck, as the sultan continued to smile. "Haris, I have been told how after you were taken from your home in Lezhe, you were raised in Adana in the house of Haytac."

"Yes, Your Royal Majesty."

"I understand them to be a strong, God-fearing, loyal family."

"Yes, Your Royal Majesty. That is how I remember them."

"And they gave you the Islamic name Haris. Do you know why?"

"I was told it means one who is vigilant, as is a watchman."

"And—?" Suleyman pried.

Haris took a moment to remember before replying. "When I first arrived at the Haytac home, I spent weeks keeping watch at the window in my room, waiting and hoping that my birth parents would arrive to take me home. I suppose my actions reminded my hosts of a watchman."

"Then you were aptly named," Suleyman said. "What academic skill did you choose to perfect, as is required of each Janissary?"

"Writing, Your Royal Majesty."

"Why of course," Suleyman responded with amusement. "I am a writer as well. I think it a virtuous talent. However, there are those who perceive writing as effeminate and a weakness. When I first became sultan, the Europeans viewed me in this way—as if I were a lamb." His judicious tone disintegrated into one of bitterness. "They soon discovered their mistake. Their Ottoman lamb was really a lion, and now they fear me. Do you fear me, Lezhe Haris?"

"Yes, Your Royal Majesty."

"Why? Have I not treated you with respect?"

"Yes, Your Royal Majesty, but I only fear that which I do not understand."

"And what is it you do not understand?"

"Why you have summoned me here today, Your Royal Majesty."

Suleyman turned from Haris to catch a warm breeze blowing from off the sea, gently ruffling the diagonal opening to the front of his gown. "Do you remember your Christianity?"

Haris followed Suleyman's surveillance of the sea. "Some of it . . . yes I do."

"What passage do you remember most often from the Christian Holy Book?"

Haris paused for a moment, before answering. "'He that troubleth his own house shall inherit the wind'."

Suleyman turned back toward Haris with his black eyebrows lifted simultaneously, as though they were joined together across his forehead. "And from the Quran?"

"'Observe justice in dealing with your children in the same manner in which you expect them to observe justice in being kind and good to you', "Haris responded confidently.

Suleyman produced a slight frown. "Both passages are similar. You harbor troubling memories of your father?"

"He was a good father, Your Royal Majesty. There is only one moment between us which haunts me. It is the time my father purchased my future with a sack of gold coins for the devshirme."

"Your heart is hardened, Lezhe Haris. You must not be so harsh toward your father. I have no doubt his wish for you was a noble one." Suleyman folded his hands behind his back. "My gift to the parents of my Janissaries is a life well lived for many of their sons. And some may one day attain a lofty status within my empire, such as rising to the position of grand vizier, as did Ibrahim."

Haris nodded.

"What do you know of my children?" Suleyman asked.

Haris took a deep breath, before summoning his education. "I know the royal house is blessed with three *sehzades*." He decided to refrain from identifying the sultan's deceased children, and naming only the living instead. "Sehzade Mustafa is your oldest son. He is followed in order according to age by your daughter Fatma Nur Sultan, your son Sehzade Abdullah, a daughter Mihrimah Sultan, your sons, Sehzade's Selim and Bayezid, and your youngest daughter, Raziye Sultan."

"Abdullah was killed by the pox," Suleyman corrected. "Sehzade Mehmed is my second oldest son."

Haris bowed his head. "Forgive me, Your Royal Majesty."

"My oldest, Sehzade Mustafa is fifteen years of age," Suleyman described. "When I reached the age of fifteen I became sanjak-bey of Sarki Province in Anatolia. Someday, Mustafa will inherit my throne, and I believe the time has come for him to become more astute in learning the delicate balance required to rule an empire. He must appreciate how occupying a throne is not merely about birth rite. Rather it is about earning admiration, and most importantly acquiring respect." Suleyman turned away from Haris to gaze out upon the sea again. "Gaining respect does not come easy, but is acquired through knowledge and experience. My son has been tutored by the best scholars, philosophers, and religious leaders from across Europe. Thus, I have trust in his growth in these areas." He swung back toward Haris. "I believe what he lacks lies in the area of military training. The backbone of my empire is my army, without it the Europeans would devour the land I rule and along with it my peoples, making it their mission to sweep away all memory of the Ottomans. What keeps my army loyal and adept at war, is their respect for their sultan. To be successful when his time comes, my son needs to earn their respect. As a Janissary, do you not agree?"

"The tulips are witness to your wisdom in this matter, Your Royal Majesty."

Suleyman grinned. "I wish for you to tutor him in military strategy, as well as in the art of soldiering."

Haris felt a wave of excitement surge throughout his body with the sultan's request; but remained quiet, realizing he had no choice in the matter.

Suleyman turned from Haris, and slowly approached his flower garden, leaning forward to gaze closely at the vibrant, intricate petals. "Lezhe Haris, there are those who question my wisdom in appointing you to train my son."

The wave of excitement Haris had felt energizing his body only moments before, had suddenly waned.

"Those who question me agree how you are a very good warrior," Suleyman continued. "But they say you ask too many questions. They say a good soldier is one who is trained to respond to an order for the strength and safety of the orta, not to waste time thinking about why the order was given. They say that perhaps you think too much, as though the independent individual inside of you usurps the disciplined soldier. What do you say to this?"

Haris swallowed hard, quickly assembling a response. "Your Royal Majesty, only moments ago you were speaking of my heroism in Vienna. My actions that night were the result of my military training."

Suleyman pulled himself away from the garden, turning to face Haris once again. "You are a good soldier, of this I am certain. But I also respect the opinions of those who question you."

Haris' stomach churned.

"Nevertheless, I have given much thought to this. It is not that I wish Mustafa to be a valiant warrior—only to expose him to the art of battle for the purpose of gaining respect as a leader of soldiers. I understand this is how European kings prepare their sehzades, or rather their princes, and it is also how I was trained in preparation to become sultan. For as much as I detest European arrogance, and their strange fondness for wanting to destroy one another, I do admire their obsession with royalty." He paused. "Ah—but I stray from the subject at hand."

Haris watched as Suleyman took a moment to gather his thoughts, before resuming his words. "You were at Vienna, and saw how the ortas made the decision to abandon the siege. At first, I was angered by this. But the more I have pondered their reaction, the more I have begun to understand you can only push men so far before they break—even Janissaries devoted to a sultan. As a leader of an army, one must not simply be able to understand the art of war he must also have the compassion to understand how men react under the stress of battle. I sense compassion about you, Lezhe Haris, and your intelligence shines brightly. That is why, despite what some may say, I know you are most capable for the task of training my son. And so, it is my wish you should do this."

The knot in Haris' stomach faded, replaced by a warm feeling of adrenaline pumping his ego.

Suleyman continued. "Your assignment will require that you relocate from your current barracks, to lodgings here inside the Yeni Saray among those assigned to work within the *Enderun*— the Interior Service of the Imperial Court. You will answer to the *Agha* of the Gate of Felicity."

Haris stiffened his posture, and bowed his head low in the direction of Suleyman. "Your wish is my command, Your Royal Majesty. I will not fail you."

CHAPTER SEVEN

A few days after meeting with the sultan, Haris stood alone in an open area of the imperial stables. He wiped the perspiration from his brow, as the morning rays of an early April sun burned brightly overhead.

Haris waited patiently after having been led to the stables by the Agha of the Gate of Felicity, who he recognized as the same African Janissary who had interrogated him at that very gate days before. After a brief, superficial conversation, Haris' new commanding officer left him to wait the arrival of the sehzade; although the sultan's son was late for his first lesson.

Haris decided the first lesson would be with the sword, but the strict requirements against anyone carrying such weapons, aside from the immediate guards of the royal family, had forced him to improvise his approach by using a severed broom handle instead. Standing in the center of an area squared off with a wooden fence, he settled his nerves with some basic calisthenics. Before too long, his solitude was interrupted by a procession of men passing through an opening in the fence on foot. They marched toward him in two parallel lines, as if it were a small parade. At the front of one line, Haris quickly identified the grand vizier pacing alongside a tall, lanky male clad in a Janissary's blue dolama, with both individuals wearing conical headgear. Six Janissaries each armed with swords—an indication of the status of the young man they protected—marched behind the lanky male, and six paraded behind the grand vizier.

Both lines came to an abrupt halt only a few rods from Haris, who stood at attention, with his head bowed.

The grand vizier stepped forward. "Sehzade Mustafa, I present to you Lezhe Haris!"

"Lezhe Haris, you may address me," the lanky male decreed.

Haris lifted his head, to gaze upon the slim build and young, bronzed face of the boy standing before him. "It is a great honor to meet you, Your Royal Highness. The sultan speaks highly of you."

The boy lifted his chest and produced a wide grin. "You are to teach me soldiering, Lezhe Haris. You must be a great warrior."

"Again, you honor me with your words, Your Royal Highness," Haris replied. "However, a great warrior is not necessarily the greatest teacher. I claim to be neither."

"I believe my father wishes only what is best for me, so I am to assume you are the best," Mustafa announced brashly. "There is a Janissary assigned to me, with whom I believe is unmatched in military skill. My father ignored my wishes to have him for my teacher, and instead has chosen you. It is my wish to settle this discrepancy by having the two of you duel one another before my training begins. Then I may be assured my teacher is indeed the best."

Haris recognized how the grand vizier expressed surprise with Mustafa's wish. "Your Royal Highness, I must object to your request on behalf of your father. I beg the Sehzade's pardon, but there exists no discrepancy. The sultan based his decision to have Haris as your teacher for many reasons beyond military prowess."

"Nevertheless, *he* will be training *me*, and not training my father," Mustafa countered. "Shall we precede, Lezhe Haris?"

Haris gathered in a breath. "As you wish, Your Royal Highness."

"Serkan!" Mustafa called out. Suddenly, a Janissary stepped from out of the line behind the sehzade. Slightly taller than Haris, the warrior filled out his uniform with a muscular physique. His dark eyes were placed deep, set beneath a protruding brow on either side of a long slender nose.

Haris held out his arms. "I'm certain Your Royal Highness can see that I am at a disadvantage without a sword. Would it please Your Royal Highness if we used these sticks instead?" He pointed to the two halves of the broom handle set on the ground beside him.

Mustafa turned to Serkan and nodded his head. In return, the warrior removed his curved sword from his waist, dropping it to the ground. Haris picked up the wooden clubs and smiled to the warrior, tossing one of the halves to his opponent.

Serkan snared the broom handle, and returned the gesture with a serious grin. Both men addressed the sehzade, bowing their heads before facing one another. The two drew closer, before Serkan led with his left foot and instantly lunged forward, swinging his stick at an angle, left and right with strong strokes. His aggressive attack forced Haris to block each slice with his own stick, while being pressed to move backward.

Mustafa sneered at the grand vizier. "It appears all Lezhe Haris can do, is to defend himself. Shall I assume this teacher's only lesson is in the art of defense?"

The grand vizier did not respond, as both men looked on, observing the duel which continued as it had begun, with Haris on the defensive. For the onlookers, it may have appeared that Serkan had the upper hand, but Haris recognized that the duel had suddenly changed; for his opponent's attack began to slow— the warrior was growing tired. In blocking Serkan's next slice,

Haris did not move his feet, but instead surprised his opponent by maintaining his ground. He leaned his upper body backward and to the right to avoid the strike, which permitted him to bring his club down on top of Serkan's. Then he moved to thrust his club forward at his opponent's neck, while Serkan raised his arm to defend against the thrust. At that moment, Haris lifted his right foot and kicked, smashing the sole of his boot into his opponent's groin, pushing him backward. Serkan winced and doubled over, as Haris smashed his hand with the club, forcing him to drop his weapon. He finished Serkan off by using his forearm to shove him face down to the ground.

Haris, breathing heavily, extended his arm toward Serkan; but the vanquished Janissary refused to accept it, and with a scowl, pulled himself up of his own power.

The grand vizier grinned at Mustafa. "Is Your Royal Highness satisfied?"

Haris stepped toward the sehzade and the grand vizier, stopping a few rods from them, before bowing.

Mustafa produced a frown, as Serkan approached him bowing before slipping back into line. "Lezhe Haris!" Mustafa called out. "What is my first lesson?"

Haris raised his head. "You have just witnessed it, Your Royal Highness. It was a demonstration of your ability to recognize talent and skill among your humble servants."

Mustafa's frown evolved into a curious smirk. "Then what is my second lesson?"

"If Your Royal Highness would be so kind to walk alone with me that we may discuss it in private."

Mustafa hesitated in his response, scanning his personal band of soldiers. With a sigh, he commenced a haughty stride in the direction of Haris. When the sehzade had reached him, Haris bowed, before turning and beginning a slow stroll in the opposite direction, which Mustafa imitated.

"Do you trust me?" Haris asked, as they continued to walk side by side.

"What?"

"Do you trust me? An element of trust must exist between the student and his teacher before learning can take place."

Mustafa glanced back momentarily at his soldiers. "I do not know you well enough to say I trust you."

"You have made the decision to walk alone with me. Is that not trust?" Haris pressed. "As a sehzade, you could have declined?"

"You have asked me to walk with you. You are my teacher, and I am your student."

"Exactly." Haris stopped, as Mustafa, in turn ended his steps and faced him. "And as my student, what is your goal?"

"I hope to learn the art of being a warrior."

"And I am proud to be your teacher of such skills. But first you must recognize how learning is about making mistakes. You will make mistakes, Mustafa."

The sehzade gasped. "I am a sehzade! You may not address me by my first name unless it is my wish that you do so! You are to refer to me as Your Royal Highness!"

Haris did not flinch. "I am Haris, your teacher. You have my permission to address me as Haris."

Mustafa gaped. "Your permission?"

Haris maintained a stoic expression. "During our time together as teacher and student, I wish to call you by your first name. Do not view it as an act of disrespect, but as a step in your growth. I do not intend to treat you as a sehzade, but as a soldier. Should you desire to be treated as royalty, then I'm certain Serkan will be eager to oblige you, but then you will be pampered and unable to appreciate the heart and soul of a Janissary. This would be a disservice to you, for you must learn to think as we think, fight as we fight, and feel as we feel, so that you may truly come to appreciate what it takes to lead such men. Do we have an understanding?"

With Mustafa's stunned expression, Haris sensed how the sehzade was taken aback by his audaciousness. He guessed very few men had the courage to speak to Mustafa with such brazenness, outside of the sultan. Nevertheless, he hoped his directness and confidence had made a strong impression; for he realized that in training the sehzade, he was not only acting on behalf of the sultan's wishes, but also out of a strong determination to successfully complete his assignment.

Mustafa glowered. "Yes, teacher Haris, we have an understanding. But heed my words. If at any point in my education I should feel you have betrayed your desire to teach me properly, then you shall pay dearly!"

Haris assumed the threat was Mustafa's attempt at reasserting recognition of his royal status, but he would have none of it. "Strong words from a boy."

Mustafa's eyes widened. "I am not a boy! I am a young man! I am the sehzade!"

"Not in my school," Haris replied. "Not yet anyway."

With face flushed, Mustafa abruptly spun away from Haris, beginning a pace toward his entourage.

"With my help, I have no doubt in time you will become a man!" Haris exclaimed. "And in the process, become a great leader as well!" He watched as Mustafa stopped, turning back to face him with contempt.

"You have my word, Mustafa—I will not fail you!" Haris said.

He guessed by the diminishing of the sehzade's rigid posture, Mustafa's ire had begun to slowly dissipate.

Mustafa took a deep breath. "You seem very sure of yourself, teacher. I think you are either very stupid, or very wise."

"I assure you it is the latter."

"This remains to be seen."

"Then allow me to show you."

Mustafa's frown remained constant for a minute or two, before erupting into a small grin. "All right, teacher. Where shall we begin?"

Haris approached Mustafa. "First, it is important we conduct our training in private. As I said, learning is about making mistakes. You will make mistakes, so I think it is best that you concentrate on being trained without having to worry about embarrassing yourself in front of an audience."

"But it is dangerous for a sehzade to be alone with one man."

"I return to my original question, do you trust me, Mustafa?"

Mustafa hesitated briefly, before nodding his head. "Yes, Haris. I guess I must," he said, before walking back toward the grand vizier and the Janissaries, dismissing them all. When they had left the area, Mustafa returned to Haris. "I must tell you how I am surprised that you defeated Serkan. He is very strong and one of the best Janissaries in my protection."

"If the winner between us were to have been decided in the best two out of three matches, I would have lost," Haris revealed. "He was outsmarted. His weakness was in showing off for you. He is strong, but allowed his pride to guide him. Wisdom triumphs over strength every time."

Haris detected respect growing within his student, shown by the intensity on Mustafa's face.

"All right teacher, what is next?"

"Show me your sword."

Mustafa pulled his sword from his sheath, and held the weapon with curved blade up for Haris to see.

"The Ottoman sword is called a *kilij*," Haris said.

Mustafa frowned. "I know what it is called."

"Good. Now how is it held?"

Mustafa gripped the handle firmly, and began slicing the air from right to left.

"You're holding it too tightly," Haris said. "Hold the weapon as you would hold a bird—lightly so the bird cannot escape, but not so tight that you will crush it. It is important to have flexibility in your wrist when working the kilij." Haris held out his hand. "Allow me to show you the starting position when using the sword."

Mustafa hesitated momentarily, before deciding to pass the weapon to Haris.

Haris grabbed the sword from the sehzade and pointed the tip of the blade at Mustafa's throat. "How do you know that I am not going to kill you with this sword?"

Mustafa's face cringed. "I trust you?"

"Trust no one!"

"But teacher, you have just spent time trying to convince me to trust you! You are confusing me!"

Haris faced Mustafa. "Look me in the eyes! Trust is to be earned, and not to be assumed! You and I have only met! I have yet to earn your trust!" Haris lowered the sword. "But in time, I will. As the sehzade, you cannot risk being so cavalier with trust. Such a mistake will cost you your life. Is this understood?"

Mustafa, wide-eyed, nodded.

"Now, about positioning your body in holding a sword," Haris said. "Watch carefully." He placed his left foot out in front, slightly bending his knees. "Your left foot is the lead foot. It is the front foot, assuring your body weight is evenly distributed. Your hips should face your opponent's and not be turned sideways, while holding your kilij at shoulder level.

"Next, you will bring the sword forward, closing the line between you and your opponent." Haris displayed the pose. "Step toward your opponent with your right foot, but not directly. Your step should be slightly to the right and will force your opponent to lunge toward you. When he does, lower your blade and strike him," he continued, demonstrating as he spoke. "Now, your turn." Haris handed the kilij back to Mustafa.

Over the next thirty minutes, Mustafa practiced the move until Haris was satisfied the sehzade had become mildly proficient at it.

"Now, to defend yourself—" Haris began.

"Haris, they tell me you are Croatian?"

Haris relaxed his body. "Yes."

"And as a young boy you were taken from your mother and father and placed in the devshirme."

"My father arranged it, but it is true that I was forced to leave them as a result."

"Do you miss your mother and father?"

"I received a message from my brother a few years ago describing how my father is dead," Haris replied. "As for my mother, I only wonder about her safety."

"You and I are similar when it comes to our relationship with parents," Mustafa remarked. "I rarely see my father, and when I do, it is often at some ceremony or celebration with hundreds of people around. I don't feel as though I know my father as intimately as a son should."

"And your mother?" Haris asked.

"I do see her more often than I do my father, but once again, there are so many servants meandering about. Our quarters in the harem are regimented with countless rituals, as if we are always on display," Mustafa lamented. "It is hard to imagine how one can be surrounded by many people, yet be so alone."

Haris studied his student with compassion, realizing how perhaps Mustafa was correct; for neither one of them could relate to experiencing the closeness of being part of an intimate family. For Haris, such fond memories once existed, but had begun to fade with time. He broke the short silence. "Well, you need not worry about crowds here . . . for we are alone—you and I."

Mustafa smiled. "Yes, but for once I do not feel alone."

Haris nodded. "Shall we return to the lesson?"

"Yes,—the defense position." Mustafa raised his sword, before abruptly lowering it. "It is my hope that you and I will become friends, Haris."

"Yes, Mustafa." Haris grinned. "But first I must teach you how to fight."

CHAPTER EIGHT

By late June, Haris' training of the sehzade took place consistently three days a week, with the only exception occurring during the month long religious celebration of Ramadan, when it was reduced to once a week. The time spent together between Haris and Mustafa worked to solidify the relationship between teacher and student, as well as fortify the foundation of a deep friendship. Ten years of age separated the two, but Haris could sense how Mustafa—who had three younger stepbrothers—began to view him as an older brother. This became apparent when, in between rigorous physical workouts and training in the knowledge of handling artillery, the two would discuss the challenges of growing up as young men. Haris convinced himself that such delicate discourse contributed to the sehzade's personal growth; although Mustafa often did not hesitate to reveal the interrelationships between the many members of the sultan's extended family—information Haris felt Suleyman would most certainly frown upon.

Friday, June 27, 1530

On this morning, Haris worshiped at Yavuz Sultan Selim Mosque, a place of worship that had been commissioned to be built by Suleyman in honor of his deceased father. The domed mosque, flanked by two minarets, was set majestically atop a hill north of Constantinople overlooking the Golden Horn. After the service, an excited Haris quickly found his way back to the capitol, where from there he moved on foot through the city streets toward the Hippodrome. As Mustafa's guest, he had received an invitation to attend the celebration following the *khitan*—the circumcision of three sehzades: Mustafa, Mehmed, and Selim.

After his name had been verified from a lengthy guest list, Haris entered a festive atmosphere. Set with an impressive display of colorful tents lining each of the elongated sides of the spacious oval shaped area, the Hippodrome pulsated with activity, most of it involving the preparation of food. A large presence of Janissaries could be seen stationed at various points around the Hippodrome, assembled for the sultan's protection. Haris realized he would have been assigned to the guard detail, had he not been elevated to the position of training the sehzade, and felt privileged to walk freely about, partaking in the jubilant atmosphere as a guest.

He moved throughout the sharply dressed crowd of prominent men representing positions of power, and wealth. They had traveled from every corner of Suleyman's empire in their desire to honor the sultan and his sons on this day, hailing from as far east as Algiers, and as far west as Baghdad, as well as from the multitude of cities lying in between. Adding to the energy swirling about the Hippodrome were royal event planners, servants, cooks, and musicians hustling into their designated places, working frantically to complete the final preparations before the arrival of the sultan and his family.

Suddenly, from behind, Haris heard his name being called, surprised to see his former Corbaci Kamil, wearing a blue kaftan and his feathered bork, moving toward him. Haris formed a rigid pose, conditioned to stand at attention, which produced a laugh from Kamil.

"Perhaps I should be standing at attention for you!" Kamil said. "For you are a member of the Enderun."

Haris relaxed his posture, returning the smile. "You still out-rank me."

"I'm not so sure. Tell me, how is the sehzade's training proceeding?"

Haris expressed surprise. "How did you know of my new appointment?"

Kamil laughed again. "Secrets are harder to keep when they involve those closest to the keys of the kingdom. There are many who envy you, and some who hover like vultures waiting to swoop in for the kill."

Haris felt troubled by Kamil's words. "What are you saying?"

"As I see it, your greatest challenge is not in training the sehzade, but will be in keeping his alliance. It is said the sultan's moods can be as fickle as the change in the direction of the wind. And with the sehzade, the apple does not fall far from its own tree," Kamil said. "But I have not sought you out today to worry you with words of warning. It brings me much joy to see you again, Haris."

Haris' angst faded, returning a smile to his face. "And it is good to see you as well. The training of the sehzade is going smoothly. I think it is safe to say he and I are becoming friends."

"That is good. I'm sure the fact you are here today as a guest, is a sign of that growing friendship."

"I want to thank you, Corbaci, for your recommendation to have me placed within the silahdar. Without the transfer, I don't think I would have been in a position to have been noticed by the sultan. I still wonder who exactly recommended me for the assignment to train the sehzade? Whomever it may be, I am very much indebted."

Suddenly, the sound of horns, drums, cymbals, and bells could be heard in the distance, bringing the boisterous crowd to a hush, as all eyes focused on the gate at one end of the Hippodrome opposite the stone serpentine column of Byzantine ruins. The crowd's attention was drawn to a parade of Janissaries composed of several ortas marching rigidly, positioned in front of a company of uniformed musicians playing while passing through the celebratory ground's makeshift entrance. These were followed by seven riders on horseback, with a lone rider in the lead. Haris recognized the three men on horseback trailing the lead rider as the sultan, the grand vizier and the yeniceri agasi, while behind them rode the three sehzades. All seven of the horsemen's prestige was reflected in their headgear—a conical shaped felt design for the sultan, his sons, and the grand vizier, while the lead horseman and the yeniceri agasi donned elaborate feathered borks.

Haris watched with curiosity. "Corbaci, who is the lead horseman? I've seen his face around the imperial stables, but I have never met him."

"He is called Rustem. He serves the sultan as the *mirahur-I ewel*, the chief supervisor of the imperial stables. They say that like the grand vizier, he is very close to the sultan. His position this afternoon as master of the horse confirms his favored relationship with Suleyman, for it is considered a great honor to be given the assignment of leading the sultan's steed."

"This Rustem, what is he like?"

"I've never met him. Those who have, describe him as being very smart, with a steady calmness about him."

Haris' attention turned back to the parade, where pacing behind the horses could be seen three of Constantinople's Islamic religious leaders. Each imam wore a long cloth robe, as well as a short rounded cap made of coarse cloth. Behind them, two black African servants clutched long poles within each hand, carrying a sedan, with one servant walking in the front and the other in the rear of the covered chair. Behind it, strolled two women clad in glittering silk robes, with an elaborate belt worn around the waist from which a small embroidered key purse was hung. The women moved slowly, walking parallel to one another and at some distance apart. Each of their wrists had been weighed down with a number of gold bands, and they wore a fez on their head with a flat top that rose a few inches, wrapped with a thin white scarf that dropped upon the shoulder before being fastened around the chin. Although their faces were concealed behind black silk veils, Haris was sure their identities consisted of the two mothers of Suleyman's sons.

"Of the women, who is who?" Haris pried.

Kamil lowered his voice to a whisper, producing a smirk. "They are the real power behind the throne. The elder woman who rides inside the sedan chair is known as the Valide Sultan, the most powerful woman in the empire, for she is the Queen Mother Ayse Hafsa Sultan, Suleyman's mother. Each of the other two women are the sultan's favorites who have each bore him children. They are given the title of *Kadin*. On the side closest to us, dressed in black, is Mahidevran Kadin, the mother of Mustafa, and to her right, dressed in turquoise is the redhead Roxelana, also called Hurrem Kadin. She is the mother of many of the sultan's other children, including Mehmed and Selim."

"Mustafa has told me of the great tension that exists between these women," Haris said.

"Of course, one is protective of her son as sultan, while the other two desires their sons to be the next sultan."

Close behind the three powerful females strolled dozens of women from the sultan's harem, clad in fine silk garments adding a rainbow of colors to the parade.

"Ah, the *gedikli*—maids in waiting," Kamil described. "It

is said that in Rumelia one can find some of the world's most beautiful —"

Suddenly, Kamil was interrupted by a strong hand on his shoulder, causing both he and Haris to turn, finding an Ottoman soldier clad in chainmail wearing a pointed helmet, standing firmly.

The officer cast a scowl. "Corbaci! Are you enjoying yourself? Why are you not inspecting your troops?" He switched his glare to Haris. "And you! Why are you not at your post? Do you think you are here as invited guests?"

"No! I . . . I —" Kamil stammered.

"It is I who has taken the corbaci away from his duties here," Haris interjected boldly. "I am Lezhe Haris, personal trainer to the Sehzade Mustafa. I am an invited guest. The corbaci was once the commander of my Janissary orta, and I recognized him here today."

The soldier scrutinized Haris. "Lezhe Haris, I must advise you there is a time and place for everything. This is not the time for old acquaintances to be sharing memories! The corbaci is on assignment here today!"

"Please let me continue," Haris said. "As I have only been the sehzade's trainer for a few weeks, I needed assistance in identifying many of the royal figures present today. It is actually my duty this afternoon, as it is the wish of the sehzade that I find assistance in this matter," he fibbed.

The soldier threw an unconvincing glare toward Kamil. "Corbaci, do you make it a habit of having a soldier of lower rank speak in your defense?"

Haris grew angry. "Do you realize you are speaking to members of the sultan's Janissaries? Is that what this is about?"

"I know with whom I speak!" the officer growled. "No matter if you are Janissary and I am sipahi, any tension between our military branches is inconsequential when it comes to the security of our sultan and his family!"

"The officer is correct," Kamil said calmly. "The security of the sultan is most important." He looked the warrior in the eyes. "I am assisting the Janissary, and will return to my orta at the conclusion of the procession."

The soldier frowned, followed by a long sigh, bringing his attention back to Kamil. "Very well," he acknowledged with slight reluctance, before stepping away into the crowd.

Kamil looked at Haris with a frown. "Thank you, Haris. I owe you."

"We are Janissaries—the right arm of the sultan! The Turk had no right to question either of us!"

"On the battlefield or within a sultan's palace it is true we hold higher status. But when assigned to a security detail for the sultan at an event such as this, any branch has the right to question another."

"It is clear that the sipahis carry a deep jealousy for the Janissary infantry!"

"If I remember correctly, for a brief time you were once a member of the sipahis," Kamil said.

"I was a member of the *kapikulu sipahis*—Janissary cavalry!" Haris corrected. "He is a *timarli*—Turkish cavalry! I find the Turks look upon the Janissaries with disdain because we are not their kind!" He grimaced. "It is the timarli who visit me in my nightmares, reminding me of the time I was taken from my home as a boy in Lezhe by the very same branch of Turkish soldiers!"

"You forget that I am Turkish myself."

Haris was surprised. "I did not know you were Turkish?"

"On my mother's side."

"I meant no offense with my words," Haris offered.

Kamil nodded that he understood, before bringing his attention back to the parade where he beheld the last stragglers of the harem. "The real disappointment is that as a result of our interaction with the timarli, we have missed viewing most of the beautiful women!"

Haris grinned. "Yes. So many women for one—" He paused when his eyes caught the figure of a slim maiden dressed in a sapphire robe with her long blonde hair bouncing with each step, as she paraded past him. "It is her! The prisoner I saw in our camp back in Vienna! A veil conceals her smile, but I'm sure it's her!"

"And what if it is?" Kamil asked. "Every woman within the sultan's harem is either a captured slave or a gift to the sultan from some tribe or kingdom."

"I remember her eyes," Haris recalled. "They were emerald and sparkled like gems."

"Her presence here today means that she is a *gozde*—a potential favorite of the sultan."

"The sultan has taken her to bed?" Haris asked, with a slight irritated inflection in his voice.

"It depends on whether she has received a scarf."

"A scarf?"

"These women are all virgins. But should the sultan desire one of them, he makes his intentions known to her by placing a scarf over her shoulder."

The two men watched the group of women follow the parade route to the far end of the Hippodrome, where a throne had been set up beneath a large, dazzling crimson canopy embroidered with gold. As Suleyman took a seat on the throne, his sons settled into seats set to the right side of their father, while the grand vizier and the yeniceri agasi sat to his left. The queen mother and the mothers of the sultan's sons were positioned behind their sons, while the maids in waiting sat together in an area to the back and left of the sultan's throne. Once all were seated, the standing crowd slowly drew closer to the canopy; although they were kept at a moderate distance from the throne by a battalion of Janissaries forming a human barrier.

The grand vizier rose to offer a complimentary and exhaustive introduction of the sultan. This was followed with great applause coupled with laudable chants, before Suleyman rose from his throne, first offering praise to Allah, followed by a boastful recognition of his three sons. Next, the Ottoman leader acknowledged and thanked the crowd for their presence, before finally retiring back into his throne. A queue quickly formed composed of distinguished dignitaries, Kurdish emirs, and Venetian ambassadors—each bearing a variety of gifts for the sultan and his sons.

As the gifts were laid at the sultan's feet, Haris' attention was drawn to the area of maids in waiting, where he identified the blonde woman in sapphire, seated on the end of the last row. "There she is!"

"Who? The blonde? Still you are obsessed with her?" Kamil bemoaned. "Forget her, I tell you."

"I must speak with her."

Kamil grabbed a hold of Haris' arm and pulled him close. "Do you not understand? These women are unapproachable— they are the property of the sultan!"

"We are also the property of the sultan!"

"If you should as much as throw a glance in the direction of one of these women, let alone speak with anyone of them, it could cost you your life!"

"And if I don't make an attempt, then perhaps I will have cheated myself of this challenge in life."

"And should death be the consequence?"

"Then I know Allah will have disapproved."

Kamil sneered. "I don't think it is Allah you should be worried about!"

"Then I shouldn't be worried," Haris replied. "Corbaci, I need your help. There is a Janissary stationed only a few rods from where she is seated. Is he assigned to your orta?"

"No. The men of my responsibility are positioned just inside the gate."

"No matter, for as a corbaci, you outrank him, and he will have to take orders from you."

Kamil frowned. "What are you thinking?"

"If you would relieve him from his duty for only a moment, and send me in to replace him, I may be able to get her attention."

"Do you hear what you are saying? This, from the man I recommended for the silahdar, as well as to train the sehzade?"

"Then it was you!" Haris reached out to hug the corbaci. "I am very grateful!"

Kamil pushed him away. "There are many eyes and ears about us! If someone should see what you just did, then we will be questioned!"

"I'm sorry. Why didn't you tell me the recommendation came from you?"

"Because your assignment has only begun, and I did not want you to blame me if it should fail! But after what you're proposing today, I'm surely to be beheaded anyway! You must forget this crazy idea of yours!"

Haris grinned. "But you forget that you owe me." He sighed. "Come, whatever may happen, you have my promise that you will not find yourself involved in this matter."

Kamil twisted his head, glancing to his left and right before directing his stare back at Haris. "You are a stubborn one. All right, I shall help you!" He lifted his head to the sky. "Allah challenges us this day!"

Haris began moving across the grounds of the Hippodrome in the direction of the seating area, with the reluctant, nervous Kamil in tow. When they were nearly twenty rods from the women, both men noticed the Janissary assigned to stand guard near to them, and stopped to plan their next move.

"So, you would like that I pull this guard away from his assignment?" Kamil asked.

"Yes. What will you say to him?"

Kamil thought for a moment. "Perhaps I will ask him to identify himself and his orta's corbaci, while inspecting his uniform."

"Good, then I shall move in to fill his vacancy."

"What do you hope to gain from this stunt?"

"Only her attention."

Kamil frowned. "Do not be long, Haris! Every second allows for more time for you to be caught!"

"I understand. It shall be quick."

The two men approached the soldier, who stood at attention less than a rod away from the seated maidens. Wearing a serious demeanor and an authoritative cadence, Kamil asked the soldier to step with him some distance away from the area of women. Haris immediately relieved the soldier from his post, making sure he positioned himself even closer to the women. With rigid posture, he stood staring outward into the Hippodrome's intermingling crowds, while delicately removing a green handkerchief from the pocket of his breeches, concealing it within the palm of his hand.

Suddenly, Haris turned toward the blonde woman and said softly in Turkish, "My lady." As he did, he bent over, reaching his hand to the grass as though he were picking something up from off the ground. Rising up, he was sure to keep his head bowed with eyes cast downward, while at the same time holding out his hand to reveal the handkerchief. Continuing to converse in Turkish he said, "You dropped this." The woman, who was now staring at him, began to utter a response, when Haris quickly interrupted with a whisper. "Vienna." And then in the German language he continued, "Remember? In Vienna, you fell, and I helped you to your feet?"

Haris could see the woman's eyes light up with astonishment.

"Do you remember?" Haris repeated, still speaking in German.

The woman glanced about at the maidens seated around her, before turning toward Haris and taking the handkerchief from his hand. With a cautious whisper, she replied, "*Danke*," followed quickly by, "Jaheem." Her response did not go unnoticed by the other women, as they glared in her direction.

Haris could not make sense of her reply; but realized how too many eyes and ears now shared their communication. Fortunately, Kamil had returned with the Janissary, and ordered him back on duty. Both men quickly began pacing away from the area of women, strolling side by side.

"Well?" Kamil asked, without looking at Haris.

"I made contact with her, but I'm confused by her response."

"What did she say?"

"I'm not sure?"

Kamil stopped, which brought Haris to a halt as well. The corbaci looked him in the eyes. "What you did just now is foolish and dangerous! Do not allow your lofty position within the Enderun to cloud your vision, Haris! The fate awaiting one with such ignorance is a bow string wrapped around his neck! I recommended you for the position of the sehzade's trainer because you are not only a good soldier, but a young man with a good head on his shoulders! It would be a shame for you to lose that head!"

CHAPTER NINE

A week and a half passed before Haris felt confident his foolish attempt to speak to the harem maiden had not fallen upon vengeful ears. The fact that no one approached him on this matter left him wondering if his stunt had been viewed as favorable by the blonde woman; although he was still left pondering just what it was she uttered to him.

On a July day, the sehzade's military training would advance from sword play to archery from horseback. Haris arrived early for the lesson, waiting inside the open air enclosure near to the stables; but he also awaited the arrival of Rustem, the chief supervisor of the imperial stables, who would bring the sehzade's horse to the training. Haris realized he would finally come face to face with this rising star within the Enderun.

As he stood in the center of the large square area flexing his bow string, Haris looked up to see a man on foot clutching the lead line of a small, black, Arabian stallion. The man moved toward him at a leisurely pace, wearing a tight black turban. With a slim build and average height, there was nothing particularly remarkable about his appearance, aside from how the man looked to be a few years older than he.

"Merhaba," the man greeted with a smile set beneath a pudgy nose. "Haris, I presume?"

"Yes." Haris noticed how the man's hazel eyes glinted on a fair-skinned face partially obscured by a thick, well-groomed beard.

"I am Rustem. You are here in my stables two or three times a week it would appear, and yet I have not found time to introduce myself. Please accept my apology."

"We are all very busy in service to the sultan," Haris replied.

Rustem smiled. "May I ask where was your place of birth?"

"I am Croatian, but was raised in Lezhe."

Rustem produced a wide smile. "What a coincidence, for I am Croatian as well, born in Skradin, and I believe we fought together at Mohacs."

Haris nodded. "I was in the cavalry division at Mohacs."

"As was I."

"Then we have something in common," Haris remarked.

"Yes, and we both live and work here in the Enderun—within the inner circle, so to speak." Rustem reached out to pet the horse's dish-shaped face. "And this beautiful animal is the Sehzade Mustafa's horse, Clovis."

"Clovis?"

"Yes. Apparently the sehzade was fascinated by an old tale told to him by one of his European tutors about an early Frankish king—a fifteen year old boy named Clovis—who united the tribe of Franks into a powerful Christian kingdom. I think perhaps Mustafa dreams of playing such an important role someday." He stroked the horse's fine coat before turning toward Haris. "Lofty aspirations, wouldn't you say?"

"No more so than two Croatian boys who find themselves within the Enderun of a powerful sultan."

Rustem chuckled, waving his index finger at Haris. "You are a witty one!"

Haris looked beyond Rustem to see Mustafa strolling through the entrance of the riding area.

"Time for schooling, I see," Rustem recognized. "It was a pleasure to meet you, teacher. You have a challenging task ahead of you—schooling the future sultan that is."

Haris guessed that Rustem's comment was meant to elicit an unflattering response, but he would not take the bait. "The sehzade is a good student. He is up to the task."

Rustem grinned, and began walking toward Mustafa. Haris watched how he stopped to greet the sehzade—the two men sharing small talk, before the chief supervisor of the imperial stables moved on and out of the area through the gate, just as Mustafa reached his teacher, wearing a smile.

"Merhaba, Haris!" Mustafa brought his head alongside that of the animal, before placing his cheek against the side of the stallion's head. "Merhaba to you as well, Clovis!" He turned back toward Haris. "What do you think of my stallion?"

"He is a fine specimen."

"I agree," Mustafa replied. The sehzade observed a narrow leather container, filled with arrows resting at Haris' feet, in addition to the bow he held within his hand. "I remember how today the lesson is archery from horseback."

Haris picked up the quiver, slinging it over his right shoulder, before sliding the bow over his left. "May I have the honor of riding Clovis?"

"Why, of course teacher."

Haris stepped up to the beautiful equine, softly petting its long nose before approaching its left side. Haris mounted the horse, settling onto the felt cushioned red saddle adorned with ornate gold patterns, and grabbed the reins, giving the animal a gentle kick sending the stallion in motion. Instantly, the horse broke into a trot, with Haris guiding the animal around the square several times—at first with a repetitive canter, before using his legs and reins to summon the stallion into a full gallop. Once Haris was sure that he and the horse were comfortable with one another, he guided Clovis back to where Mustafa stood.

"Mustafa, over the past few weeks I have seen you use the bow and arrow. You are very good at it—when you are stationary." Haris leaned forward in the saddle. "Today, you will learn what separates the Janissary's cavalry from the enemy's—archery from a moving horse. It is a skill first effectively put to use by the Mongols, who built the world's largest empire by mastering the talent. This tactic of warfare found its way to Turkish tribesman, even before the days of Seljuk."

Haris corrected his posture. "When riding into battle or on the hunt, an archer clutches the reins of his horse with the right hand, and holds his bow with his left." Haris slid the bow from off his shoulder and gripped it with his left hand. "Thus, the first important step to learn is to be able to have the confidence to ride your horse in full gallop, with only one hand holding the reins."

"I have ridden horses since I was a child," Mustafa said. "I am confident I can ride in the manner which you describe."

"We shall see," Haris responded. "And if so, then it shall be a quick transition for you to the next step, which is to have confidence in riding with no hands on the reins, for it takes two hands to shoot an arrow with a bow. Keeping your balance on the back of the horse, as well as knowing just when to let the arrow fly, are important for the shooter's accuracy.

"The archer's quiver is slung over his right shoulder in order to reach behind with the right hand to retrieve an arrow, while remaining focused on what is ahead without holding the reins. After retrieving the arrow, it can be brought to the bow, and released while the horse is galloping."

Mustafa did not respond, which Haris interpreted as a sign

the sehzade was bored with the instruction; yet eager to see his teacher perform the feat.

"But, as I said before," Haris resumed, "the most important action involved in this skill, is to recognize when is the right time during the horse's gallop to release the arrow."

"How do you know when?" Mustafa asked.

The sehzade's question brought a smile to Haris' face. "During a horse's gallop, there is a beautiful moment when the animal has all four hooves off of the ground. As a rider, you will learn to feel when the horse is in flight. If you do not fire at this point, the jolt that occurs when its hooves are brought back to the ground will disrupt the flight of the arrow. Is this understood?"

Mustafa nodded with a sigh. "Jaheem warned me this would be a difficult lesson today."

Haris froze. "Jaheem?"

"Yes, I had a conversation with him only moments ago as I strolled through the harem. It is why I was delayed."

Haris' curiosity was piqued. "Who is he?"

"Why do you care?"

Haris realized he had been caught off guard by mention of the name. "I don't care. Let us return to the lesson."

Mustafa smiled. "Jaheem is the *kizlar agasi*—the chief black eunuch of the sultan's harem."

Haris' concentration slipped again, as he began to imagine the blonde maid in waiting.

"Well?" Mustafa proclaimed, breaking Haris' daze.

"Well . . . what?"

"Are you going to demonstrate this archery skill you have just described?"

"Yes—yes, of course. Observe how I will let the arrow fly when all four hooves are off the ground." Haris pulled on the reins and with a firm kick from both feet, sent the horse into a full gallop.

The stallion and its rider circled the area several times before Haris let go of the reins, pulled an arrow from his quiver, and fixed it to the bow string. At one end of the square was planted a tall wooden pole, and with the horse in full stride moving toward the object, Haris waited for the moment his body could recognize when the animal was airborne. In an instant, he fired his arrow at the pole, striking the object with deadly accuracy. He repeated the successful shot on a second gallop around the square, before rising up in his saddle, and balancing himself on the stirrups in a standing position, as the galloping horse streaked toward the target for the third shot.

Mustafa's eyes widened, as he beheld the skillful teacher, and without fail, Haris' third arrow found its mark as well. He retreated into the saddle, grabbing the reins to slow the stallion to a trot.

"Very impressive, Haris!" Mustafa praised. "It surprises me that you are a member of the Janissary infantry and not a member of the sipahis. Your skills on horseback with the bow and arrow are notable!"

Haris dismounted the horse. "I began with the sipahis. My experience at the Battle of Mohacs forced me to ask for reassignment within the infantry."

"What happened?"

Haris took a breath. "In the middle of the battle, my horse was shot out from underneath me and when it fell, I found myself trapped from the waist down beneath the weight of the wounded animal. Helpless to defend myself, a Hungarian soldier saw my situation, and rushed to strike me with his sword. Another Janissary came to my defense, killing the man just before the Hungarian went to plunge his blade into me. The experience told me I'd rather be free, fighting on my feet, than to be dependent upon an animal."

Mustafa stood silent. Haris interpreted the quietness to be an indication of the sehzade suddenly grasping how far removed from the reality of battle his military training seemed to be.

"Now it's your turn," Haris said. "I want you to practice at riding with one hand first, and when you have succeeded, ride with no hands."

Mustafa nodded and mounted the horse to begin guiding it around the square. Before long, the sehzade let the steed out to gallop, working diligently at holding the reins with one hand, while maintaining his balance as the horse moved briskly. Haris recognized how this skill did not take very long for the sehzade to accomplish, and instructed Mustafa to try it with no hands. Soon, Haris could see how this proved more difficult, as the sehzade struggled to maintain his balance on the galloping steed. After twenty minutes had passed, Mustafa slowed his horse to a trot, steering it toward his teacher.

"It is more difficult than I thought," Mustafa said.

Haris noted a disgusted look envelop the sehzade's face. "Nothing comes easy without practice."

"If I can't ride a moving horse without holding the reins, how am I ever going to master shooting an arrow from the back of one?" Mustafa groaned.

"Mustafa, it takes years to perfect such a skill," Haris said. "Remember, you are a sehzade. Your role is to lead such men into battle, not to be a great archer yourself. Those who serve you want only to believe their leader understands the art of war, for you will be the architect of the battlefield strategy that will guide them, and they will entrust their lives to you."

Mustafa sighed. "But what if my stepbrother masters this skill or any skill before I do?"

"Your stepbrother, Mehmed?"

"Yes . . . or Selim, or even Bayezid! Any one of them!" Mustafa growled. "Should any of them gain the favor of the troops over me, then I am a dead man!"

Sensing Mustafa's frustration, Haris softened his tone with the sehzade. "Do you have a strained relationship with your stepbrothers?"

"No—we are cordial with one another, but they are young, as am I! I would be foolish not to think that the future may change our relationship! There may come a time when my brothers and I will be enemies!"

Haris frowned, looking away.

Mustafa gripped the pommel tightly. "Haris, you think I'm mad to worry about such things? It was my great, great grandfather Mehmed who passed the Law of Fratricide! I only learned the meaning of the word last year from my European tutors! It means to kill one's brother or sister!"

"I know it's meaning," Haris said.

"The law was passed because the sultan suggested how it is best for the empire if the siblings of a sultan should die, as a way to prevent civil war!" Mustafa's facial features grew more animated. "And my grandfather Sultan Selim invited both of his brothers to a dinner party shortly after his father died, and had both murdered! For this he was given the nickname ferocious!"

"I have heard such things." Haris sighed, glancing up at Mustafa. "But you have the upper hand, for you are the oldest."

"Yes, and so then when I am sultan, I should have my brothers murdered?" Mustafa mocked.

"As the sultan, you will have great power. You will have the power to change such traditions. You worry about having the skill to be a warrior as though leading with the sword is the only way.

But leading an empire is done with the heart," Haris expressed, pounding his right fist against his own chest. "And it is done with the mind!" he continued, bringing his index finger to his temple. "These are more powerful than the sword!"

Mustafa sighed, nodding in agreement with Haris, before dismounting the horse. "Perhaps you are right. But I still worry I may not get the chance to make such changes!"

"Now is not the time to become belabored with such thoughts," Haris said. "You should be concerned only with that which you can control." He grinned. "At this time, there is not much you can control, aside from learning how to ride Clovis with no hands on the reins."

Mustafa stared Haris in the eyes, forcing a smile. "You are correct, teacher. I only hope you are with me when that day comes for me to be in a position to make change."

CHAPTER TEN

Mustafa's mention of the name Jaheem had struck a chord with Haris, and after careful deliberation, it all began to make sense to him. *The blonde maiden, who was taken prisoner in Vienna, had become a member of the sultan's harem, and Jaheem held the position as the harem's chief black eunuch. Unfortunately, the sultan's harem existed only for the sultan's pleasure, and to challenge that precedent would be dangerous. Yet, on that day at the Hippodrome, the maiden's utterance of Jaheem's name may have been a signal on how the chief eunuch possibly possessed the means of establishing discreet communication between anyone foolish enough to risk contact with a maiden of the harem. But what did this reveal about Jaheem? Could the black eunuch's assistance and discretion be purchased? More importantly, was the blonde maiden worth the risk?* Haris convinced himself she was.

Since having been appointed to the Enderun, Haris' living quarters had changed from the barracks in the Et Maydani section of Constantinople to the dormitory within the third courtyard of the Yeni Saray, set aside for members of the silahdar who had been assigned special duties on behalf of the royal family. Haris viewed this as an opportunity to observe Jaheem before approaching him. He realized how the chief eunuch, like the maidens and their servants, was essentially a prisoner inside the walls of the harem—an area off limits to most—and laying eyes upon him, let alone speaking with him, may prove to be an impossible task.

The friendship between Haris and Mustafa continued to

grow stronger; but Haris thought it unwise to share with him his secret desire to meet the blonde maiden. Surely the sehzade could help identify Jaheem, but it seemed to be a subject too personal and laden with potential danger.

Haris decided to alter his daily routine in the hope he might stumble upon a moment of opportunity to see the chief eunuch; however, days and weeks passed without any activity at the harem's Royal Gate. Finally, one Thursday at mid-morning, while Haris was passing the harem on his way back to the dormitory after training with Mustafa, he observed a wagon full of fine silks and colorful linen parked outside the gate. Suddenly, the doors of the gate parted slightly, and out through the opening stepped a man with skin the color of ebony. The African conducted business with the wagon driver with an air of confidence, carrying himself as though he were a man of some importance. Convinced this man had to be Jaheem, Haris made certain to return to the Royal Gate at the same time on the following Thursday, finding the scene repeated. He now had a time and place where he could observe the chief black eunuch.

In the following weeks, Haris' initial scrutiny of Jaheem became limited to identifying the African's physical characteristics. The eunuch was short and stout with shiny black skin, and cropped hair. He exhibited a perpetual smile reflecting a friendly, gregarious demeanor—a trait Haris imagined to be welcomed and pleasing to the many women of the harem. However, the physical trait Haris would find most advantageous about the man, was his pudginess around the waist; for it was obvious Jaheem enjoyed food.

Haris, whose Janissary wage totaled thirty *akces* every three months for the purchase of weaponry, and twelve *akces* for clothing and other incidentals, would on occasion, spend a small portion of his salary treating himself to a delectable pastry. This proved to be a very convenient acquisition for him, since his place of residence inside the dormitory set less than one hundred rods from the Gate of Felicity, allowing him easy access to the palace's kitchens and bakeries. Guessing that Jaheem may himself be in possession of a sweet tooth, Haris concocted a plan to use food as a way to arrange a meeting between the two.

The plan unfolded one Thursday morning just after the wagon unloaded its delivery of silk and linen at the Royal Gate. Haris had made sure to time his movements precisely to pass the gate just as the wagon pulled away, and as Jaheem was making his way back through the opening. Haris—carrying an object wrapped in paper—moaned as he fell to the ground. His actions did not go unnoticed by Jaheem, who stopped to observe Haris in a sitting position, grimacing as he reached for his ankle. The chief eunuch gave him assistance, and in return, Haris rewarded him the contents wrapped in paper, which much to Jaheem's delight contained the sweet dessert pastry baklava. This strange introduction evolved into a weekly routine over the next month, as Haris stopped by the Royal Gate every Thursday morning with the edible gift for his new acquaintance. Even the armed black African soldier who stood guard outside the Royal Gate had begun to look forward to the weekly visit, for Haris made sure to include the particular harem sentry in the delectable gesture as well; although he could not help but find it odd how the guard would smile upon receipt of the pastry, without ever once expressing a word of gratitude.

With each delivery of baklava, small segments of conversation would erupt between Haris and Jaheem, affording each man the opportunity to delicately unwrap each's true character with a friendly, but guarded approach. Haris compared it to slowly pulling the skin from an onion with care to avoid being brought to tears by the pungent vegetable. Eventually, he learned Jaheem had been born and raised in a village just outside of Timbuktu, the great African city within the Mali Empire of West Africa. He had been captured by Arab slave traders, castrated before puberty, and eventually sold to a wealthy merchant in Constantinople, who in turn, presented the African slave to Suleyman as a gift upon his ascension to the throne of the Ottoman Empire. Over time, Jaheem had used his charm, personality, and wit in advancing from his role as a servant assigned to the harem, to eventually reaching the position of the kizler agasi.

With each passing week, Haris sensed that Jaheem began to suspect there was more to their benevolent fraternization than simply sharing pastry. And so, it came as no surprise to him that on the fifth consecutive Thursday, Haris detected a touch of curiosity surfacing from within the chief eunuch.

"Lezhe Haris," Jaheem addressed, with high pitched voice, and a wide smile, brandishing sparkling white teeth. "I have asked myself for the past several weeks why I—a humble servant of the sultan's harem—should continue to receive the generosity of the sehzade's Janissary trainer. For I know, as you know, that everything has a price."

Haris grinned. "You are very observant, Jaheem. So, I must be honest and tell you that I do seek information. But I am hopeful our new friendship will not be affected by what I am about to ask of you." Haris glanced toward the African soldier standing guard at the gate.

"You need not fear speaking in front of him," Jaheem explained. "He, like many of the servants inside the harem, is deaf and mute. The sultan and his family feel less threatened when surrounded by afflicted peoples."

"That explains the guard's silence over these past weeks. But you—"

"I am no exception, for I am a eunuch—less of a man," Jaheem described, still smiling as though he had come to terms with his situation long ago. "Before you proceed with whatever it is you intend to ask of me, you must understand my loyalty lies with the sultan."

"As does mine," Haris replied. "But what the sultan does not know cannot hurt him, and it is not my intention to do so." He studied Jaheem silently for a moment, until convinced he could proceed with his request without objection. "There is a woman within the sultan's harem. She is Viennese or German—a blonde European who was acquired in Vienna last year. I am hoping you may help me speak with her?"

Haris noticed how Jaheem did not express surprise at the request, reacting as though he had anticipated it. "There are several women who meet your description."

"She has the most stunning emerald eyes with the power to command one's attention, as does a pair of gems sparkling in the moonlight."

"You know of course that all women of the harem are off limits to everyone but the sultan?"

Haris nodded. "Yes, I know, and I am hoping not only for your help, but for your word in keeping our conversation a secret."

"Then you risk everything by attempting to speak with her. I am the kizler agasi—the chief black eunuch of the harem," Jaheem reminded him. "It is a position I have earned by thinking ahead, being resourceful, and knowing when not to be seen and heard. But most importantly, my value lies with the trust given to me to keep secrets." He lowered his voice to a whisper, as if he too were suddenly concerned with ears attached to undetected faces. "The harem contains many women who are imprisoned behind these walls. Constantly under surveillance, they have very little freedom to express their thoughts, fears, dreams. They are like beautiful jaded birds in a gilded cage. Peace of mind for each rests with sharing their secrets with me." He paused, leaning closer to Haris. "I can keep a secret, Lezhe Haris, this I can assure you. Why should I risk placing myself in danger for *your* secret?"

"I have only one answer which makes sense," Haris offered.

"And—?"

"On the chance that somewhere, within her secrets and desires, I exist. Then, in taking me to her, you would be bringing her pleasure in fulfilling her dreams. I imagine keeping the sultan's harem satisfied is your responsibility, is it not?"

Jaheem's smirk expanded into a wide smile, revealing his teeth once again. "You are unlike any Janissary I have known, Lezhe Haris! Although trained to devote complete loyalty to the sultan with mind, body, and heart, you possess a free spiritedness about you that tests what you have been trained!"

"Believe me, Jaheem, when I tell you how my loyalty is with the sultan, as well as my devotion to the ways of a Janissary."

"I believe that you want to believe it is the truth! But you are blinded by your youth!" Jaheem explained. "One day your eyes will be opened, and when it happens, you will not like what you see, for the truth will then be visible. Although I fear a long life lived is not in the future for such a courageous man as you!"

Haris' eyes widened and his smile faded. "You will not help me?"

Jaheem stared back at him. "I too have a secret." Slowly he reached into the pocket of his kaftan, pulling out a green hand-kerchief. "You have indeed existed within her dreams."

"My handkerchief!"

"I have known about your real intentions since our second meeting," Jaheem revealed. "The blonde maiden you seek has been confiding in me with her own dreams. But I had to give it time to learn if you could be trusted. She is very dear to me, and is unlike most of the women within the harem."

"What is her name?"

"Ah—this I will not tell you. The less information you receive from me, the better for me," Jaheem explained, still smiling.

"What did you mean she is unlike others within the harem?"

"She is full of life—rebellious and not submissive like the others. I liken her to a caged lioness which does not accept the situation in which it finds itself. But most importantly, she has a good heart, and treats the servants as equals. This is why I have agreed to help the two of you meet—I like this one very much. Fate has brought you together, so it must be the will of Allah."

"How do I meet her?"

"Allah has brought you this far in your quest to meet the maiden," Jaheem said. "If Allah wills it, your meeting will happen. I know a way in which to move you beyond the Royal Gate unnoticed, but it must be at a time when the sultan is away from the harem. I am not saying you will have less danger with him gone, but it should be less complicated that way. When the sultan is present, everything is done with utmost efficiency. My advice is for us to continue to meet as we have here at the Royal Gate each Thursday. When I have information, which will allow us to move with greater freedom, I shall reveal it to you."

CHAPTER ELEVEN

By the advent of autumn, Haris' patience in waiting for an opportunity to set into motion the plan to meet the maiden had begun to waver when suddenly, Jaheem learned of preparations being made to entertain an Austrian diplomatic mission arriving at the palace. The mission of the seven men sent by Austria's King Ferdinand, was an attempt to persuade Suleyman to return a large portion of Hungary to Austria—territory which the Ottoman sultan's army had captured four years earlier.

Of course, Haris and Jaheem were less concerned by the nature of the diplomatic visit than to its timing, as they realized most of the sultan's morning duties would place him within the Divan Square's Imperial Council, where foreign and domestic state affairs were often conducted. Because this council met within the second courtyard, they reasoned the situation would present the chief eunuch with opportunity to discreetly move Haris inside the harem.

Thursday, October 2, 1530

As planned, Haris met Jaheem near the linen and silk wagon, under the watchful eye of the African guard. The two men exchanged small talk and baklava, before Jaheem said goodbye, carrying the day's shipment inside the open gate. Haris began walking in the opposite direction as the wagon pulled away, when suddenly Jaheem rushed back outside calling for the wagon to stop, motioning for the guard to run after the vehicle. As the guard pursued the wagon, Haris quickly slipped inside the gate opening.

After the guard brought the wagon to a stop, the chief eunuch obtained another bundle of linen from the merchant. Jaheem used sign language to express his thanks to the deaf guard, before slipping inside the gate. He closed the door, finding Haris waiting in the shadows of a second wall containing three doors. Jaheem instructed Haris to remove his bork, conceal the headgear within a piece of cloth, and quickly cloak his own body in linen, while shielding his head and all but his eyes with silk.

"Which door do we take?" Haris asked.

"All three doors will eventually bring us to the fourth courtyard where the gardens and pavilions are located," Jaheem explained. "The door on the right leads to the sultan's quarters. The door in the middle leads directly to the Court of the Queen Mother, and the door on the left leads to the Court of the Concubines."

"Then we shall take the door on the left."

Jaheem shook his head. "No. Remember, the sultan is not present within the harem at this hour. We have less risk of being seen should we take the door on the right. We will be able to move unnoticed until we reach the courtyard of the Queen Mother."

Haris noticed how Jaheem had lost his customary smile, replacing it with a distressful look, lowering his voice to a whisper. "What we are doing is dangerous!"

Haris wrapped his face with the veil. "Yes, I know, we've been through this."

"No! You don't understand! It has become even more so since yesterday!" Jaheem exhaled. "Come, we must not stand here! We must move!" He began dividing the bundle of linen and silk among the two of them. "Carry this and you will look less suspicious, and with your hands full, you will be less likely encouraged to perform sign language." He stepped up to the doors, choosing the one on the right. "Walk alongside of me." They began a steady pace through a narrow corridor featuring high white walls, with its ceiling open to the blue sky overhead.

"I was approached yesterday by a man seeking answers to questions about our relationship!" Jaheem revealed. "He seemed to know about recent meetings you and I have had at the gate!"

"Who is he?"

"I do not know his name, nor did I ask, but I believe he may be a member of the martolos!"

"Martolos?"

"It is a security force that the sultan relies upon in the Christian areas of Rumelia. These are not good men!"

"Rumelia is far from here! It is the land where I am from!"

"Yes, but it is rumored how some of these men work secretly here in Constantinople for the sultan. I have seen his face only once before—years ago when several Janissaries were arrested here inside the Yeni Saray."

"What were the charges against these men?"

"I cannot be certain, but their strangled corpses washed up on the Bosporus shoreline three days later! The martolos have the power and freedom to create rats where no rats exist!"

"This man—he knew my name?"

"Yes. You shouldn't be surprised by this, for you work closely with the sehzade. I should have known better to have gone this far with our plan! But I, as do you, have special feelings for the maiden. She would be disappointed."

"What did you tell him about us?"

"Only how we are friends with the same passion for pastry."

While conversing, Jaheem guided Haris through the corridor until pausing at a doorway appearing on their left. "At the end of the corridor, you will find the sultan's quarters." He pointed. "We will take this doorway that leads us across the courtyard of the Queen Mother." He led Haris through the opening, and into a spacious area of paved tile centered by a large circular fountain. Both men moved at a hurried pace, around the fountain, and across the opened area. Their worrisome discussion had ended, and now the two moved silently but swiftly, with hearts pounding. Haris noticed a few people moving about, mostly African servants, before one suddenly stopped them, using his hands to communicate with Jaheem. With head bowed, Haris held his breath as the chief eunuch exchanged sign language with the man, before the unsuspecting servant moved in the opposite direction.

Sighing simultaneously, they resumed their pace, this time without interruption. Suddenly, Jaheem stopped when they came upon a large domed area with small glass clerestory windows.

"What is it?" Haris whispered.

The anxiety in Jaheem's sulking face shown with widened eyes. "We are in the heart of the harem! Beneath the dome is the hammam, where the sultan and queen mother bathe. The bath links the apartments of both royals."

Jaheem nervously lifted his right foot and stepped forward to resume his pace. Soon both men were relieved to find themselves on the other side of the courtyard, before they came upon a wide, paved bridge connected to a circular pavilion set at its end. The dazzling shelter, with eaves and arches adorned with vivid colors, was positioned some twenty feet above a small garden, and featured a narrow, stone staircase that led down to the botanical display, where paths of paved stones wound around vibrant beds of flowers.

Leading the way, Jaheem negotiated the staircase, arriving beneath the bridge where adjacent to the garden they found four doors. The chief eunuch used a key to open one of the doors, hurriedly ushering Haris inside. The room was cool and dark, containing a mound of topsoil, gardening tools, and two wheelbarrows, with its only source of light coming from a grilled window set in the wall across from the door.

"I will go and signal the maiden." Jaheem announced rapidly. "She will seat herself on the bench situated on the other side of the window. You will be able to speak with her very easily through the window grill undetected. I will be watching. When I see her leave the bench, I will know you have finished, and shall return to unlock the door to remove you from here."

"Jaheem!" Haris called out. "Thank you."

"Save your thanks for when we are safely back on the other side of the Royal Gate." Jaheem quickly exited the room, locking the door.

Haris grabbed a wheelbarrow, and flipped it upside down. He seated himself on the barrow, and peered out through the window's intricate grill design. His anxiety began to subside while gazing upon the stunning view of the many varied flowers gathering in the warm sunlight, with their opened petals painting the garden a rainbow of colors. Haris found the striking scene matched in beauty and perfection only by the sultan's tulip garden—until the blonde maiden entered the view. She sauntered around the flower beds, and slowly approached the stone bench set below the window grill, clad in a long robe with its color resembling the greenish hue of shallow seawater. Above her waist she wore a beige kaftan, and her golden locks hung down from beneath a pinkish veil covering the top of her head, concealing her face below the eyes.

Delicately, the maiden lowered her body onto the bench, moving her head back and forth in a judicious manner. With the back of her head near to the window grill, she sat with erect posture, staring forward into the assemblage of flowers. "*Hallo. Wie geht es dir?*" she asked in German.

"I am fine," Haris responded, also in German. "And you, my lady?"

"I am well," she replied. "It seems you have followed me here to Constantinople from where we first met—last month . . . in Prague?"

Haris hesitated for a moment confused by her facts, before smiling to himself. "I must correct you, my lady. We met outside of Vienna nearly one year ago."

"Then it is you," she remarked. "I was testing you. What is your name?"

"Haris, and yours?"

"They call me Badra, but my Christian name is Verena."

"My Christian name is Jadran."

"You were forced to change your name as well? I thought such a practice was reserved only for women of the harem?"

"All servants of the sultan—his Janissary, members of his harem—all enslaved Christians must replace their names. It is as if they have been reborn in service to the supreme ruler."

"Yes." Badra sighed. "But I will not abandon my Catholic faith. Some women of the harem believe they have a better chance of gaining their freedom should they switch their faith to Islam, although we are not required to do so."

"A Janissary is required to convert to Islam."

"You are a Janissary?" she asked. "I remember you as a soldier in Vienna, but I did not know what kind. I have heard legendary stories of the Janissary's prowess on the battlefield. I cannot see you, but I am guessing your face is rugged and scarred from battle."

"No scars to impress you with, I'm afraid. I have been told my face looks much younger than my age. I'm sorry to disappoint you."

"I did not get a good look at your face when you passed me your handkerchief at the Hippodrome. I was too frightened. But I find your description of yourself to be handsome. What is it you find most attractive about me?"

"Your eyes—your emerald eyes. They captured me."

Badra fell silent.

"Have I embarrassed you?" Haris queried.

"No—not at all," she stammered. "As a converted Muslim, I assume you've read the Quran? I have read passages from it, and have found them to be very lyrical."

Haris smiled to himself, recognizing how fast she moved to change the subject. "I find the Bible is much longer and filled with so many stories of who is related to whom. It's been some time since I have read the Christian holy book, but I remember how confusing it can be trying to keep up with so many names and places. Yes, I have read the Quran and found it is more poetic but requires deep thought for one to focus on the meaning of each passage. This can prove tiresome."

"I see," she said.

As each one paused to select the next question to ask, the conversation's lull grew awkward. Haris realized how this was probably not for a lack of questions, but rather because they both attempted to prioritize their many anticipated queries in the essence of time. Suddenly, in an effort to break the silence, their simultaneous questions collided, producing an eruption of laughter from both.

"I'm sorry. You were saying?" Haris apologized.

"No, no. Please, you first."

"Your name, Badra, it means full moon . . . if I am not mistaken?"

"Yes. After we were taken in the siege of Vienna and brought to Constantinople, I spent many terrifying, lonely nights gazing at the moon, wondering about my future, and if any of my family were still alive. I began asking myself, should they be alive, do they stare at the moon and think of me, as I think of them?" She paused giving Haris a moment to memorize the maiden's heavenly voice. "Just the idea of believing how there is a possibility we may be gazing upon the same object, at the same time, although separated by great distance—such a thought seemed to be . . . well, in a small way, a great comfort to me."

Suddenly, through the grilled window, Haris could see two maidens appear from around a floral display, and he realized Badra had become lost in the conversation to a point where she allowed her vigilance to relax. The two women approached the seated maiden, and expressed their concern about hearing voices, convinced Badra was speaking indistinguishable words to herself. Haris quickly leaned back away from the grill into the shadows of the room as Badra, thinking fast and now speaking the Turkish language, thanked the women for their concern, explaining in a few words that she was simply praying aloud. The women appeared satisfied, moving on past the seated maiden, and when she could see them no longer, Badra resumed her discourse with Haris in German.

"I did not see them approaching," she confided.

"Are you all right? You seemed to stammer with your reply to the women?"

"It is my Turkish—I'm still learning, and it is weak at best," she explained. "Where are you from?"

"Rumelia. I am Croatian."

"Yet, you speak German?"

"Yes—and Croatian, Albanian, Turkish, Arabic. The education of a Janissary is very advanced."

"We—the women of the harem that is—" Haris smiled to himself as Badra's speech became sardonically flamboyant. "We are schooled as well, mostly in the art of how to appease the sultan with the way in which we move, dress, and speak. In addition to Turkish, we are being taught how to speak French," she continued, her tone returning to its lovely cadence. "It seems as though the Ottomans view French society as the most refined of all European peoples. Oh, if only the villagers back in Vienna knew of this. They would be appalled to have the French language shoved down their throats!"

"What exactly is it that you do for the sultan?"

"He takes me to bed with him, day and night."

Haris did not respond.

She giggled. "I am teasing, Haris! He loves my voice. I sing for him and he enjoys hearing Viennese ballads. He doesn't seem to desire me sexually. I know what I'm about to say makes me sound prudish, but there are attractive girls within the harem, some gifted with stunning beauty that I would think any man with a beating heart would desire. However, many such women the sultan ignores sexually, and instead selects them for reading poetry, the playing of a musical instrument, or for dancing, among other skills. Yet, Hurrem Kadin, who is a very pretty woman, but one who many judge as far less attractive than most women within the harem—this woman becomes one of the sultan's favorites in the bedroom! Perhaps it is her red hair that excites him?"

"You sound jealous?"

"I am not," she scoffed. "I don't see myself as one of the beautiful women I described. Believe me when I tell you how I am frightened about the possibility of the day coming when I may be selected to share his bed. The thought of this has brought me to tears on many occasions."

"I'm sorry to have raised the subject."

Badra sighed, before chuckling. "You are how I imagined."

"And how is that?"

"Polite. After all, you did offer to help me to my feet in Vienna," she recalled. "Yet, you are a Janissary—men of wondrous talents on the battlefield." Haris recognized how the bubbly tone of her voice seemed to drop away. "You are the same as the soldiers who brought such death and destruction to my city—the same as those who snatched my freedom from me like thieves in the night, tearing me away from my family, and bringing me to this place to be of service to a sultan."

Haris suddenly sensed he was on the defensive. "If you harbor such feelings, why did you agree to speak with me today?"

"Because despite your military bravado, I detect a difference about you. I sensed it, and Jaheem confirmed it. And because we—you and I . . . all of us—cannot help the situation in which we find ourselves." She sighed. "What can be done about the power cravings of rulers, whether they are sultans or kings? We are only pawns in this wretched game of theirs for empire—powerless to do little more than what we need to do to survive. There exist both good and bad people under the banners flown by all kingdoms. All we can do is to choose our allies and pray they are likeminded."

"Then it is my friendship you seek?"

"Friendship always seems to be the appropriate beginning, would you not agree?" she asked. "Tell me, what is it you seek, Haris? Why are you here risking so much to speak with me?"

"I'm not sure."

"Well, then you will have time to figure it out, for I must leave now. Soon the garden will attract more maidens."

"When will I see you again?" he asked in earnest.

"It is for fate to decide. Maybe you will come to your senses and realize our friendship will not serve you well under the Ottoman banner . . . for I am a maiden in waiting to the sultan, and you are his loyal Janissary." She rose to a standing position. "Clearly we are trying to make our own rules in a game we cannot win."

"A man determines his own fate," Haris replied with a cautious whisper. He watched Badra walk away without turning, leaving him unsure that she had heard his reply.

What Haris could not see as Badra moved gracefully away from him, was the satisfied smile illuminating her face beneath the pinkish veil.

CHAPTER TWELVE

Within days following Haris' clandestine meeting with Badra, he began to question his own security, as a member of the Enderun. *Perhaps living and working, so closely to the keys of the kingdom carried with it the high price of greater suspicion and less privacy. Did the sultan have spies in Constantinople?* Whether it was true or not, Haris decided it would be prudent to operate less carelessly; although this did not dissuade him from longing for more communication with the lovely maiden. It only reinforced, that for the moment, contact between the two could not be made in person.

After careful deliberation, Haris' solution for continued interaction with Badra would be accomplished through the writing of letters. He reasoned Jaheem could discreetly pass written correspondence back and forth between the two; although the plan still reeked of danger should the letters be intercepted. To be careful, within his first letter to the maiden, Haris emphasized that once read, each correspondence should be destroyed. Badra agreed, and so with Jaheem's assistance, the communication commenced.

In an attempt to prevent even more suspicion, Haris and Jaheem decided not to interrupt their Thursday "pastry" ritual, fearing that a sudden cessation of the meeting might invoke even more questions. More importantly, it would become the method for exchanging the letters—concealing them inside the baklava's paper wrapping. In return, on those Thursdays that Jaheem had a letter to deliver from Badra, the chief eunuch would hand Haris a bundle of cinnamon sticks—one of which would contain her tightly rolled correspondence hidden within the hollow dried bark.

By November, the passage of letters was in full swing, although written communication was not exchanged every week. The depth and detail of the words being swapped within the correspondence provided the seedlings for a budding friendship, full of flirtatious language. The secrecy of their communication proceeded flawlessly, with much confidence placed on Jaheem as the liaison for both; however, the security of their operation would be put to the test by events unfolding northwest of Constantinople.

Earlier in the month, the relaxed atmosphere within the Ottoman capitol grew tense when word reached the Yeni Saray that Ferdinand's Austrian forces launched an attack on the city of Buda in Hungary. The city on the Danube was under the control of self-proclaimed king and Ottoman ally, John Zapolya. The surprise attack by the Austrians had been planned in response to Suleyman's October rejection of the Viennese delegation's request the sultan return Hungarian land to Ferdinand. In response, Suleyman decided to send an army of Janissaries to assist Zapolya, although the sultan himself did not join the military campaign. The fact that the Ottomans were involved in a new military operation, placed Constantinople under heightened alert, permitting all military units within the city to carry swords throughout the duration of the campaign, and of course, to be diligent about reporting anything out of the ordinary.

By late December, Constantinople's weather had turned cooler with frequent rainfall. It was under these conditions in which Haris found himself, on a gray, overcast Thursday morning during a light drizzle, as he left the second courtyard's bakery with his purchase of baklava. He strolled along a tree-line path with the collar of his dolama pulled up to protect his neck from the cold air, slouching slightly forward to protect the pastry and its paper wrapping he carried, from the dampening elements. Pacing briskly in the direction of the Gate of Felicity, the foul weather would prove less disconcerting than the man who suddenly stepped out from behind a tree, startling him. The stranger stood facing Haris, wearing a black kaftan with black breeches and boots, his attire reflecting the mood of the morning.

"Lezhe Haris," the man remarked, not as an inquiry, but with a tone of self-assurance.

"Yes—?" Haris replied warily, noticing how the sheepskin kalpak the stranger wore on top of his head rose to a crown with its brim turned up all around the headgear.

"More baklava for your friend, Jaheem?"

Haris did not respond, taking note of how the man's skin was ghost white as is the shade of squid after being hauled from the sea, and how his brown eyes, which were nearly as dark as his pupils, created the appearance of two large, cold, black holes, focused now on the wrapped pastry Haris carried.

"Or maybe Jaheem is not a friend?" the stranger continued. "Maybe he is an accomplice?" The corner of his mouth curled slightly, causing his upper lip to disappear beneath a bushy dark mustache.

"Who are you?" Haris replied quickly, with an annoyed cadence.

"I am called, Megara Ali."

"What business of yours is my choice of friends?"

"It is the sultan's business," Ali replied with a cold directness. "And the sultan's business is my business."

Haris took a moment to study the stranger with an alarmed curiosity, realizing he could be a member of the martolos. He noticed how the slope of his long, angular nose was crooked at the bridge, indicating it had been broken more than once; yet despite the slight deformity, the strength of his high cheek bones drew attention away from the appendage, presenting an approachable appearance—one that Haris believed could work to ensnare his prey, as how the sweet nectar from a Venus fly trap entices the unsuspecting insect.

"I know that your pastry is a gift for the chief eunuch of the harem," Ali said. "What I would like to know, is what does Jaheem give you in return? Perhaps you two are lovers—the passion that men from Rumelia have for the same sex is widely known."

Haris chortled, brushing off Ali's attempt at agitation. "Where are you from, Megara? Maybe you have firsthand knowledge of what men from Rumelia desire."

"I wonder if your common sense is as sharp as your tongue."

"You hound me over delivering pastry to a friend? What are you, the sultan's personal chef?"

Ali chuckled. "Let us say, I am his gardener."

"Gardener?"

"My job is to identify the weeds growing within the empire, and then to extract them before they begin to sprout and spread their destruction."

"The sultan's empire is very large. There must be weed infestation everywhere, perhaps even in Rumelia," Haris countered, remembering Jaheem's story of the martolos' origins. "I'm sure that makes you a very busy . . . *gardener*."

Ali sighed, appearing unamused by the comment. "Every garden needs weeded."

"What does this have to do with me?"

"Perhaps nothing," Ali replied. "But it is important to be sure the sultan has planted the correct flowers within his garden.

Sometimes, what plants may seem deceptively harmless, may in fact be the most poisonous."

"And you see me as a poisonous weed because I share baklava with a friend?"

Ali grinned. "Everyone has a price."

"What is your price for me sharing with you the secret of my gift of baklava?"

Ali hesitated in his response, surprised by the question. "I have no price, for it is your duty to report all activity involving the sultan."

"And how does my friendship with Jaheem involve the sultan?"

"You are both members of the Enderun, thus everything you do involves the sultan."

"Is it unlawful for friends, even inside the Enderun, to engage one another?"

"I am not concerned with the law—rules and regulations to keep the sheep within their pen," Ali barked. "No, my focus is on the wolves—those clever enough to operate within the framework of the law in an attempt to do their ill will. The justice I bring is retribution outside of the law."

The two men stared at one another, before Haris slowly leaned forward. "Here is my secret," he whispered, drawing Ali closer. "Jaheem has a sweet tooth for honey." He smiled, pulling back away from the stranger.

Ali stood with a scowl, but gradually a smirk began to form as if he knew something Haris did not. The stranger lifted his left hand, and brought it to the kaftan, slowly brushing the light rain drops from his garment. It was at that point when Haris noticed the stub where Ali's left little finger was missing.

"Are we finished here?" Haris asked.

"We are done for today. But I sense that in the greater scheme of things we are not yet finished."

"Is that a threat?"

"I do not threaten," Ali replied. "I only warn, and I only ever give *jedan upozorenje!*" he added, holding up his right index finger.

Haris understood the Croatian words—*one warning*—and he trembled slightly from hearing his native tongue being used by Ali.

"View our meeting this morning as your one warning." Ali's grin quickly evaporated, as he began a march in the opposite direction.

Haris watched his movements carefully, before the stranger vanished within the shadows of an alley.

Standing steadfast, Haris shuddered to think how perhaps it didn't matter that he had been appointed by the sultan to train the sehzade; for there could be greater powers at work. *Greater powers at work than the sultan?* The thought haunted him.

CHAPTER THIRTEEN

The passage of two years reflected little change in the eyes of those beyond the walls of the Yeni Saray, much like the perspective of an amateur stargazer who watches a deceptively constant nighttime sky, oblivious to celestial changes within distant galaxies. In the same way, unforeseen forces were at work altering the dynamics of life within the Ottoman palace.

Behind the harem walls, Suleyman could find time to relax from the business of warfare after Ottoman forces successfully assisted his Hungarian ally in repelling the threat of Ferdinand's attempt to reclaim all of Hungary. A time of tranquility was restored to the Ottoman Empire, although the Austrian king's forces had been able to capture a number of fortresses along the Danube, raising the possibility of future hostility.

The sultan's family continued to grow, as Suleyman sired the birth of a fifth son to Hurrem Kadin, named Changir. Since her second oldest son, Abdullah, had died from disease at the age of three, Hurrem could now boast of having four sons in line to be the next sultan, a fact that brought more angst to Mustafa.

Haris' encounter with the dark stranger, who called himself Megara Ali, would haunt him for weeks and months afterwards; however, the passions of youth would not permit Haris much opportunity to look over his shoulder. As the months turned into years, eventually the passage of time worked to diminish Ali's threat.

Meanwhile, the correspondence between Haris and Badra

continued, leaving both to wonder just how long they could pursue their reckless course before the martolos intervened. Complicating matters was Haris' undisciplined desire to set eyes on Badra whenever possible. In this pursuit, he was aided by Jaheem, who found opportunity to sneak Haris inside the harem on six occasions within the past twenty-four months, taking advantage of those opportunities when the sultan's business was scheduled outside of the harem. They were playing with fire and they knew it; but the excitement it generated for all three, seemed to be a welcomed diversion from the daily routine of palace life.

With Mustafa's ongoing training, it made sense to elevate Haris to a position among the Janissary assigned directly to the sehzade as a personal bodyguard. The two friends had become almost inseparable, making Haris well aware of the political advantages associated with their friendship, and more importantly alerting him to how others within the Enderun could perceive him as a threat.

Constantinople – April, 1532

Although the return of spring to Constantinople brought a welcome change from the damp and cooler temperatures of winter, a heavy rainfall one April morning forced Mustafa to remain indoors. Having acquired a fascination for military history, he took advantage of the inclement weather by spending a portion of the day within the Enderun's library.

It was there on a Wednesday morning where Haris found his friend seated cross legged on the floor, resting on large comfortable pillows within the quiet room. He found nothing unusual about Mustafa's desire to bury himself in past tales of the architects of military history, since the sehzade's winter training amounted to similar sessions within the library.

Haris moved within a few feet of Mustafa and stood above him, noticing how the sehzade's attention was held captive by the contents within a book he held open. "Merhaba, Mustafa."

The sehzade raised his head from the book and smiled at Haris. "Why doesn't my father organize his Janissaries on the battlefield into phalanxes?"

"Phalanxes?"

"Yes—the groupings of soldiers into block-like formations. Alexander the Great used this most effectively."

"I know what a phalanx is," Haris said. "I'm just surprised by the question."

"Why does our army not use this method?"

"Well, it proved effective against charioteers, as horses are smart enough to recognize when they are charging into a group of men with long spears pointing at them," Haris began. "But a disadvantage of the phalanx is that when penetrated by the enemy, the spears are too long of a weapon to be useful in hand to hand combat."

Mustafa sat back, resting the book in his lap, continuing to give his attention to Haris. "Alexander was a very clever leader."

Haris sensed an opportunity to query his student. "Why do you say this?"

Mustafa thought for a moment before answering. "It was how Alexander would structure his attack to divide the opposing army. He realized he could not defeat a larger army by just engaging on a battlefield. He used deception and knowledge of the landscape to force the enemy to break down into smaller units, making them more vulnerable."

"Yes, a leader needs to be confident and spontaneous on the battlefield, for a moment's hesitation can change the course of the battle," Haris expressed. "He must know his enemy intimately in an effort to exploit its army's weakness."

Mustafa's face shone with excitement. "I wish to someday find myself in a similar situation."

Haris scoffed. "Ah—be careful what you wish for."

Mustafa's elation evolved into a look of puzzlement. "But history remembers the Macedonian general as Alexander the Great!"

Haris grinned. "What happened to Alexander's empire?"

"I'm not sure?"

"After his death, his empire broke up." Haris stepped over to a large bookshelf gracing one wall of the library, and ran his fingers along the binding of a book. "Alexander, much like the Mongol leader Genghis Khan, built his empire by shedding blood and instilling fear in the population he conquered." Haris slowly turned toward Mustafa. "Keeping a conquered people suppressed by fear and bloodshed has its limits. Eventually the vanquished will overcome their situation. It may take generations, but history tells us it is inevitable. When a people's customs and traditions are threatened, rebellion is in the air. Your father knows this. That is why the provinces stretching across his empire have their own millets."

"Yes, religious communities of Christians and Jews with their own rules and regulations," Mustafa said.

"As long as the peoples of the sultan's empire are permitted to live with assurance of their own customs and traditions unchanged, they remain loyal and at peace."

"Christians and Jews," Mustafa mumbled. "Who was the leader of the Muslims that chased the Christian Crusaders from Jerusalem?"

"The Kurdish leader, Saladin."

"Yes, I remember! Tell me about him again!"

"It has been recorded that the siege of Jerusalem produced a horrific battle, with many Christian and Muslim warriors slaughtered," Haris said. "But after the Christians were forced to surrender the holy city to Saladin, the Muslim leader did not force those captured to be ransomed as slaves, and instead set them free. He also permitted Christians and Jews to remain as residents of Jerusalem without persecution, and promised that all Christian pilgrims to Jerusalem would be granted safe passage. Today, Christians, Jews, and Muslims still live and worship side by side in peace within Jerusalem."

"Jerusalem would seem to be a very important city within the Ottoman Empire, but my father rarely speaks of it," Mustafa said. "However, my father did choose wisely in selecting you as my teacher. How do you know so much?"

"Like you, I enjoy books," Haris revealed. "My Muslim guardians in Adana possessed a great collection of books. After learning the Turkish and Arabic languages, I wasted no time in devouring their contents."

Mustafa rose from the floor. "With your knowledge and skills, you should be of service in some higher position within my father's empire."

"I can think of no higher position than teaching you."

Mustafa smiled. "Someday you will be my grand vizier!"

Haris raised his eyebrows with a look of surprise. "Be careful of promising things you may not be able to keep."

"Why do you doubt me? I am next in line to be sultan, and you are my best friend. Who is more qualified to hold the position of grand vizier than you?"

Haris smiled. "Thank you, Mustafa. If such a day should come, I will be more than honored to serve you."

The discourse between the two friends was suddenly interrupted by a servant who entered the room with head bowed. "Excuse me Your Royal Highness, but I have a message from the grand vizier. He would like to meet with Lezhe Haris, and awaits him in Divan Square's Domed Chamber."

"You are in high demand today, my friend," Mustafa remarked.

Haris left the room accompanied by the servant. Within a few minutes, both had arrived within the second courtyard, where Haris entered the Domed Chamber alone, finding the grand vizier seated comfortably on a wide red velvet cushioned chair. Haris stood within the center of the room, facing Ibrahim with his head bowed. "My Lord."

"God's peace, be upon you, Lezhe Haris."

As Haris raised his head in the direction of the grand vizier, his eyes caught sudden movement off to his right, and he turned to see a long grilled window set in the wall; however, the darkness beyond the grill obscured any presence.

"Haris, our meeting is the desire of our sultan," Ibrahim announced, bringing Haris' attention back to the grand vizier. "He wished for me to express his pleasure in the progress of Sehzade Mustafa's training. The boy has grown up considerably over the past two years while under your tutelage. I too am witness to his growth and applaud you."

Haris bowed his head again. "It has been an honor to serve the sultan and the sehzade."

"I have news for you, Haris," Ibrahim continued. "Ferdinand of Austria has resumed his attempt to pull all of Hungary under his dominion. The sultan is determined to prevent Ferdinand from succeeding and has decided that once again the time has come to teach the Austrian dog a lesson. The sultan plans a major military campaign to conquer Vienna, which will commence before the end of the month."

Haris produced a rigid stance. "I am at your service."

Ibrahim grinned. "Do you believe Sehzade Mustafa to be ready for military action?"

"As a Janissary?"

"As a leader of Janissaries. Upon your recommendation, the sultan would appoint the sehzade to the rank of *sanjak-bey* for this campaign. He would be given responsibility for one orta of eight hundred Janissaries under the command of one corbaci and four *boluk-aghas*. This is so that he shall have officers with military experience at his side." The grand vizier stroked his bearded chin. "In your opinion, is the sehzade ready for such responsibility in the field of battle?"

Haris took a breath. "I believe the sehzade is prepared for anything he may be asked to do. I have complete confidence in his ability, and would trust my life under his command."

"It is good to hear you speak such words, for you will be promoted to the rank of *boluk-bashi*, allowing you to operate as the personal assistant to the sehzade during the military operation. The sultan believes Sehzade Mustafa would feel comfortable with your assistance. Do you have any questions?"

"Shall I inform the sehzade?"

"No. The sultan has expressed his desire to inform his son personally," Ibrahim revealed. "You are dismissed—Boluk-bashi Lezhe Haris."

Haris bowed his head, turned and paced across the tiled floor before disappearing through the opening.

When Ibrahim was certain Haris had left the chamber, the grand vizier stepped over to the grilled window, facing it. "He was the right choice for Mustafa's teacher."

"Yes—at present it would appear so," the faceless voice of Suleyman replied from within the shadows behind the grill. "Though I wonder what else it is that my son is learning from his teacher?"

CHAPTER FOURTEEN

Austrian Campaign – Spring and Summer 1532

Suleyman assembled an Ottoman army of over two hundred thousand men and left Constantinople in late April to lay siege to Vienna once again. Unlike his attempt to conquer the Austrian capitol three years earlier, on this occasion the sultan planned to attack Vienna from out of the west. By mid-July, the impressive assemblage of warriors, horses, camels, and some of the world's largest cannon had crossed the Drava River and reached the Croatian town of Osijek. In an effort to keep the planned route to Vienna accessible for his heavy artillery, Suleyman ordered a number of his Janissary ortas to branch off, and advance ahead of the main army with the goal of destroying villages and capturing castles.

By early August, Suleyman learned that the imperial army of the Holy Roman Emperor Charles V, led by the Habsburg monarch himself, had set out to block the sultan's advance toward Vienna. When the Ottoman army had reached the village of Koszeg along the Austrian-Hungarian border, Suleyman made the decision to lay siege to the town, recognizing how the miles of flat, open terrain surrounding Koszeg would allow for a larger engagement. The sultan's initial goal had been to capture Ferdinand's Vienna to keep the Austrians out of Hungary; however, what he desired more was a confrontation with Charles—his greatest nemesis. Thus, Suleyman decided Vienna could wait, and instead prepared to use Koszeg as bait for a confrontation with the Habsburg monarch.

As Suleyman prepared to lay siege to Koszeg, the Janissary orta led by the Sanjak-bey Mustafa—sent north on foot toward the Austrian capitol to remove any obstacle to Suleyman's army—arrived on a wooded cliff overlooking the tranquil Austrian village of Berndorf, located in a mountainous region lying south of Vienna. The previous two days of marching had been through steady rainfall; but their arrival to the outskirts of the Austrian village saw a return of clear blue summer skies, creating drier conditions beneath a glistening, sun-spotted, leafy canopy.

The orta halted their undetected advance to observe the scene below, appreciating how the village had been carved out of the forested hillside. The densely-built dwellings populated both sides of a series of winding stone streets, forming arteries linked at the bottom of the hill to a wide central road, running along a level plain dominated at its eastern end by a stone church with a lofty, gothic octagonal tower. To the east of the church, vineyards and fields of wheat brought uniformity to the geography, while the movement of tiny images about the town, indicated most of the inhabitants were outside this day enjoying the pleasant weather.

The feature generating the most interest among the Ottoman warriors was an imposing medieval castle made of stone, strategically built on an isolated rocky crag encircled by a gorge—an island among the hills—positioned above the village, and separated from the community by a wide dirt road.

The polygonal-shaped fortification sprouted from the crag as though the fortress itself was an extension of the unique geographic formation, with its centrally located keep appearing as a man-made peak. The castle's imposing stone curtain wall, with rectangular gaps set at intervals, rose forty feet in the air and was studded with circular towers equipped with arrow slits. Two projecting towers were positioned on either side of the gate, which featured a portcullis with a lattice grill, while a paved stationary stone bridge, supported by four arches beneath it, crossed one section of the gorge intersecting the main road.

After finally catching his breath from the arduous morning's climb through thick forest vegetation littered with boulders, Mustafa asked Haris to step aside with him out of earshot from the others. They found a secluded location within the wood that continued to offer a vantage point of Berndorf, and relaxed their bodies against the massive trunk of a beech tree.

Mustafa peered down the mountainside to gaze upon the town. "It is a beautiful site—the village that is." He turned toward Haris. "Though from what I have seen thus far since the arrival of our troops into this country, I fear it will not be long before we replace such serenity and beauty with death and destruction."

"Sadly, yes, Sanjak-bey," Haris replied. "It is the way of war."

"Why must it be so? Removing the castle as a threat to the sultan's advance is our goal. Why can't we leave the village alone?"

"Because, unfortunately the villagers will not leave us alone. The only way to lay siege to the castle is to bring the village under our control."

"But how do we take control of the castle? We have no cannon. The artillery is with the sultan."

"It will be difficult, but there are ways. Our task is to force the occupants of the castle to come out and fight us, or for us to penetrate the walls of the fortress and bring it down from within."

Mustafa frowned. "This is my first mission, and I am not proud to admit that I am frightened to fail. I already sense that some of the men doubt my ability because of my age, and because my position as sanjak-bey has not been earned, but was given to me by my father. Take for example Serkan, who has been promoted to one of the boluk-agha's on our mission. He has always been extremely loyal to me, but now I see distrust in his eyes."

"He is envious of our relationship—yours and mine."

"Perhaps, but at a time when I need his loyalty the most, it is not to be found."

"Mustafa, the grand vizier asked me if I thought you were ready to lead such a mission, and I said yes." Haris delivered the statement with a piercing look of sincerity that he was certain Mustafa could feel, as well as see. "You have earned this position. I have seen it with my own eyes, so believe it is true."

"Thank you, my friend. I will need your help, though."

Haris turned toward Mustafa, holding out his clenched right fist. The sehzade responded by placing his left fist on top of it. "Be strong. We are in this together."

Mustafa nodded. "What should be our first course of action?"

"Do you have a plan?"

Mustafa thought for a moment. "No."

"Do you think any one of us has a plan?"

Mustafa looked back at the orta, before turning his attention once again to Haris. "I think we should find out."

"Very good, Sanjak-bey," Haris said with a smile.

Mustafa returned the smile. "Thank you for honoring me with the title of sanjak-bey, instead of using my first name."

"You are our commander. We are on the battlefield, and not at school." Haris grinned. "When we return to Constantinople, I will be happy to use your first name again."

Mustafa laughed. "Yes—in Constantinople."

"It is an old castle, probably several hundred years, don't you think?"

Mustafa spun back to look at the castle. "I . . . I'm not sure."

Haris flashed a look of reassurance. "Take my word it is a very old castle." He glared back at the fortress. "Its appearance tells me that they have not updated the castle with new defenses. This could be used to our advantage."

Mustafa nodded in agreement, before ordering all of his officers to gather together in a small clearing. The location was removed from the regular Janissary soldiers, who rested quietly on the ground spread out under the cool shade of the multitude of leafed out trees.

The seven officers found their way to the clearing forming a circle, using tree trunks and boulders to lean upon. Haris studied their resolute faces before giving a nod in the direction of his friend the Corbaci Kamil, who returned the acknowledgment with a nod of his own.

Mustafa cleared his throat. "The task before us is to capture the village and the castle, eliminating the threat to the sultan's army. The castle seems to be our largest obstacle." He spoke with a jittery delivery, before pausing to take a deep breath. "Officers of the Janissary—" He hesitated. "This is my first operation, and my first command. I am relying on your experience and judgment to help devise a plan of attack, recognizing how many heads are better than one."

Haris stirred with a sense of pride in his young student, observing how the officer's postures changed, as if suddenly awakened from a deep sleep. They seemed to appear slightly encouraged by Mustafa's words, perhaps recognizing that they too were part of the conversation, and not simply a liaison between the commander and troops.

"We have no cannon," an officer volunteered. "A direct assault on the castle may be fruitless."

"Yes—yes, your point is well taken," Mustafa eagerly acknowledged. "However, it is a very old castle—I think perhaps several hundred years old." He threw a quick glance to Haris. "Perhaps they have not updated their defenses?"

Several of the officers nodded in agreement, and began to throw out ideas incessantly.

"We could dig beneath a section of the castle wall to create a tunnel, so it may be ready for the sultan's army when it arrives with gunpowder," suggested an officer.

"My men are Janissaries, not sappers," challenged another. "We are not here to dig tunnels."

"Build a siege tower and attack the castle from above," voiced another.

Kamil interjected. "Absolutely not. There is no doubt the castle is equipped with cannon that would blow up any tower, as well as tear our men to pieces. Just because the castle is ancient, doesn't mean we have to devise an ancient battle plan."

Serkan spoke up. "Starve them into submission. I say we surround the castle with our troops and besiege them with arquebus fire and arrows, making it our objective not to permit any supplies from going into the castle. If they fail to surrender by the time our sultan arrives, then Ottoman artillery will reduce the fortress to dust with cannon fire."

"I don't think the sultan will be very pleased if he arrives and finds the castle has not been overtaken," Haris said.

Serkan glared at Haris. "Well, then what do you suggest, Boluk-bashi?"

"I believe we need to take the castle down from within."

Serkan scoffed. "From within? And how do we accomplish that?"

"*Sprechen sie Deutsch?*" Haris uttered.

The officers fell silent, and Haris could see how all stared at him with bewilderment. "I speak the tongue of the Austrians. I may be able to use my knowledge of their language to gain entrance undercover, and open the gates from within."

Serkan sneered. "These people know one another! They see each other every day and work in the fields and shops together! They will be able to smell you out in minutes and kill you!"

Mustafa quickly interrupted. "All of your suggestions are appreciated and each has merit. But two facts are very apparent to me in our situation. The first is that the sultan will most likely expect the castle to have been taken by the time his forces arrive." He noticed the scowl forming on Serkan's face. "And the second is that since we have been assigned a mission reliant upon speed and stealth, we have no siege cannon. Thus, the sultan has placed his faith in our creativity to dispose of this ancient road block." He turned toward Haris. "The boluk-bashi's plan to bring the castle down from within is creative. Although we may lack heavy artillery, we may be able to use knowledge of their native tongue as a weapon."

Haris nodded. "As the Sanjak-bey has pointed out, the castle is probably at least several centuries old. Although here on this ridge we are located far from it, the gleam from the sun striking the gate tells me it is a portcullis made of metal, which one man should be able to lift from the inside using its winch."

One of the boluk-agha's stepped forward. "Are you just hoping to knock on the gate of the castle, speak a little German, and expect they will permit you to enter?"

"No. I suggest we attack the village first, but we stagger the attack to give some of the townspeople time to flee toward the castle for safety," Haris explained. "Then I will blend into the fleeing crowd, and hopefully the chaos will allow me to gain entrance."

"It is a good plan. I think I would feel better if you are not acting alone, just in case something goes wrong," Mustafa decided.

Serkan scoffed. "But who else among us speaks the tongue of the Austrians?"

"We can make it look as though a second man is injured and cannot speak, so it is less likely he would be questioned," Mustafa offered.

"This is madness!" Serkan blurted. "We are engaged in war among men! We are not playing a child's game here!"

The comment had produced a wave of silent tension within the circle of men, and all eyes focused on Mustafa, awaiting his response.

Mustafa's face grew angry. "Are you suggesting I am a child?"

"Forgive me, Sanjak-bey." Serkan lowered his head. "My tongue spoke before my heart and head could intervene."

"Then perhaps I should have your tongue cut out of your head!"

Serkan remained steadfast, with head bowed.

Mustafa breathed heavily, before scanning the faces of his officers. "We shall attempt to infiltrate the castle with several men!"

"I suggest we should attack tonight, allowing the darkness to help conceal our men," Kamil proposed. "As for now, each of the boluk-aghas should assign a guard detail rotation throughout the afternoon, so we are not detected before nightfall."

"Thank you Corbaci, I agree," Mustafa said.

"The fact that the people of this village have not yet sought the safety of the castle, tells me that they are unaware the sultan's army lies southwest of here," Haris remarked.

Kamil nodded in agreement. "Then Vienna must also be anticipating an attack coming from out of the southeast, and not from the west."

"My officers shall meet again in this clearing at the first sign of dusk to go over the final details of the attack," Mustafa commanded. "God willing, we shall have control of the castle before dawn! Praise be to Allah!"

"Allah Hu Akbar!" the officers called out in response, and began to break from the circle.

Haris approached Mustafa. "I am proud of you."

"Do not get yourself killed, my friend."

"I will do my best not to." The two men nodded at one another, before Mustafa turned and walked away.

Haris noticed Serkan also moving away and called out his name, before quickly catching up with him.

Serkan turned to face him with a grimace. "Haris, you're a fool! You're going to be killed tomorrow and jeopardize this operation!"

Haris grinned. "You underestimate Mustafa. He's been trained well."

"Ha! By you? You will be dead by dawn, and Mustafa will be left trying to explain to his father why the castle still stands, blocking the road to Vienna!"

Haris rubbed the sleeve of his kaftan against his lips. "Serkan, the day we fought for the sehzade's pleasure, I did not realize when I kicked you in the groin that your brain is in the wrong place!"

Serkan groaned, instinctively reaching for the handle of his sword, hesitating to pull it from its sheath.

Haris did not flinch. "And another thing, do not underestimate me either! I will see you inside the castle!"

CHAPTER FIFTEEN

Later that afternoon as the sinking sun set the Alpine skyline afire, draping the creeping shadows of lofty peaks across the forest canopy, the officers met once again to design their plan of attack. It wasn't until the dark horizon revealed a partial moon that Haris and three boluk-aghas led four hundred Janissaries down the hillside. They moved through the wood in the direction of the village, while simultaneously, Mustafa, Kamil, and Serkan led four hundred Janissaries in the direction of the castle.

By the time the Janissaries had reached the tree line southeast of the village, the nightfall had chased most of the villagers inside, assisting the secrecy of the Ottoman approach, which assembled undetected in front of the church located at the end of the main street. Haris realized how the ease in which the Janissaries had slipped into the village could afford his troops the opportunity to overrun the town quickly; although the plan called for commotion, as it would drive many of the townspeople in the direction of the castle. Thus, the advance into the village center had to wait until after the Janissaries invaded their first shelter—the housing for the village priest—which set adjacent to the Catholic Church.

After being pulled from the house, the elderly priest turned three shades of white when he set eyes upon the presence and size of the Janissary army. Speaking German, Haris demanded that the clergyman enter the church and ring its bells or be put to the sword. The holy man complied, and when the bells were sounded, scores of seemingly dazed villagers wandered into the main street of the town.

Haris ordered the boluk-aghas to instruct the Janissaries under their command to fire their arquebuses over the heads of the townspeople, and only to fire directly at those individuals who chose to take up arms against them. The soldiers did as they were told and when the townsfolk realized the gunfire had originated from a large, shadowy presence situated in front of the church, a wave of panic sent villagers scattering like a herd of deer fleeing the hunter. Many returned to their homes, while others moved quickly up the main street to seek refuge inside the castle.

From among the Janissaries, Haris chose the accomplices needed to infiltrate the castle based on their fair complexions, so they might easily blend into the crowd of Austrian villagers. He and his men set about invading a home, finding enough men's clothing to disguise themselves as townsfolk. They replaced their borks with low, soft narrow brimmed hats, and left their kilijs and arquebuses with the boluk-aghas, carrying only a dagger tucked inside the waistband of their breeches.

Haris cut off a section from his shirt sleeve with the dagger, before using the blade to slice open the palm of one of the other Janissaries. He instructed the soldier to clutch the torn piece of shirt within his bleeding hand, until a dark stain of blood saturated the cloth. The bloodied garment was placed around the man's chin and tied at the top of his head, giving him the appearance of having been wounded in the neck. With their disguises complete, the three prospective spies ran ahead of the army, toward the fleeing crowd.

As the Janissary troops continued to advance through the town, Haris and his two companions soon found themselves traveling with the flow of panicked refugees, moving within the dark forest along a narrow, ascending, dirt path located west of the village. Haris noticed how the evacuees made very little noise aside from a few sobbing women and children, while marching with purpose, as though such a flight of refuge was familiar to them.

After nearly thirty minutes and aided by a faint moonlight, Haris peered through gaps in between forested trees where he distinguished a stone bridge, realizing they would soon be at the castle's gate. He looked at one of his companions and nodded, sending the man moving out of the crowd and into the forest. "Go and take your piss!" Haris yelled out in German. "We are not waiting around for you!" A few bystanders glanced at Haris, but their hurried intent to reach the castle prevented any interest or suspicion in the man's sudden departure.

As the villagers continued advancing toward the stone fortress, the Janissary who had stepped away from the crowd quickened his pace, moving among the trees in a southerly direction. After covering about two hundred rods, he was surprised by a man in a Janissary uniform who stepped out from behind a tree, pointing the barrel of an arquebus in his direction. Speaking Turkish, the man in Austrian garb identified himself as a fellow Ottoman. The uniformed man lowered his weapon, and rushed him over to where Mustafa and Kamil were positioned behind a large fallen timber, where they could safely view the castle.

The Janissary spy reported the situation to Mustafa, who turned toward Kamil. "They should be close now. Look for one of our men to stumble to the ground as a signal they approach the gate."

Haris and his companion had crossed the stone bridge, guessing correctly that a number of Janissaries hid beneath one of the bridge's arches, and as the two neared the gate, the crowd suddenly stopped, bunching together at the castle entrance. Haris was surprised by this, since the portcullis had been pulled upward. He nodded to his companion and quickly the man dropped to the ground on one knee as planned. As Haris helped him to his feet, they witnessed a man being pulled from the crowd by two armed men, who ordered for him to drop his breeches, before they checked his manhood. Haris reasoned they were inspecting each unrecognizable male, using circumcision to identify non-Christians. Apparently satisfied, the armed men permitted the man to rejoin the crowd. Haris turned to his companion and without uttering a word, flashed a worried look.

From his vantage point, Kamil could discern the stalling of the crowd at the castle's entrance. "Sanjak-bey, the crowd has slowed to a stop at the gate! If they are checking suspicious individuals, our men will be caught!"

Mustafa realized something needed to be done, and called several Janissaries to his side. "Run up and down our line and tell the men that as soon as I give the order to fire, they are to shoot their arquebuses at the castle wall! But they are to aim their shots well above the heads of the crowd! Go—do it now!"

Outside the gate, Haris and his companion had moved closer to the entrance, when one of the castle guards called for the two of them to stop. "What are your names?" The guard pushed his way through the crowd. "I do not recognize you!"

"We are brothers," Haris lied in German. "The name is Weisman."

"I do not know of any Weisman in Berndorf!" The guard looked closely at Haris' companion, studying his head wrapped in the blood stained cloth. "What is his injury?"

"He has a deep cut beneath his chin," Haris replied. "I think it may be serious."

"Let me see it!"

Haris took a deep breath, slowly placing his hand on the waistband of his breeches, finding the handle of the dagger. Suddenly, an explosion of arquebus fire erupted overhead, causing the crowd to panic and push forward at the gate. The guard who had been questioning Haris stepped away from him, yelling for others inside the castle to permit the entire crowd entry without delay. Once all of the people had rushed across the threshold, the gate abruptly closed, stranding stragglers who were forced to hide in the wood or return to the occupied village.

The eruption of the Janissary's firearms had unleashed return arquebus fire from the castle walls, but Mustafa ordered his troops to cease firing once the gate had closed.

Within the castle, Haris and his companion moved with the village crowd who were ushered into the fortress casemate by the castle's militia. There, the two men sat down on the stone floor of the vaulted chamber, and waited for the commotion to settle, before making their next move.

* * *

Just after midnight, when the lull in the fighting was into its third hour, Haris and his companion decided to leave the casemate, with the excuse that they could lend assistance to the castle's defense. As the casemate was located directly beneath the inside of the castle's entranceway, the two men had only to climb a short stone stairway before arriving at the gate, where they found two Austrian guards carrying flat swords. Speaking German, Haris asked if he and his friend could be of help, but before the guards could respond the two men overpowered each guard, quickly disposing of them with daggers to the throat.

Haris moved to the winch set to the right of the gate, and began turning the hand crank on the large spool. The device pulled on a thick chain, raising the portcullis, while his companion stood guard—now armed with an Austrian flat sword. Haris locked the portcullis at about six feet, before retrieving a burning torch from the metallic holder on the wall, waving the flame back and forth over his head in the direction of the wood. Within minutes, a flame appeared in the distance, when suddenly from over both sides of the stone bridge poured Janissaries.

Castle defenders perched on the walls above the bridge were quickly alerted to the breach at the gate and sounded the alarm; but it was too late. Before the hour was up, scores of Janissaries swarmed every corner of the castle, using their expertise as elite swordsmen to overrun the larger number of inexperienced Austrians. In the process, they worked to keep the gate opened until Mustafa arrived and could move the remainder of his troops safely inside the castle. The violent confrontation left scores of defenders slaughtered, while the Janissaries endured only minimal casualties.

* * *

After a restless night in which the invaders received only a few hours of slumber—sleeping in shifts wherever they could find a place to lay their head—Mustafa and Haris, having bedded near to each other alongside a group of Janissaries inside the chapel, rose with the crack of dawn. Their first order of business was to determine in which direction from the castle was southwest; for that would point them in the direction of the Arabian city of Mecca. In a display of irony, they prostrated themselves on the floor of the chapel facing in the direction of Islam's holiest city, and recited a series of Islamic verses from the Quran. When they had finished their morning prayers, together Mustafa and Haris set out to inspect the situation within the captured fortress. In no time it became evident to both how efficient the Janissaries had been in assuming control of the castle, finding the gunpowder storage room secured, as well as Janissaries perched on the castle walls and at the gate. In addition, there were those who kept guard over the many Austrian prisoners—soldiers and civilians clustered together in the casemate.

As Mustafa and Haris were reviewing the casemate, they could hear a rumpus commencing from the stone stairwell, and realized it originated from the courtyard above them. Rushing up the stairs, they stepped from out of a doorway to witness Janissary soldiers forming a large circle around a dozen Austrian males who were forced to kneel barefoot with their hands tied behind their backs. Some of the prisoners were whimpering aloud, while others pled for mercy, as Mustafa and Haris beheld the ghastly sight of two bodies lying in a pool of blood, separated from their heads, with Janissary soldiers jeering. At that moment, a Janissary standing within the round, grabbed one of the prisoners by his arm and dragged him into the center of the circle where another Janissary stood over him, gripping his curved sword that dripped with blood.

"Stop!" Mustafa yelled. Immediately the group fell silent, as he pushed his way into the circle. "Who is your boluk-agha?" he demanded of the assassin. Before any could respond, Serkan stepped from out of the circle across from where Mustafa stood.

"Serkan!" Mustafa exclaimed. "What is this?"

Serkan bowed his head before lifting his eyes to Mustafa. "Sanjak-bey, it is the execution of those prisoners who took up arms against the forces under your command last night!"

Haris could see the agitation spread across Mustafa's face. "For what reason do you execute them?" Mustafa demanded. "They are our prisoners! We've taken their weapons and boots from them!"

Serkan yelled as though he wished for all present to hear. "They are Christian! Infidels! Non-believers! If we allow them to live, they will fight against us another day! It is for us then not only to destroy the enemy of Islam, but to teach other non-believers who shall bear witness to this, that to shed Muslim blood will be met with the shedding of Christian blood!" The impassioned boluk-agha's proclamation was met with a clamor of support from among the Janissaries.

Mustafa turned toward his boluk-bashi. "Haris?"

"It is the method of dealing with the enemy," Haris replied. "But it doesn't have to be. One may use fear as a method of maintaining order, another may use compassion. Neither makes him weak—but one makes him stronger. Remember the story of Saladin?"

Mustafa took a deep breath, before turning away from Haris. "Serkan! Approach me!"

Serkan marched proudly across the circle, stopping before Mustafa and bowing his head.

"Look at me!" Mustafa commanded. Serkan lifted his brown eyes to meet Mustafa's. "We are here to capture a castle, and prevent its use as a weapon of war! Not to slaughter its inhabitants!"

"Yes, Sanjak-bey, but your father —"

"My father is my father!" Mustafa interrupted with a furor. "And I am his son! Tell your man to clean his sword and sheath it! There shall be no more display of butchery!"

Serkan bowed his head. "Yes, Sanjak-bey."

"And Serkan! When that man has cleaned and sheathed his sword, I want him beaten on the soles of his bare feet with the *falaka* cane!" He watched as anguish twisted the features of Serkan's face. "As boluk-agha you are responsible for him, thus it will be you who administers the punishment!"

Serkan sighed heavily, glaring at Mustafa. "Yes . . . Sanjak-bey."

* * *

As the day evolved, Mustafa sent Kamil with a group of soldiers down into the village to assess the situation. The corbaci returned to the castle over an hour later, reporting that all resistance to the Ottoman presence in the town had been eliminated, confirming how their orta had secured the entire area.

Satisfied by the results, Mustafa ordered two Janissaries to take horses and ride south to Koszeg to inform his father that Berndorf's castle along with the village, had been captured, clearing the road to Vienna.

CHAPTER SIXTEEN

Two days had passed without any news from events in Koszeg, leaving Mustafa and Haris concerned by the continued absence of the sultan's army. With an abundance of food within the village, the Janissaries were eating well, and certainly relishing the reprieve from marching and combat. The villagers were somber but cooperative, and there were no serious confrontations or misbehaviors on the part of the Janissaries or their captives, aside from occasional verbal insults exchanged between both groups.

On the fourth day following the capture of the castle and village, Haris sought some solitary time away from the center of town, reflecting on Badra and longing for a resumption of their correspondence. Finding a spot not far from the church, he planted himself against a wooden fence, and gazed across a golden field of wheat with his eyes transfixed on the snow-capped mountainous landscape rising beyond the field. He became lost in his appreciation of a rock-strewn hillside, situated well below the snow peaks—its stony crags splattered with blotches of white edelweiss—when his moment of solitude was interrupted by a Janissary with news of six men captured by an Ottoman patrol in the wood south of the village. Realizing his knowledge of the German language would be needed, Haris quickly headed off in the direction of the church, where he encountered Mustafa, Kamil, and a great many Janissaries hovering over the prisoners outside of the building.

Haris approached the captives, seated on the ground, appearing weary with dazed looks splattered across faces blotched with dried sweat and dirt. He looked up at Mustafa. "Landsknecht?"

"I don't know. I have never seen landsknecht," Mustafa replied. "They were found moving in a northerly direction, and are in possession of many gold coins. Maybe they are thieves?"

Haris pored over their flamboyant clothing; although he was taken aback by the ragged, dirty appearance of their garments. "I'm certain they are landsknecht, which I assure you to be a profession that reeks of thievery. It looks as though they haven't bathed in a while. You say they were found south of the village? Perhaps they have come from Koszeg?"

"Perhaps. The Janissaries who discovered them found them to be very much surprised by our presence here. They didn't have time to react when they were overrun."

"Then they had no idea we control the village or the castle." Haris paced over to where the six men rested, followed by Mustafa. He studied each face carefully, moving from right to left; but when coming upon the last man, he stopped abruptly, and gawked.

Mustafa glared at the blonde haired blue-eyed prisoner before looking at Haris. "What is it?"

Haris turned his back on the man and addressed Mustafa. "Sanjak-bey, I would like to speak to this man alone."

"Why him, and not the others?"

"I think I may know him." Haris spun back toward the prisoner. "On your feet!" he commanded in German.

The surprised man sluggishly rose to his feet, as Haris unsheathed his kilij, pointing the blade at him.

"You know him? How?" Mustafa pressed.

"I will tell you later. But I think I may be able to gather information from him."

"Shall I accompany you?"

"No. Let me handle this alone, Sanjak-bey." Haris turned away from Mustafa. "Come!" he yelled to the prisoner. "Inside the church!" he demanded, leading the man with the point of his kilij inside a side door to the house of worship.

Within the two-story church with its nave divided horizontally by rows of wooden pews, the two men could see a wooden crucifix hanging from the wall of the church's eastern end, set behind a stone altar, and moved toward the first row of pews nearest the doors.

"Sit down!" Haris ordered.

The young man cooperated, dropping down into a pew, just as his face lit up with excitement. "It's you! Isn't it?"

Haris frowned. "Your name is Ademir, is this true?"

Ademir smiled. "You remembered!"

Haris did not return the smile. "When I hesitated to take your life back in Vienna, I warned you to give up the career of a landsknecht!" He paused to glance with disdain at Ademir's brightly colored outfit. "But I see you failed to heed my words."

"It pays well, and the women are attracted to such a profession," Ademir said. "Besides, I have become very good at soldiering."

With the quickness of a striking serpent, Haris brought his curved blade to Ademir's Adam's apple. "A good soldier doesn't allow himself to be captured in the forest—certainly not twice!"

Ademir's smile suddenly faded. "You make your point well."

Haris lowered his sword. "What are you doing here?"

"Tell me your name?" Ademir countered.

Haris remained silent, continuing to stare down his prisoner.

"You've known my name for three years," Ademir reminded him. "If you want me to answer your questions, then at least allow me to know your name."

Haris grimaced, raising the kilij once again. "I am not here to bargain with you! You are my prisoner and without my intervention, you most likely would have been executed by now!"

"Execute me then!" Ademir leaned forward in the pew. "Execute us all! And when you do, the information that we possess, which I'm certain will be of use to you and your army, dies with us!"

Haris lowered his sword, and studied him with a perplexing stare. "You have indeed grown up since last we met. I'm not sure I like it."

"Your leader—he appears to be younger than me. What is he, a prince?"

Haris gnashed his teeth, avoiding a response.

"When first we met, I would not have imagined you, the great Ottoman warrior who I witnessed easily dismember three landsknecht singlehandedly, taking commands from a boy!"

Haris grew agitated. "Well, Ademir," he sputtered, followed by a long sigh. "You leave me with no other choice! I will bring each of the five men who were captured with you inside the church one at a time! Until you tell me what I want to know, I shall proceed to execute each of them here before your eyes, spilling their blood on this altar of your faith!"

Ademir slumped back against the pew as Haris turned for the door. "All right!" he shouted. "It is a pity that you and I are on opposite sides . . . for I think we would be friends."

Haris stopped and spun around. "You and I have little in common! You have the freedom to make whatever you desire out of life, yet you choose the path of war! My path has been chosen for me!"

"My homeland has been besieged by warfare since my birth," Ademir countered. "I've known nothing else! Freedom? Ha! I have been a slave to warfare for as long as I can remember!"

Haris growled. "All right, landsknecht." He drew a long sigh. "You have your wish. I am called . . . Haris."

Ademir nodded his approval. "Haris? It sounds strong. I think it fits you."

Haris grew impatient. "Now, tell me what you are doing here?"

"Well . . . Haris—after you spared my life in the forest outside of Vienna three years ago I decided to stay in Austria and made a home here in Berndorf. Warfare in these mountains brings a steady income for a landsknecht. Think about it, one moment the Austrians are trying to prevent a Turkish invasion, and in the next they are being led by Ferdinand to attack Hungary. With such a hearty thirst for blood in these parts, I am certain to remain steadily employed."

"Berndorf is your home now?"

"Yes. It's beautiful, is it not?"

"Then you did not know we had taken the village or castle?"

"The castle has also fallen?" Ademir shook his head. "Well, your conquest will be short-lived."

"What do you mean?"

Ademir hesitated, swallowing hard. "I feel as though I am betraying my people by revealing what I'm about to say, but you did spare me from the sword three years ago."

"What information do you have?"

Ademir frowned. "I want your promise that my fellow landsknecht and I will not be harmed! And that you will not lay waste to this village!"

"I am not the sanjak-bey. I cannot promise what he will do."

Ademir produced a quizzical look. "Sanjak-bey? Is that the title given to the boy? It sounds important. I'm guessing he out ranks you. Yet it is apparent that you have influence over him. When we were outside the church, I could see the intensity in his face as he listened to your words. Sultans, kings, sanjak-beys—they piss on those who they see us as unequal in their eyes! But no, this young officer looks at you with respect! If you tell him not to harm us, then he will listen. Give me your promise, Haris!"

Haris, visibly annoyed, turned away from Ademir, bringing his eyes to the crucifix, before focusing back on the young landsknecht. "You are of the Roman Church—that is what you told me when we first met. And I too was raised Catholic. I wonder whose side God favors in all of this?"

"Perhaps God hasn't chosen sides?"

Haris winced. "All right, you have my promise Ademir, that you and your accomplices will not be harmed—only if I deem the information you possess as essential!"

"And the village?"

"The village will be spared."

"I believe you," Ademir replied.

"Now, what is your information?"

"Haris, your sultan and his army are on their way back to Constantinople as we speak. They retreated after laying siege to the castle that defends the city of Koszeg. I know of this, because I was there. That is where we were returning from when captured in the forest. We were aiding the people of Koszeg. They paid us in gold."

"You're lying!" Haris exclaimed. "I was at Koszeg before the siege began! I know the size of Suleyman's army and the number of cannon he brought with him! Koszeg could never have survived an Ottoman assault! Vienna, perhaps, but not Koszeg!"

"I speak the truth! I swear it!" Ademir pled. "I fought alongside very brave men—Croats who refused to surrender for nearly a month! Some say our numbers inside the city totaled only seven hundred—only seven hundred against infinite numbers of Ottomans!" Ademir paused momentarily, allowing Haris to scrutinize the landsknecht, sensing from his serious expression that his word was genuine. "At one point, Ottoman sappers brought down a large section of the castle wall! Yet, we fought on, enduring nearly twenty assaults on the city, and refusing to surrender! It reminded me of the Ottoman assault on Vienna when you and I first met! Then the rains came, and apparently your sultan had had enough! Frustrated by our bravery and by the wet summer weather, he negotiated terms of surrender with our leader, Nikola Jurisic, who permitted only a small force of Ottoman attackers to enter the castle and raise an Ottoman flag! There was nothing else negotiated! So much death and destruction for the purpose of raising a flag! Soon after, the Ottomans retreated and headed off in the direction from whence they came."

"Why should I believe you?"

"Because it's the truth!" Ademir plead. "And because it is my way of repaying you for sparing my life in Vienna!"

"Yes, I spared your life, but how has your tale affected me? I find your information interesting, but not life-saving!"

"But I haven't finished—there's more! Charles' army marches toward Koszeg," Ademir said. "Although when he arrives he will learn what I have just told you about the Ottoman retreat. But there was a messenger who passed us on the road traveling with urgency to get news of events in Koszeg to the people of Vienna. He told us that a tercio of Spaniards sent ahead of Charles' army had reached Aspang-Markt when they learned of the Ottoman retreat."

"Aspang-Markt?" Haris asked.

"It is a village lying southwest of Berndorf," Ademir explained. "They are now moving north toward Vienna to reinforce the capitol, should the Ottoman sultan change his mind. They are about a half a day behind us and heading this way. I suspect they should be arriving in Berndorf soon, and I don't think they will be overjoyed with what they may find. What do you think?"

Haris frowned. "If I find you are lying to me, I will personally hunt you down, and do what I should have done to you when first we met!"

"You don't really mean that, do you?" Ademir jested.

Haris growled, just as Mustafa exploded through the doorway behind him with his sword drawn.

"Haris?" Mustafa called out, speaking in Turkish. "You have been in here long enough! What is it that you've learned from this man?"

"Your father's army has retreated from Koszeg, and is headed back to Constantinople!"

"What? I don't believe it! He would have sent word to us!"

"He may have tried. It's possible the Spanish may have intercepted the Ottoman messengers you sent." Haris sighed. "At any hour three thousand Spaniards will be arriving in Berndorf."

"This man revealed all of this to you? Can you trust him?"

"I'm afraid we have to. Come, we need to get word to our troops around the village and in the castle. And you need to order our complete withdrawal."

"Do we march north toward Vienna?" Mustafa asked.

"No, back the way we came, south toward Osijek. If we move north we will be caught in between the Viennese and the Spanish who march this way, to be followed shortly by the imperial army of Charles."

"But by marching south, we march directly into the Spanish forces!"

160

"Let us pray they take the road," Haris said. "We shall take the mountains."

Mustafa pointed at Ademir. "What of this one?"

"We leave him here, as well as the others. We leave this village as we found it."

"Haris, if we do not punish the village it may be a sign of weakness!"

"If we take the time to punish the village, we will find ourselves entrapped by a larger army of Spaniards! The amount of lives your withdrawal will save will be an example of strength, not weakness!"

Mustafa drew a heavy breath. "Very well. Let's do as you say."

Haris turned toward Ademir. "Be well, Ademir," he wished in German.

"And you as well, Haris," Ademir mumbled under his breath. "And you as well—"

CHAPTER SEVENTEEN

Two hours later—which in Haris' estimation was two hours too late—the village populace watched the sudden departure of the Ottoman orta, as it headed south in the direction from which they had invaded. Being careful to avoid the main road, the Janissaries climbed and descended the first of what they remembered promised to be a grueling homeward trek, involving many heavily forested hills and mountains.

Nearing the bottom of the first hill, the men of the orta approached an area of thinning forest through which they could distinguish a valley, bereft of trees. A wide, shallow brook separated the vale, cutting a meandering channel through an area of tall grass, splashed with pockets of vibrant wild flowers. Across the valley, which Haris guessed to be nearly a mile in width, the tree line reappeared at the base of the opposite hill, with its forest ascending as the topography climbed. Suddenly, the boluk-aghas ordered their Janissaries to an abrupt halt; for movement was sighted across the valley, where flurries of dark figures began to emerge from out of the tree line at the base of the opposite hill. At first, Haris guessed that the shapes were packs of wolves appearing from beneath the forest canopy in great numbers that seemed to be unending. However, soon it became clear that the figures were hundreds, if not thousands of soldiers, armed with arquebuses and flat swords.

Alarmed by how soon the Janissary orta had encountered the enemy since leaving Berndorf, Haris huddled behind a group of trees with Mustafa, and the two were soon joined by Serkan and Kamil.

Mustafa looked at Haris. "It would seem your prisoner was telling us the truth about the Spanish."

Haris nodded. "But I guessed wrong about them using the road. Why do they march over rough terrain and not use the highway? This land belongs to people who hold their allegiance to the same emperor as the Spanish. The landsknecht may not have known we had control of the village and castle, but it appears the Spanish knew."

Kamil stared at the figures crossing the valley floor. "Maybe they captured the messengers the Sanjak-bey sent to Koszeg. Under torture they may have revealed our location."

Haris sighed. "It's possible. No matter how they've learned of our presence, I believe the Spanish didn't take the road because they're trying to prevent our escape."

"Well, we can't go around them," Mustafa said.

"And we can't go back the way we came." Kamil frowned. "Allah challenges us this day."

"Perhaps we can negotiate to pass one another harmlessly," Serkan jested. "Boluk-bashi, do you speak Spanish as well as German?"

Haris produced a scowl. "No, I'm afraid I do not. We could take up positions here on the hill, wait for their arrival, and see which side is left standing after the ammunition runs out. But I'm afraid we are outmanned and outgunned."

Mustafa stared off into the forest. "What would Alexander do?"

"Alexander?" Serkan questioned.

"Yes . . . yes," Mustafa rambled. "I believe I may have a plan!"

All four men held their tongues.

"How much time before the Spaniards will reach us?" Mustafa asked.

"Within the hour," Kamil replied.

Mustafa wiped his forehead with his shirt sleeve. "We need to work fast! I think it would be best if we descended at least another twenty rods! That should place our arquebuses well within range of the valley floor, and still keep our men hidden in the forest! I want all of the men of the orta to spread out forming two rows, stretching shoulder to shoulder westward in the direction of the road!"

"You wish to take cover behind trees and shoot at them, Sanjak-bey?" Haris asked, in a tone laced with doubt.

"Yes, but only at a crucial moment! When the entire Spanish army moves to the northern side of the stream, one boluk-agha shall lead his men from the point farthest west of our line, and attack the Spaniard's flank by first laying down a volley of arquebus fire from behind the trees! After we have fired on them, those same men of ours will charge the Spaniards and engage in hand to hand combat in the valley! How do you think the other Spaniards will react to this attack?"

The officers looked at one another with confused expressions, before Serkan volunteered. "They will shoot at our men and kill them!"

"No, they will not!" Kamil interjected. "The Spanish will not risk firing at their soldiers! They will come to their aid like a swarm of bees, and fight us with their swords!"

Mustafa smiled. "Yes Corbaci, I think so too! And when I see this happening, I will order a retreat, but instead of falling back into the forest, our men fighting the Spaniards will cease their fighting and run, just beneath the tree line in a westerly direction!"

"The Spanish will believe they are retreating toward the road!" Haris added. "They will not know the size of our army!"

"Yes!" Mustafa agreed. "As the Spaniards pursue them, the remainder of our corps, stretched out and hidden behind the tree line, will open up their arquebus fire, shooting up and down the line!"

Kamil nodded. "It might work! But the Janissaries sent out to set the trap will be bound to suffer many casualties. Sanjak-bey, who do you think should lead the charge?"

Mustafa pondered the question. "I wish not to compel a reluctant man to commence the attack . . . for the men who will be forced to follow him must be led by his courage. I am hopeful Allah will reveal such a man."

A few moments of silence passed before Serkan spoke up. "I will lead the charge!" He stood erect with chest out. "God willing, we shall succeed, Sanjak-bey!"

Mustafa grinned. "Very well. You're a good and brave soldier, Serkan."

Haris felt a hint of jealousy with Mustafa's words of praise for Serkan; however, he recognized that the sehzade spoke wisely.

"We haven't much time!" Haris warned. "We need to get our men into position as quickly and as quietly as we can!"

Immediately, Serkan and the other boluk-aghas broke from their meeting, and gathered the men under their individual command. Within thirty minutes, two straight lines together totaling nearly eight hundred Janissaries stretched across the forest just above the tree line, hidden behind trunks of spruce, oak, and chestnut trees. A series of candles set inside tin lanterns were ignited, and passed up and down the lines so that each man could light his arquebus match cord. Once all the cords had been lit, they waited, watching the army of Spaniards wade through the shallow brook, until most of the unsuspecting members of the tercio had crossed the stream, moving toward the tree line.

Mustafa took up position alongside Serkan's men near to the far right of the line stationed closest to the road, and as the first group of Spaniards neared the tree line, the sanjak-bey ordered Serkan's men to fire. A burst of arquebus fire exploded from out of the wood, cutting down a large number of Spaniards with deadly accuracy. Serkan's troops dropped their firearms and unsheathed their kilijs, as Mustafa ordered them to charge the remaining Spaniards. The quickness of the Janissary strike did not allow time for the Spaniards to load their firearms, forcing them to counter the attack with the use of their own swords.

The clash of men and steel jolted the serenity of the valley, invoking bloodcurdling cries of men struggling against one another. As the hellish sound of battle echoed throughout the basin, the bodies of fallen soldiers from both sides quickly began to desecrate the landscape.

Haris moved from his position to join Mustafa. "Your plan seems to be working!" The sanjak-bey did not reply. Haris studied Mustafa's face, recognizing how pale it had become. "Mustafa?"

Mustafa turned slowly toward Haris. "When we had taken the castle, I did not arrive until after the fighting inside the fortress had ceased! Now here in this valley, I see the cruelty of combat! I do not think I like war very much!"

Haris didn't know how to respond, nor did he believe the time was right to do so, and returned his focus to the battle. "The other Spanish soldiers are rushing to aid their men! You need to order the Janissary retreat!"

Serkan stood in the valley next to a Janissary carrying a horn, positioned just beyond the base of the tree line so that he could witness both his group's battle with the Spaniards, as well as having a view of Mustafa. When he saw the sanjak-bey raise his arquebus over his head with two hands, Serkan recognized the signal to retreat, and ordered his soldier to sound the horn. The Janissaries began to fall back at the sound of the blaring instrument, and bravely, Serkan rushed into the melee with sword drawn.

The group of Janissaries, having begun their retreat, fled from the Spaniards in a westerly direction, running along the brook toward the road. The bulk of the Spanish tercio took the bait, believing they had turned the tide of battle, and commenced their pursuit of the fleeing Janissaries.

Mustafa looked at Haris. "When shall I order our men behind the trees to fire?"

Haris held out his hand. "Wait! We need to be certain that Serkan's men are safely beyond the aim of our troops in the forest!"

Both men watched events unfold with great intensity, roiling their faces until Haris felt the last of the Janissaries were out of harm's way. "Now! Give the order now!"

Raising the arquebus again, Mustafa gave the signal to fire, and instantly the tree line roared, spitting fire and smoke simultaneously. Hundreds of Spaniards, hit by a barrage of lead balls, dropped to the earth with their final breath. When they realized another army lay hidden behind the tree line, the tercio shifted their charge from pursuing the fleeing Janissaries to attacking the hillside. Suddenly the second line of Janissaries fired their arquebuses, inflicting even greater damage. The Spanish commanders, discouraged at the carnage suffered by their troops, ordered a retreat, forcing what remained of their tercio to fall back across the brook.

Haris slapped Mustafa on the back. "You did it, Sanjak-bey! Your plan worked!"

Appearing dazed, Mustafa shook his head, swallowing hard. "Praise be to God!" he offered feebly. "What now, Haris?"

"We keep the troops under the cover of the trees, and move westward toward the road to meet up with Serkan!"

"What about the threat of another attack by the Spanish?"

"If we stay here in the valley, I think such an attack may be likely! That's why it is important to get to the road before they can regroup!"

* * *

Within the hour, the Ottoman orta had reached the dirt road safely, reuniting with the surviving members of those brave men who had led the charge. Mustafa and Haris moved about the unit congratulating these Janissaries, when they stumbled upon two men lying on the road with life threatening wounds. Both Mustafa and Haris were shocked to discover one of the two injured men was Serkan, bleeding profusely from a deep wound to his left thigh.

A tourniquet was applied to Serkan's leg, while Janissaries fashioned stretchers from tree limbs and pieces of material from uniforms. With days of marching still ahead, Haris realized without proper medical care, the two would perish before they reached the town of Osijek.

On the following morning, after marching throughout the night to place distance between themselves and the Spaniards, the Janissary orta was surprised by the appearance of two Ottoman soldiers on horseback, approaching from out of the south. The two soldiers brought with them a third horse, void of a rider. Upon reaching the haggard Janissaries, the riders were directed to Mustafa, who could be found marching among the middle of the Ottoman orta alongside of Haris. As the riders approached the sanjak-bey, an order was issued to bring the Janissary's march to a halt.

One of the riders dismounted and approached Mustafa, carrying a rolled parchment. "Your Royal Highness?"

"I am he!" Mustafa replied.

The Janissary bowed, before lifting his head and handing the parchment to Mustafa. "We are messengers sent from Sultan Suleyman with instructions to deliver this message to you! Praise, be to Allah that you are safe!"

Mustafa read it silently. When finished, he raised his eyes toward Haris. "The sultan's seal confirms it is authentic. His army has left Koszeg and is on its way home to Constantinople. He awaits me in Belgrade within the Sanjak of Smederevo. The third horse without a rider is for me. The sultan's wish is that I should accompany these men back to Belgrade on horseback." Mustafa rolled up the parchment and handed it to the messenger. "Bring me the two wounded men on stretchers!" he called out. Immediately, four Janissaries disappeared within the orta, only to reappear again moments later, carrying the two stretchers supporting the wounded men.

"I am not going anywhere without my orta!" Mustafa declared aloud, for all to hear. He addressed the messenger. "Return to the sultan and tell him I have decided to stay with my men! We have marched into this country together, and shall march from it onto Belgrade together! As for these wounded men, they are in desperate need of medical care! Their need to travel by horse greatly outweighs mine, for their lives depend on it! I command that you place each of these men on horseback! You and your fellow messenger can share the third horse! Ride to Osijek with these men, and get them medical attention! I am entrusting their safety and medical care to you!"

The messenger flashed a confused expression. "But Your Royal Highness, your father's instructions are specific! If I do not return to Belgrade with you, the sultan will have my head!"

Mustafa huffed. "Very well. Then I shall save my father the time, and take your head instead!" He nodded in the direction of one of the Janissaries, who unsheathed his kilij.

The messenger's eyes widened, before he held out both hands. "Of course!" He bowed his head. "You are very wise, Your Royal Highness! May Allah forgive me for offending Your Royal Highness! We are honored to be within your presence and to serve the Sehzade Mustafa!"

Mustafa bent over Serkan as he lay on the stretcher. "Can you ride a horse in your condition?"

"I will have to, Sanjak-bey," Serkan delivered with a weakened voice.

"I will see you in Osijek," Mustafa said, before several Janissaries lifted both men from the stretchers, placing them onto the saddles of the horses. One of the Janissaries handed Serkan his bork.

Haris stepped beside the horse, raising his head toward Serkan. "Serkan, what you did yesterday in the valley—it was very brave."

Serkan grinned, as he grabbed hold of the horse's reins. "You would have done the same, Boluk-bashi."

"Yes—but *you* did it. Every one among us owes his life to you."

Mustafa placed his hand on Serkan's boot. "May God be with you."

"Sanjak-bey," Serkan addressed. "This is for you," he said, reaching down and handing Mustafa his bork. "You have earned it. You are a Janissary." He smiled. "You are one of us."

Haris could see how Mustafa accepted Serkan's headgear with pride. Clearly overcome with emotion, the sanjak-bey's speech fell silent, and he could only nod his appreciation to the wounded Janissary.

CHAPTER EIGHTEEN

Constantinople – November, 1532

After six months away from his capitol city, Suleyman finally returned to Constantinople with his army just as the November air began to acquire a pesky chill. Despite not having set eyes on Vienna or Charles' imperial army, the sultan proclaimed victory for his military campaign, touting the surrender of Koszeg as well as the capture of seventeen castles—many of which were located inside the border of his ally Hungary—to support his claim of success. The result was five consecutive days of celebration throughout Constantinople filled with music, dancing, fireworks, daily parades, lavish food provisions, and flattering speeches delivered by significant government officials, including Suleyman himself. It was a celebration of power and might, focusing on the longevity of Ottoman rule, coupled with adoration for the sultan.

Most of the military parades moving through the streets of Constantinople during the days of celebration showcased every branch of the Ottoman war machine, including branches absent from the most recent campaign, such as the sultan's prestigious navy. Each unit's march culminated inside the grounds of the Hippodrome before an elaborate throne set beneath a large tent where the sultan sat, surveying his grand military.

On the third day of the celebration when the various ortas were being recognized, dozens of Janissaries from within each orta were selected to perform a ritual sword dance—a display that brought beauty, poise, and athleticism to the art of wielding the kilij. The final choreographed movement of the sword dance featured the Janissaries quickly forming two parallel lines in which the soldiers faced one another in a rigid military pose. When the command was issued, the Janissaries simultaneously and slowly raised their curved swords above their heads, extending the weapons forward so that the blades from both lines touched one another, forming a long arch of steel. Beneath the raised kilijs, the military leaders of each specific orta paraded, eventually emerging from underneath the blades in their approach to the sultan.

It was evident to all that Suleyman was very much enjoying the skillful exercise, when he suddenly beheld Mustafa pacing beneath the swords of the men assigned to the sehzade's orta. He watched as his son strode haughtily between the soldiers, and when he had passed by the final two Janissaries, a boisterous cry of "Mustafa!" erupted from among the orta, evolving into a repeated chant of his name that echoed around the Hippodrome. Suleyman noted how no other commander had received such an energetic response of admiration as did Mustafa, and although it appeared to please the sultan, the respect he had for his son became tempered slightly by a touch of jealousy.

* * *

A week had passed, when Suleyman summoned Ibrahim to meet with him within the Audience Chamber of the Yeni Saray. The grand vizier found the sultan standing alone, dressed in a long cashmere gown, staring at the portraits of sultans adorning the white, blue, and turquoise tiled walls of the chamber's smaller front room.

"Sultan," Ibrahim called out, after entering the room with his head bowed.

Suleyman turned his head slightly to glance at his friend from over his shoulder. "Ibrahim."

"God's peace be upon you, Sultan."

"And God's peace, be upon you as well, my friend." Suleyman brought his attention back to the portraits.

"We have news today?" Ibrahim asked, after raising his head and moving toward the sultan.

"Yes. The messenger should be along shortly."

"I see that you are preoccupied with portraits," Ibrahim noted. "Are you pleased with your own?"

"I am merely pondering history. It is believed that my great grandfather Mehmed was poisoned by his son, my grandfather Bayezid." Suleyman remained fixated on the portraits. "My father Selim fought his father for control of the empire."

"And so, you find yourself troubled by your family's past?"

The sultan turned away from the wall, adjusting the cummerbund at his waist, and paced slowly through the entrance into the main chamber room. "I was very surprised by the army's reaction to Mustafa at the Hippodrome last week."

Ibrahim stepped behind him. "You should be very proud."

Suleyman marched to the far end of the chamber, where he climbed a raised platform and took a seat on the throne. "I am indeed proud of Mustafa," he acknowledged. "Lezhe Haris has done admirable work training my son. But when I dwell on the recent history of my family, should I be concerned with Mustafa's sudden popularity among my army?"

"Sultan, Mustafa was cheered by the orta he commanded. You elevated him to that command. The respect your son received is what you wanted for Mustafa all along. It is why you appointed Lezhe Haris as his trainer, is it not?"

Suleyman softly stroked his bearded chin. "But what is the

price to pay for nurturing such respect? Have I unwittingly unleashed a tiger?"

"I have watched Mustafa grow up. He is a good son, and I believe Lezhe Haris to be of good character, as well as a loyal Ottoman servant. Allow the student to emulate his teacher, and do not be haunted by your family history."

Suleyman nodded in agreement. "Your words bring me peace Ibrahim . . . for the moment that is."

Suddenly, the door to the chamber opened, revealing a chamberlain with his head bowed. "Your Royal Majesty, the messenger has arrived."

Suleyman nodded toward Ibrahim. "Send him in," the grand vizier commanded.

Passing through the doorway, Suleyman and Ibrahim beheld a short, olive toned man carrying a rolled piece of parchment tied with a silk bow. He moved with his bowed head wrapped within a green turban, followed closely by two chamberlains. Stopping before the sultan's chair, he waited until receiving Suleyman's permission to lift his head, revealing eyes that slightly bulged as does a frog's, while flashing a perfect half-moon shaped smile that made his cheeks puff as though he were storing dates within his mouth.

"In the name of God, most merciful and most compassionate," the man began with a gentle, warbling voice. "As the earth welcomes the dawn of every new day, Ghafir, Your Royal Majesty's humble servant, cowers before thee with deep respect, always extremely honored to be in Your Royal Majesty's presence. Praise, be to Allah for protecting me on my journey to Constantinople."

"Ghafir, it always brings me pleasure to see you," Suleyman replied. "You are like a window to the world with the news you bring."

"You honor me with your words, Your Royal Majesty." Ghafir once again bowed his head slowly. The two chamberlains who stood close behind him stepped forward and each grabbed one of Ghafir's arms, holding them outstretched as the three men approached the raised platform. Suleyman bent forward and extended his left arm toward Ghafir, who in turn, kissed the sultan's hand, before being gently pulled back away from the platform. The chamberlains released their hold on him as one of them removed the scroll from his grasp, inspecting it briefly, before returning it to Ghafir.

Suleyman wiped the top of his hand with a handkerchief. "Ghafir, in spite of my joy in seeing you, it is a shame that we must take such precautions. I am certain it makes you feel like a criminal, but the procedure has its roots in an earlier time, after a Croatian sought an interview with the sultan . . . and then murdered him."

"Your Royal Majesty, I take no offense in being restrained in your presence, and I thank Your Royal Majesty for the compassion behind the Sultan's explanation."

"Let us begin with my empire," Suleyman instructed. "My beylerbeys and sanjak-beys, who I have entrusted with ruling the far corners of my empire, are very competent in providing me with their reports. However, I realize that embellishing information for personal gain is a weakness of human nature. Thus, I place much credence in what news I receive from you. So, tell me, what is the status of my empire?"

Ghafir raised his head. "You are very wise, Your Royal Majesty." He took a moment to unroll the parchment. "I am happy to report that Your Royal Majesty's empire, stretching, as it does, across the Mediterranean Sea from the northern coastline of Africa eastward to the Tigris and Euphrates Rivers and Caucasus Mountains, and extending from the lands of the Danube River southward to the Arabian Sea—an empire so large that every other monarch on earth envies the sultan who rules over it—your empire is prosperous and peaceful. The people have become accustomed to calling Your Royal Majesty, *Suleyman the lawgiver* in every corner of the empire, bearing witness to how the laws stemming from the stroke of your pen have brought justice and fairness across the land. Even the Mamluks of the *eyalet* of Egypt, who have given Your Royal Majesty much trouble in recent years, now enjoy the fruits of Ottoman rule because of your wisdom."

Ghafir took a breath before continuing. "It is evident that Allah has reflected His pleasure with Your Royal Majesty, who as Caliph leads the Muslim world as the protector and guardian of the true faith, in addition to safeguarding Islam's three holiest cities, Mecca, Medina, and Jerusalem. It is obvious how Allah continues to bless the empire with a consistent strong harvest, so that none go hungry. The merchants continue to turn a sizable profit, mostly from trade with the Far East, especially now since Your Royal Majesty has seen to it that the Silk Roads are closed to European traffic. Within the millets scattered across the empire, Christian and Jewish subjects continue to sing Your Royal Majesty's praises for his benevolent tolerance in allowing them to worship freely and keep their traditions. In mentioning Jerusalem, I am also happy to report how Bedouin invasions of the holy city have steadily decreased. As a result, the population of Jerusalem continues to grow."

"Despite my father's desire to neglect Jerusalem, I judge it to be a city of much significance in sustaining the longevity of my empire. I am determined to use whatever resources are at my disposal to preserve its religious connection to the peoples of my realm," Suleyman said. "What about the Druze in the Sanjak of Safad?"

"After years of fighting amongst the various chieftains of the Ma'n Dynasty, and as a result of Your Royal Majesty's very wise decision to give them self-rule, the violence in Mount Lebanon has appeared to be ended."

"Yes, the wisdom of permitting self-rule," Suleyman interjected. "Why rustle a hornet's nest when it is far from your home? What of my navy, Ghafir?"

"Under the leadership of the Kapudan Hayreddin Barbarossa Pasha, the Venetian threat to the eastern Mediterranean has declined dramatically, establishing the Ottoman navy as the dominant presence in this area."

"Ghafir, the news you bear certainly warms my heart, for your words reflect an empire stronger than ever, and more importantly, they confirm that my people are content." Suleyman paused to clear his throat. "But, as is the case with everything, good news certainly precedes the bad. As the Quran teaches 'He hides from the people because of the bad news given to him. Shall he keep it in humiliation, or bury it in the dust?' Ghafir, I anticipate news from beyond the borders of my empire is dark, but as your sultan and your caliph, I shall neither keep it to myself, nor bury it in the dust. Tell me what dangers lurk outside of the Ottoman borders, so that I may address them appropriately."

"Your Royal Majesty's insightfulness is unmatched," Ghafir acclaimed, before returning his attention to the scroll. "The news I bring from beyond your borders is not devastating, yet unfortunately the lands outside of your realm are splattered with your enemies, many who fear Your Royal Majesty's power, and those who seek to destroy not only the Ottoman way of life, but Islam as well."

Suleyman played with the long sleeves of his robe, his expression undaunted by the messenger's words. "What news do you bring me from the lands bordering my empire to the east?"

"From the lands beyond the Indus River, the great Mughal Emperor Babur is dead, and his son, who is called Humayun, has ascended the throne. Not much is known about the new emperor, other than the fact that he is very young."

"The Mughal rulers are Sunni Muslims, as are we and their lands lie beyond nearly impassable mountain ranges," Suleyman explained. "Neither do I desire the land lying to the east of these mountains, nor do I believe the Mughals would attempt to expand west of them."

"The wisdom of Your Royal Majesty shines like a thousand suns," Ghafir praised.

"What of the Persians?"

"As you are well aware, Your Royal Majesty, with the death of Shah Ismail, like the Mughals, youth occupies the throne of the Safavid kingdom with Ismail's son, Tahmasp," Ghafir reported. "It has been nearly a decade with Tahmasp in power, and my informants tell me the young shah is one to watch carefully. It is reported he has organized an elite fighting force made up of Armenians, Circassians, and Georgians."

"It sounds similar to your Janissaries," Ibrahim interjected.

"It is believed Tahmasp has an interest in expanding his empire into the area of Baghdad," Ghafir added.

Suleyman produced a look of concern. "It makes sense that he would try this. They tell me the heretic Shia movement, which exists to pit Muslim against Muslim, is very strong and infects the cities and villages on the eastern border of my empire. These Muslim hypocrites would surely welcome the Shia Safavids. I fear Tahmasp and I may be on a collision course."

"Tahmasp would be wise to keep his distance from Baghdad," Ibrahim remarked.

"Yes—but he is young and filled with much pride, two qualities that often stifle wisdom." Suleyman frowned. "What is the situation in Europe?"

"Spain continues to grow wealthier with her colonization of the new world. It appears this land located across the great ocean, is much larger and filled with more riches than anyone could have dreamed," Ghafir described. "Your Royal Majesty is unquestionably the richest man in the world, but Charles grows wealthy with each Spanish fleet laden with gold and silver returning from the new world."

"What do they call this new world?" Suleyman asked. "I have heard the term before, but I have forgotten it."

"It is called America, Your Royal Majesty," Ghafir clarified. "It is named for a Florentine map maker."

"Florentine, Genovese, Napolitano!" Suleyman blurted with disdain. "They are map makers, painters, sculptors, writers, inventors—all who continue to leave their mark in European affairs. With such talent among them, why can they not form a united kingdom on their peninsula? Do they not pine for the return of the Roman Empire? But it is not these Europeans who trouble me!" Suleyman exclaimed, pounding the armchair with his right fist. "It is Charles who infuriates me! He continues to avoid direct battle with my army, yet the Christian dog has most of Europe under his spell! And now it appears his wickedness is set to poison this—this, America!"

"Your Royal Majesty, I have some interesting news on the subject of combatting Charles," Ghafir revealed. "The Spanish Emperor has formed an alliance with Venice in his desire to protect the Pope, Clement."

"I have not threatened the Catholic leader of infidels!" Suleyman barked.

"It is not protection from you, Your Royal Majesty. Rather it is protection from the King of France. Both Spain and France have competed for the Pope's recognition for a decade or more, and Clement has played both sides against one another. At one point, Clement gave his support to the French King Francis, but the Pope switched his loyalty to Charles after the Spanish king invaded Rome, imprisoning Clement. My informants tell me the possibility exists that France may wish to seek an alliance with Your Royal Majesty to counter the Spanish-Venetian alliance."

"It has always been a goal of mine to turn St. Peter's Basilica into a mosque, as we have done with Hagia Sophia." The sultan brought his hand to his face and cupped his chin within his palm. "These Europeans—French, Spanish—they share the Catholic faith, yet they fight one another. Do they not remember their Charlemagne? If they would put their differences aside, they could become a formidable opponent. They are all fools!"

"And Christian Europe continues to splinter, as the dust from Luther's Reformation has still not settled," Ibrahim added.

"This so called Reformation has been troublesome for Christians, but beneficial to Islam. As they fight one another, my empire grows stronger," Suleyman explained.

"Your Royal Majesty and his Grand Vizier are very astute," Ghafir described. "Charles is having much difficulty with the Christian kingdoms of Central Europe, which continue to sever ties with the Catholic Church."

"What of Catholic England?" Suleyman inquired.

"Ah—another trouble spot for Charles and Clement is indeed England, Your Royal Majesty. It is reported that very recently King Henry, frustrated that his wife Catherine can no longer bear him a son, has secretly taken another wife, and thus the king challenges the laws of the Catholic Church which forbid such a union. It is believed the king will seek a divorce from Catherine, further aggravating the Pope. Many believe it is only a matter of time before Henry breaks with the Vatican."

"Women—they are the folly of men," Suleyman growled. "History tells us the stories of many great kings who were brought to their knees over the lust for a woman outside of marriage. 'Whoever marries a woman for nothing but to cast down his eyes, guard his private parts, and join a relationship, Allah will bless him through her and vice versa', " the Sultan recited.

Suddenly, the door at the far end of the chamber thrust open, as a guest barreled through unannounced, while the rear guard stood silently with head bowed. When Ibrahim spied the woman stomping across the chamber floor, with her bouncing red, shoulder-length locks of hair, he recognized her as Hurrem Kadin. As one of Suleyman's favorite consorts, Ibrahim realized she required no introduction.

Suleyman grumbled, and turned toward Ibrahim. "Speaking of women—" he whispered.

"She doesn't look very happy, Sultan," Ibrahim replied.

"I assure you, she is not."

The woman approached Suleyman with her head bowed, stopping beside the messenger, who stood with his head bowed as well.

Raising her eyes, she stared up at the sultan from beneath a black veil that hung down from the flat, black fez that set atop her head. "Your Royal Majesty, please forgive me for my interruption, but it is urgent that I speak with you."

Suleyman frowned. "Ghafir, are we finished here?"

Ghafir raised his head, careful not to glance at the woman.

"My mission is complete, Your Royal Majesty," he announced, before reaching out to hand Ibrahim the scroll.

"Very well, you are dismissed," Suleyman pronounced.

Ghafir bowed his head and slowly walked backward across the room, accompanied by the chamberlains until all disappeared within the doorway. Ibrahim understood that for him too, it was time to leave, and after saying his goodbyes, respectfully bowed to both Suleyman and Hurrem before exiting the room.

Suleyman rose up from out of his chair, and descended the steps to confront his lover, approaching her with his arms extended outwards. They locked fingers of both hands together, before the sultan gently lifted his right hand from hers, removing her veil, and gazed longingly into her hazel eyes. "My bright moon, when I summoned you, I anticipated we would meet in my apartment."

"I needed to see you now, my love," she responded. "My body aches for you. I could wait no longer."

"Did you receive my poems while I was gone?"

"Yes, my Muhibbi," she said, speaking her pet name for him playfully. "They were beautiful. They brought me such comfort, for I exist as your helpless, miserable slave, suffering in your absence."

"You are my springtime." Suleyman pulled her closer to him, as they joined their lips in a long kiss, before the sultan pulled away. "I've sent you messages nearly every day since returning from the campaign—yet you have refused to see me."

Hurrem buried her face within his chest. Suleyman reached down, placing his fingers beneath her chin, and gently lifted her head. "Your name Hurrem means smiling face, but I do not see you smiling today. Tell me, how is my infant son?"

"He is healthy. You now have four healthy sons to succeed you one day."

"Five," Suleyman corrected. "You forget Mustafa."

"Yes—" Hurrem obliged. "We cannot forget Mustafa."

Suleyman detected a lack of enthusiasm in her voice. "What troubles you, my love?"

"Did you not read the last letter I sent you?"

"Of course I did. Though I have not yet found time to respond. My love for you is unending, but I still have an empire to rule, and I have been gone on campaign for six months."

"I know how long you have been gone!" She pouted. "Every day you were away became more painful than the last!"

Suleyman ran the back of his hand against her soft face. "Within your last letter, I was confused by your words. You wrote how embarrassed you would be to show yourself to me." He frowned. "You referred to yourself as sold meat. What does this mean?"

Hurrem's head drooped. "It is Mahidevran!"

Suleyman sighed, pulling away from her.

Hurrem lifted her head and huffed. "Suleyman, she has gone too far this time! She attacked me! She referred to me as sold meat before tearing out a crop of my hair, and scratching my face with her claws!"

Suleyman scrutinized her fair complexion, finding a few small scratches beneath her left eye. "What was it about this time?"

"It is about the same thing all of the time! Her jealousy of our love—it grows more vengeful every day! We are both confined in that ancient palace on the other side of Constantinople, like prisoners sharing the same cell! I'm afraid she may try to kill me there! Oh, how I wish I could be here in the Yeni Saray each day with you!"

"Only the Queen Mother may live here in the Yeni Saray with the sultan," Suleyman reminded her. "It is tradition."

"Then break with tradition! You are the sultan! Your word is the law!"

Suleyman sighed. "I will speak with Mahidevran."

"That's it?"

"What more would you like me to do?"

"Send her away!"

"Send her away?" Suleyman grumbled. "You are both haseki's—mother of sehzades! You both hold a privileged status as the mother of my children!"

"Then Mahidevran is correct, we are both sold meat!"

"How can you say such things? My turtle dove, let me remind you it has been Ottoman custom that after a favorite has given birth to a son, the sultan can no longer take her to bed. Her duty lies with the task of raising the child and preparing him to be the next sultan." Suleyman placed both his hands on her shoulders and made sure he held her attention with his eyes. "But with you, my paradise, I continue to make love! The birth of our six children is evidence of this! I have indeed broken tradition for you, for our love has shattered the Ottoman custom of one woman, one son!" He pulled Hurrem closer to him, embracing her tightly. "You are not sold meat! You are my elixir! You are my life!"

"I love you Muhibbi," Hurrem replied softly. "I feel the weight of tradition crushing down on our desire for one another! There must be something that can be done!"

Suleyman sighed as he stroked her fiery locks. With eyes closed, she moaned softly and parted her ruby lips, luring the sultan into a wet kiss.

CHAPTER NINETEEN

Constantinople - February, 1533

As he waited to begin another lesson with Mustafa, Haris lifted Thomas Malory's *Le Morte d'Arthur* from off of a shelf within the Enderun library, and studied the book with fascination. His enthrallment was not necessarily built around an attraction to the legendary story of King Arthur, but how obsessed such a powerful sultan as Suleyman could be with almost all things European.

As he returned the book to its place on the shelf, Haris heard the door to the library open, finding Mustafa passing through the doorway with a determined stride, carrying a swagger about him that he did not recognize.

"Merhaba," Mustafa greeted, stopping a few feet from where Haris stood to face him.

"Mustafa," Haris replied, returning a probing look.

"Lezhe Haris, my education is finished. You are no longer my teacher," Mustafa announced authoritatively, with a tone Haris had not heard emit from the sehzade's lips in years. "The sultan has appointed me Sehzade Beylerbey of Manisa," he boasted. "It is the town of my birth, and now I shall return to rule over it."

Haris recognized the beylerbey title to be akin to that of a provincial governor. "Well, then I must congratulate you, Mustafa. Manisa has historically been the administrative training center for future sultans. As beylerbey, it would appear you move one step closer to succeeding your father."

"What will you do now, Lezhe Haris?"

Haris hesitated. "I'm not sure—perhaps return to the corps?"

"Wrong answer. Haris, you are no longer my teacher, because now you are one of my viziers! And not just any vizier, but my first vizier!" Mustafa flashed a large smile. "Will you accept the position?"

Haris returned the smile. "You honor me, Mustafa! There is no place I would rather be than by your side!"

"I would have not accepted any other answer from you!" He beamed. "Oh, and Haris, let me remind you that you are also my best friend!" The sehzade stepped into Haris, giving him a firm hug.

"I am proud of you, Mustafa!"

"Thank you, my friend. As first vizier, you will be involved in all decision making."

"I am pleased and flattered to be given such responsibility! When do we leave?"

"The spring equinox. I would like to be situated in Manisa before Ramadan begins. I imagine there will be banquets to attend celebrating my appointment. To schedule my arrival during a time of religious fasting would most certainly stifle the celebration," Mustafa said. "Oh, and Haris, my father wishes to see you in the Audience Chamber. I was told not to say anything, but I think he may have a gift for you," he added, grinning.

"Then I shall not keep the sultan waiting."

"One more thing," Mustafa interjected. "My father advised me that it would be prudent to have a personal physician—someone who is very good at their profession, someone willing to move to Manisa in service to me, and someone with whom I can trust. It is known that Constantinople is full of physicians, but I know not where to begin in my search. Would you find such a physician for me?"

"I will take care of it immediately," Haris said. "I think I know of just the right man for the job . . . Your Royal Highness," he added with a bow.

"It has been a long time since you have bowed to me," Mustafa said.

"When we were first introduced, you were a boy." Haris flashed a serious glare. "You are no longer a boy, Your Royal Highness. My bowing to you is a sign of my respect to you as a man who truly is deserving of it."

* * *

At the top of the hour, two chamberlains opened the door to the Audience Chamber, permitting Haris to enter. Immediately, he noticed how the Grand Vizier Ibrahim stood on the platform behind the throne of the sultan. As Haris moved in his direction, Ibrahim stepped down from the platform to greet him.

"God's peace, be upon you, Lezhe Haris," Ibrahim said, as Haris stood before him with his head bowed.

Haris lifted his head. "And God's peace, be upon you, my Lord. I was instructed to meet the sultan here at the top of the hour."

"Yes. However, I will be representing the sultan this morning," Ibrahim pulled on the sleeves of his robe. "I assure you the sultan sends his blessings, as well as his admiration for your role in Mustafa's training. The sultan is very pleased."

Haris threw a quick glance to the grill set in the wall behind the throne, wondering if the sultan or anyone sat behind it. "It pleases me to know of this."

"We stand before one another with something in common—do we not, Haris?"

Haris realized Ibrahim referenced his new position as

Mustafa's vizier. "Yes, my Lord. I am honored to have been chosen as Sehzade Mustafa's first vizier."

"It is well deserved. It is apparent that you and the sehzade are very close. It helps to have such a strong bond between men, and I speak from personal experience," Ibrahim remarked. The grand vizier glanced beyond Haris at the chamberlain positioned at the door to the far end of the chamber, before clapping his hands. With the signal, the chamberlain threw open the door and Haris turned to see a queue of beautiful women dressed in an array of vibrant colors parade through, assembling along the room's wall.

"The harem," Haris gasped, quickly bowing his head, and directing his eyes to the floor.

"Actually, they are only a small portion of the sultan's harem," Ibrahim corrected. "Thirty in fact. Go ahead Haris, you are permitted to look at them."

Haris slowly lifted his eyes to behold the youthful hour-glass shaped women, whose faces were concealed behind veils.

"Lezhe Haris, members of the Janissary are not permitted to take a wife until the age of forty," Ibrahim explained. "How old are you?"

"I am twenty-eight as of last month."

Ibrahim smiled. "I was twenty-eight when the sultan selected me as his grand vizier. It seems we are on similar paths, you and me."

"Once again, you honor me with your words."

"Yes—and as I was saying, Janissary corps members cannot take a wife until the age of forty. But you are no longer a corps member. You are a vizier—an esteemed member of the Enderun," Ibrahim proclaimed. "Thus, you are free to marry at any time. The sultan has selected these women from his royal harem, and it is his desire to gift you one of your choosing. Of course, you do not have to marry the one that you select. She becomes yours to do with her as you wish."

Haris took a deep breath, still staring at the gorgeous ensemble. "Remove your veils!" Ibrahim commanded. "Go on Haris, take a closer look. I think you will find that many of these women originate from where your heritage lies, in Rumelia. The sultan felt this fact may please you."

As the women removed their veils, Haris stepped closer to the stunning group. He began at the far left of the line, pacing slowly, while inspecting each of the beauties with an appraising eye, as if shopping for the best goods in the marketplace. However, unbeknownst to Ibrahim, Haris' assessment was merely an act for the benefit of the grand vizier, as he sought only one woman—the blonde haired, emerald eyed Badra.

Much to his dismay, when Haris reached the far right end of the line of women, he could see how Badra was not among the choices; although he realized to decline the choice of any one of them as a gift, risked offending the sultan. *He had to think fast.*

"Well, Lezhe Haris. Have you made your decision? Who shall it be?" Ibrahim inquired.

Haris turned to face the grand vizier. "My Lord, I cannot place into words the gratitude I have for the generosity of His Royal Majesty. It exceeds all of my expectations, and I am truly appreciative of the benevolent gesture," he began, choosing his words carefully. "However, I recognize that although I am now titled vizier, my teaching has not ceased, but rather, has grown more complex. I will continue to give Sehzade Mustafa my complete devotion in assisting him in his new and prestigious role as Beylerbey of Manisa. It is his next great challenge, as much as it is mine. In lieu of this fact, my time need not be complicated by the trappings of matrimony, or the pursuit of the pleasures of female companionship. There will be a time for me to marry, but this is not that time. With His Royal Majesty's blessing and understanding, I hope he will forgive my decision to decline his most generous gift, for it would be premature to accept such a prized offer, as my assignment is not yet complete."

For a moment, silence hovered about the Audience Chamber. Haris could see a stunned expression overcome the grand vizier, who appeared lost in searching for a reply. Finally, it came.

"Lezhe Haris, I am surprised by your response, for what man could resist such a luscious gift as one of these women—each one schooled in the art of giving pleasure," Ibrahim said. "Yet, you provide a most interesting defense for your refusal to accept the sultan's gift. You've placed the need of the sehzade over your own gratification."

Haris began to feel as though the grand vizier's words appeared designed to make the case for someone else's benefit—someone he could not see.

"Yours is a noble response, but should the sultan insist that you must take a gift from him, what gift would you desire, if not one of these beautiful women?"

Haris thought for a brief moment. "A horse."

Ibrahim's eyes widened. "A horse?"

"Yes, such a magnificent animal as is found within the sultan's imperial stables would be most beneficial in my travels about Manisa as vizier."

Suddenly, a door in the wall near to the grilled window opened, revealing the sultan. Immediately, everyone in the room bowed their heads, with the women quickly hiding their faces behind a veil.

"A horse?" Suleyman exclaimed. "As a gift, I give you the choice of some of the harem's most desirable women, and you profess the desire for a horse instead?"

Haris lifted his head. "Forgive me—"

Suleyman raised his hand, summoning Haris to silence. "As the good book says: 'It is Allah who provided for you all manner of livestock, that you may ride on some of them and from some you may derive your food. And other uses in them for you to satisfy your heart's desire. It is on them, as your ships, that you make your journeys'," Suleyman recited. "Lezhe Haris, despite rejecting a woman from my harem, with those words our great Prophet Muhammad reminds us of the value of a horse. You are correct when you say there will be time for marriage in your future, but you have recognized the time to own a horse is the present. I will grant you your wish as my gift. You may have your choice of one horse from the imperial stables."

"Your Royal Majesty, your gift fills me with such joy!" Haris praised.

"Everyone, leave me!" Suleyman ordered. "That is, everyone but Lezhe Haris!"

Quickly, the Audience Chamber emptied, leaving Haris standing before the sultan, who approached the throne and took a seat.

"Lezhe Haris, you heard my grand vizier sing your praises, but it is only right that you should also hear it directly from me. I commend you on your work with my son. I am very proud of the progress Mustafa has made, just as I am very proud of his architect.

"Watching my son grow up to be a man brings me great elation, for as a man sees his reflection within a mirror, I see my youth in Mustafa, and it leaves me with fond memories." Suleyman paused to adjust the opening in his robe. "On the other hand," he resumed, stiffening his posture, "as grains of sand pass boundlessly through an hour glass, my son's growth also reminds me of my own mortality. A few minutes ago, you spoke of challenges when referring to Mustafa's appointment as Beylerbey of Manisa. You are correct, as there will be many challenges ahead for Mustafa. But *your* greatest challenge Lezhe Haris, will be keeping power from going to my son's head.

"For as it is written, 'Whatever benefit comes to you, it is from Allah, and whatever misfortune befalls you, it is from yourself. Three things destroy man's spirit: following his desires, being greedy, and'—"

"Conceit," Haris boldly interrupted.

Suleyman gaped at the sudden interjection, before a small smile wrinkled his face. "Yes, Lezhe Haris . . . conceit! Your task will be to make sure my son always knows his place within *my* empire!"

* * *

Several hours later, the Jewish doctor, Jucef ben Ezmael threw open the door to his modest home located within the heart of Constantinople's Jewish community of Balat. Behind the door, he beheld three men standing in the form of a triangle, with the two in the background wearing the bork of a Janissary. The individual standing just across the threshold wore no headgear, allowing his thick, light brown hair to be ruffled by the cool breeze blowing from off of the Sea of Marmara. At first, Jucef did not recognize the smiling man. "Can I help you?"

"*Shalom*. Jucef ben Ezmael, you do not remember me?" Haris asked.

Jucef studied Haris for a minute or two before his memory rescued him. "The soldier in Vienna with his hands bitten by the cold," he recalled. "I believe your Christian name had something to do with the Adriatic."

"Jadran. My Islamic name is Haris."

"Ah, yes, Haris," Jucef repeated. "What is it that brings you to my home today after all this time? Surely it is not another medical situation?" He pored over the soldiers standing behind Haris. "Should I assume the sultan has decided to march off to war again, or have you come to arrest me?"

"Have you done something wrong?"

Jucef grinned. "It depends on the whim of a sultan. What is permissible one day, may be illegal the next."

"We are not here to arrest you, Doctor," Haris revealed. "I have a proposition for you."

"A proposition?" Jucef repeated, with widened eyes. "The history of my people teaches us to be weary of propositions presented to Jews."

"It is nothing to be alarmed about. May we enter?"

"How rude of me. Yes, please be my guests."

Inside the home, Haris peered about the small rectangular room, carpeted with an elaborate Persian rug. The room featured wooden cabinets built into the walls running the length of two sides of the room, while the wall adjacent to the street held four windows set above a long, cushioned bench. A small fire burned inside a fireplace set in the far wall, and situated in between the cabinets in the middle of the long wall was positioned an open doorway, featuring a beaded curtain.

As the three Janissaries dropped down on the cushioned bench, Jucef disappeared behind the beaded curtain, before returning with a tray of coffee, along with a plate of fresh fruit and pickles.

"Jucef, I do not recall seeing you on the sultan's most recent campaign into Austria," Haris remarked.

"My wife had taken ill, so I had to stay behind and assist her."

Jucef poured coffee from the pot, as the beverage's sweet aroma filled the room.

"I trust she is better?"

Jucef stepped toward Haris and handed him a cup. "She passed away a few months ago."

"I am very sorry," Haris said.

"The medicine I practice has saved many lives over the course of my career." Jucef frowned. "Yet, it could not save the person most dear to me."

The men found themselves with a loss for words, and were left only to throw helpless glances at one another, leaving Jucef to break the silence. "I am curious. What type of proposition is it that brings three soldiers to my home this afternoon?"

"I am no longer a Janissary," Haris revealed. "I have been promoted to the position of Sehzade Mustafa's first vizier."

Jucef nodded. "Congratulations, Haris. That would explain the absence of a Janissary's bork atop your head. I have never had a vizier grace my humble abode." He shrugged his shoulders. "I'm not sure of what the proper etiquette may be in the presence of such an esteemed Ottoman official? Would you like that I bow to you?"

Haris frowned. "That is not necessary."

"It has taken three men to bring me such news?"

"As I am now a government official, these men are assigned to me for my protection," Haris explained. "What I would like Doctor, is for you to consider accepting the position to be Sehzade Mustafa's personal physician. It would be an honorable and befitting manner in which to end your career. No more battlefield triage or endless numbers of patients occupying your house at all hours of the day and night, seeking your medical attention. I assure you the pay and living conditions would be very generous. However, it would mean that you must relocate to Manisa."

"Manisa," Jucef repeated. "I know it well. It is not far from the Aegean port of Izmir, where I once lived."

"I do not expect you to make a decision today."

"How many other physicians are your considering for the position?"

"None. You are my only choice," Haris said with a smile. "Please give it serious consideration and make an effort to give me your answer within a few days." Haris finished his coffee and rose from the bench, as did the other Janissaries. "Thank you for your hospitality, Jucef. It was good to see you again."

"Haris," Jucef called out, stopping all three. "Why me? Surely there are other physicians just as good as me, or even better. Constantinople is a very large city."

Haris turned toward the two Janissaries. "Wait for me outside," he commanded and watched as they stepped from the home, before directing his attention back to Jucef. "Yes, you are probably correct about the number of qualified physicians residing within Constantinople, but I have now met you twice, and despite the fact our meetings have been very brief, I sense you are a virtuous man—a trustworthy man. Your experience is heralded and your knowledge as a physician vast, as it would appear is the size of your heart. You are not blinded by loyalty, but rather your opinions bespeak of a righteous man. No matter how you may judge our current sultan, I assure you that if you make the decision to be the sehzade's personal physician, you will be administering medicine to a decent man. Mustafa is not his father."

"Vizier Haris, you are not the same man I met back in Vienna."

Haris interpreted the look on Jucef's face as one of admiration. "I trust that your words are a compliment?"

Jucef smiled. "You will have my decision in the morning."

"Oh—and Jucef, I am truly sorry about your wife," Haris said. "Not everyone can be saved when it is their time." The solemnity accompanying Haris' frown now transformed into a benevolent smile. "I'd like to think God chose to take your wife when He did, so you would be free to consider my proposition."

* * *

Within the hour, Haris returned to the Yeni Saray, arriving at the imperial stables. There, the chief supervisor Rustem was waiting to assist in Haris' selection of a horse as a gift from the sultan.

Rustem leaned against the top rail of the corral's wooden fence, peering over the selection of horses he had removed from the stables, before noticing the approach of Haris.

"Haris, what a pleasure it is to see you again," Rustem greeted with a large grin.

"Thank you, Rustem," Haris replied, joining him at the fence.

"And congratulations on your selection as the sehzade's vizier. You have certainly positioned yourself well."

Haris seemed confused by the statement. "What do you mean . . . I have positioned myself?"

Rustem produced a surprised look. "I'm sure you realize as Mustafa rises, so do you."

"But you insinuate I have orchestrated my appointment as vizier?"

Rustem chuckled. "You have been the sehzade's trainer for years. He has followed your lead." With a coy grin he turned away to gaze upon the horses within the corral. "It is like a trainer of horses. The beasts are taught to follow commands, so they may eventually take the rider where he desires to go."

Haris grew incensed. "Mustafa is a young man with a free will! Believe me when I tell you how my appointment was as much a surprise to me as it was to anyone! My responsibility was to train the sehzade in the art of military matters and that is all! Never did I envision to one day become a vizier!"

Rustem cast a doubtful glare upon Haris. "You and I both know the heart of a sultan's empire is his military," he said calmly. "Please do not misinterpret my praise for you. It is sincere." His grin went unchanged. "Come let us select your choice of the sultan's gift to you." He left his position on the fence to open a gate to the corral, stepping inside.

Haris followed Rustem, before both men came to stop several rods from the impressive animals.

"If you are interested in my opinion, I would select the black stallion for your choice," Rustem suggested. He pointed to one of the largest horses with a shadowy coat. "This one is a dark, magnificent, and powerful animal. I think such a horse compliments you well—a Janissary hero who vanquished the enemy and now rises to become the right hand of a sehzade."

Haris was not fooled by Rustem's exaggerated exultation. "Rustem, I have heard your opinion on one too many subjects already this afternoon, and I am not interested in what you have to say," Haris scoffed. "My choice is the white mare."

Rustem's grin disappeared. "Very well, Vizier Haris. The white mare is yours. The horse is named, Alabaster." He approached the horse, grabbed its reins and led the exquisite animal in the direction of Haris.

Haris noticed a large silver ring affixed to the horse's nostril. "I can see she is marked with a ring of distinction."

Rustem brought the horse close to Haris. "Yes, she is a smart girl and properly trained." Rustem called out a one word command, which the mare responded to by dropping down into a kneeling position on all fours.

Haris was impressed. "Have her saddled and ready for me by the morning."

"It shall be done," Rustem replied.

Haris began to walk away, when Rustem called to him. "Haris . . . do you not wonder about the timing of Sehzade Mustafa's appointment as the beylerbey of Manisa?"

Haris stopped, spinning toward Rustem. "I don't know what it is you are referring to, and I don't care. Have the mare ready in the morning!" he repeated, turning and continuing his steps.

"Hurrem Kadin complained about Mahidevran Kadin's presence in Constantinople!" Rustem exclaimed, bringing Haris to a stop again. "Mustafa's mother is being sent away—exiled to Manisa! It's convenient, wouldn't you agree? Mustafa's appointment becomes the perfect way to keep a mother united with her son, and away from Constantinople."

Haris did not turn around to address Rustem this time, but resumed his steps toward the gate.

CHAPTER TWENTY

Constantinople - Late March, 1533

For nearly a month, Rustem's words lingered with Haris, sometimes keeping him awake at night for hours. It would take an evening of celebration inside the Yeni Saray, hosted by the sultan on the eve of Mustafa's departure to Manisa, for the sehzade's new vizier to experience some peace of mind.

The following morning, Haris could feel the physical effects of the previous evening's gaiety, which had extended into the early hours of the morning. It didn't help his tired body that he arose earlier than normal in preparation for the journey, and most importantly to groom in anticipation for his role in the ceremonial send off.

By mid-morning, before a large crowd composed of members of the Enderun, he found himself leading Alabaster into the Yeni Saray's third courtyard. His decision not to mount the animal was rooted in the law which forbade anyone from riding a horse through the interior palace gates, aside from the sultan. However, on this day an exception was to be made for Mustafa, as the departing sehzade.

As Haris approached the Royal Gate, he observed the horse-drawn covered wagon train with dozens of Janissaries ambling about, preparing to provide escort. The precious cargo consisted of one hundred women from the sultan's harem divided amongst five wagons—each woman a gift from Suleyman to Mustafa. As he perused the royal assemblage, Haris recognized Jaheem standing among the crowd. He guided his horse over to where the chief eunuch was positioned, noticing how Jaheem's face burst with excitement when their eyes met.

"Is it true, my friend?" Jaheem asked. "You are the sehzade's vizier?"

"Not just a vizier, my friend, but the first vizier. I leave today for Manisa with the harem wagons. From the palace, we are to proceed to the harbor where we will board Ottoman galleys, and begin our journey by ship down the Anatolian coastline."

An officer shouted out a command, sending the Janissaries hustling into a formation of parallel lines near to the wagons. From across the courtyard, a group of women could be seen strolling toward the Royal Gate, and although their faces were hidden behind veils, Haris was certain the three were the Queen Mother, Hurrem, and Mahidevran. They approached a four wheeled carriage, where two Janissaries assisted Mahidevran inside the vehicle, as the other two women watched emotionless.

Haris turned toward Jaheem. "Well, my friend, I am required." He handed his horse's lead line to the chief eunuch. "Do me a favor and keep Alabaster company for a moment, and pray to Allah that I do not make a mistake."

Haris strode confidently toward the center of the courtyard where several servants stood, observing how Kamil joined him there. His friend nodded in his direction, before the servants handed Haris a golden robe, and Kamil a glistening sword. They were joined by Rustem, who stepped up, pulling the lead line of Mustafa's horse.

Moments later, approaching from across the courtyard, Ibrahim, Mustafa, and Suleyman appeared. As the three men reached the center, Haris, Kamil, and Rustem bowed their heads.

Mustafa returned the gesture with a stoic look, before promptly turning toward his father.

The sultan looked Mustafa in the eyes. "I, Sultan Suleyman Khan, hereby pronounce my son, Mustafa, Beylerbey Sehzade of Manisa! May God bless him and give him wisdom!" He held his hand out for the sehzade to kiss it.

After Mustafa had kissed his father's hand, Kamil stepped forward and girded the sehzade with the sword, before Haris stepped behind him, lifting the ceremonial robe for Mustafa to slide his arms through. Rustem held steady the stirrup of Clovis, as the sehzade proudly marched toward his horse, and mounted the animal.

Mustafa bowed in the direction of the sultan. "It is my honor to serve the Sultan Suleyman Khan! By the grace of Allah, I will not fail you Padishah!"

Mustafa led his horse into a trot, guiding the animal alongside the stationary caravan until he moved to the front of the wagons, flanked on either side by three sipahis on foot, leading the lead lines of their horses.

Haris hurriedly returned to Jaheem, who handed him Alabaster's lead line. "You will make a fine first vizier!"

"Thank you, Jaheem. My new role is exciting, but it also leaves me with emptiness. I suppose that for every venture gained, there is something lost."

"Then it would hold true that for every loss, there is something gained," Jaheem countered, still smiling.

Haris gave the chief eunuch a befuddled look. "I know that you know the subject of which brings me sadness. In regards to this matter, I was wondering if you may do me one last favor." He reached into the saddle bag slung over the horse, and withdrew a pastry wrapped in paper. "Yes, I did not forget your baklava."

He handed the wrapped dessert to Jaheem. "Please make sure she receives my letter. I wish I could have told her in person how painful it is for me to say goodbye."

Jaheem took the wrapped pastry from his hand. "Why don't you tell her yourself?"

"Jaheem, I am leaving—" Haris paused, before gazing at the moving wagons. "Is she . . . no it can't be? Is she among the harem that leaves in the wagons?"

Jaheem smiled. "I believe she is in the third wagon."

Haris caught his breath. "This is wonderful news! I will be with her now in Manisa!"

"As much as I will miss your generous gift of baklava, I must say it is a relief for me that I will no longer have to coordinate your secret communication." Jaheem rubbed the back of his neck with his hand. "Perhaps I will be able to keep my head a little longer."

"Jaheem, I cannot thank you enough! I will never forget what you have risked for me!"

"You are a fortunate man, Lezhe Haris, and Badra is a worthy woman. It would seem that Allah has used me as an instrument in bringing the two of you together. For this I am blessed."

"I must go," Haris announced. "Jaheem, about what you said concerning the balance of gaining and losing—now that it looks as though I may be able to continue communicating with Badra, what is it I've lost?"

"You have lost nothing it would seem," Jaheem said. "But as for me, I will lose my gift of baklava, as well as losing two good friends."

"Then you are incorrect, for I will lose a friend in you."

Jaheem beamed. "May God give you good reward!"

* * *

Once through the Imperial Gate, beyond the palace walls, Haris mounted his mare. Within a quarter of an hour, the size of the wagon train increased after linking up with additional wagons exiting the Eski Saray, carrying objects and personnel assigned to the sehzade. It would be a short ride down the hill to Constantinople's harbor, where a fleet of Ottoman galleys were being prepared to transport Mustafa and his entourage by ship to the port of Izmir on the western coast of Anatolia. As the wagon train rolled down the paved city streets toward the sea, Mustafa was joined on horseback by Haris.

"Sehzade, the air is cool, the sky is blue and the sea is calm for the beginning of our journey," Haris described.

"Yes, my friend. I hope it is a sign that Allah is pleased with my appointment." Mustafa smiled. "And it seems with your help, Allah will bless me with good health. I met Jucef, my new physician yesterday. He seems to be a decent man."

"Well, you asked me to find the best for you. By the way, I spoke with Serkan a few minutes ago. He appears to be healing well. He rides inside one of the wagons today, as he still is unable to ride a horse."

"The progress of his health is good news."

"You saved his life by giving him the horse your father sent for you."

"It is a shame how the other Janissary died," Mustafa lamented. "When Serkan's strength has finally returned, he will be assigned to my silahdar in Manisa."

"I will admit, I did not like him when we first met—challenging one another at your behest—but he is a valiant warrior and loyal servant, as he proved in the valley outside of Berndorf," Haris said. "Which reminds me, Kamil is very thrilled you have appointed him silahdar agha."

"Kamil is wisdom, loyalty, and military all rolled into one man. It was an easy choice."

"I have known him for a long time. You could not have made a better choice," Haris praised. "How is your mother?"

"She seems comfortable riding in the carriage. But I am not so sure how she may fair traveling by ship." Mustafa gazed at Haris' mare. "That is a fine horse that you ride, Haris. Is it true what they tell me—how you chose a horse over one of the women from the sultan's harem?"

"It is true."

"You are not fond of women?" Mustafa teased.

"I assure you Sehzade, I have a weak spot for the physical attributes of women. Yet, there is one woman who moves me as much with her body as she does with her mind."

Mustafa turned toward Haris with raised eyebrows. "Hmm—I am curious, where would you find such a woman?"

Haris chuckled to himself, slow to answer. "Ironically, within your father's harem."

Mustafa's eyes widened. "How did you know of her?"

"Forgive me for what I am about to disclose to you, but I will not lie to you," Haris pledged. "I first met her when she was captured in Vienna, and later I began communicating with her when I discovered she had been forced to be a member of the sultan's harem."

"How did you manage this?"

Haris grinned. "Is it important that you know how?"

Mustafa gave Haris a long, puzzled look. "No . . . of course not."

"Thank you."

As he steered his horse, Mustafa brought his attention back to the road stretching before him. "It is unfortunate that this mystery woman, the one who moves you, was not among the choices the sultan had given you. I am sure she will miss you now that you will be living far from Constantinople."

"Well—" Haris began hesitantly. "As it turns out, the woman was selected as part of the harem your father bequeathed to you."

Mustafa turned toward Haris with a surprised stare, before bursting into laughter. "You are a lucky man, Haris! It reminds me I have not yet given you a gift for your appointment as my first vizier!"

"Sehzade?"

"The woman is yours, my friend! Let her be my gift to you!" Mustafa proudly announced. "After all, what is one woman to me out of a hundred? And there are more women awaiting me in Manisa!"

"Your kindness is truly appreciated! I am forever grateful!"

"Of course you are." Mustafa flashed a wide smile. "Why don't you go and deliver the good news to her while she rides in the wagon? It may make the trip less unbearable for her. The harem will be sailing in three ships separated from us, so you may not see her for a while."

"No, it if pleases the Sehzade, I think I shall wait until we are in Manisa."

"And risk that since I do not yet know her identity, I may want to take her to bed in the port of Izmir myself?" Mustafa warned, grinning.

"Her name is Badra," Haris quickly revealed. "She is a blonde Austrian."

"So, it is the blonde ones you favor. For you my friend, I shall refrain from taking any blondes to bed before you claim her."

"That is very kind of you," Haris said flippantly.

Mustafa laughed. "Besides, if she is as smart as you say she is, she may find opportunity to jump ship, should you claim her now!"

Haris shared in the laughter. "Perhaps she would be wise to do so."

* * *

Manisa, Anatolia

A day and night of pleasant weather assisted the fleet of Ottoman galleys—each warship's multitude of oars gracefully being pulled in and out of the azure waters of the Aegean by the rhythmic motion of the crew, as the vessels hugged the mountainous Anatolian coastline. In the morning of the following day, the long, slender hulled two mast vessels dropped their anchors in the harbor of the ancient port city of Izmir.

As the galleys were emptied of their cargo, a great many of Izmir's small population turned out to welcome the sehzade's entourage with music and a variety of food items. Clear skies and warmer temperatures added to the welcoming party, and when all of the ships had been emptied, the wagon train set off in a northeasterly direction bound for Manisa.

Within the hour, the royal caravan arrived in a fertile valley consisting of plots of farm land and vineyards, divided around a wide stream called Caybasi. Beyond the stream, lying east of the agricultural fields, and spreading outward from the forested slopes of the Sipylus Mountains, the caravan's occupants could discern two minarets flanking a narrow tower soaring above city streets.

As the city materialized, within its center could be seen the large rectangular Ottoman palace covering eight acres. The royal dwelling exhibited an architectural design similar to the Yeni Saray, consisting of four courtyards sectioned by high walls, with each wall containing a massive gate. The red lattices of the tower of justice came clearly into view, centering a nearly self-sufficient complex, complete with arched-roofed buildings that mimicked the comforts and essentials of Constantinople's palaces.

For Haris, the first two days in Manisa proved to be very busy, as he spent the hours moving into his apartment, while becoming acquainted with the palace grounds. Badra certainly occupied his thoughts, but settling into the large complex became his first priority, and since the harem was off limits to all but the sehzade, he felt no hurry. It was late in the afternoon of the second day when he received a message from a servant, requesting his presence within the Audience Chamber.

Arriving at the designated hour, Haris found himself alone within the chamber, noticing how the walls of the room were stark compared to the identical room located within Constantinople's Yeni Saray. Pacing about the chamber with slight impatience, he wondered why Mustafa would find the need to summon him in a formal location, as opposed to merely approaching him directly within his apartment. As the door slowly opened, Haris began to question his friend, when he realized it was not Mustafa who entered, but his mother.

"Mahidevran Kadin!" Haris exclaimed, bowing.

"Haris, is it?"

"Yes, Kadin." Haris raised his head to gaze upon the beautiful dark haired woman, who was absent of a veil and wearing a jeweled headband in its place, standing before him dressed in a long black robe, buttoned to the neck.

"Thank you for meeting me here today. Mustafa speaks highly of you," she praised. "I wanted to take a moment and introduce myself, since we shall both be working here in Manisa together— in tutoring my son."

Haris nodded. He recognized how the wavy locks of her hair fell gently upon her shoulders, framing her clear, perfectly symmetrical face. Instantly, he realized the appropriateness of her Islamic name Mahidevran, meaning one whose beauty never fades; for he became captivated with her large caramel eyes, complimented by thin dark eyebrows and long black eyelashes conveying both a mildly suggestive, yet motherly affectionate appeal. Her smile punctuated her demeanor with warmth and unpretentiousness, and she carried a shapely figure hinting Mahidevran could play the role of seductress and nurturer simultaneously.

"I want you to know I shall be present in all government meetings involving the sehzade," she announced. "This includes issues that may arise pertaining to both local matters within the Sanjak of Saruhan, as well as with any situations involving foreign governments. My role is to assist my son in his preparation of learning how to rule as a sultan."

"Yes, I understand."

"Mustafa tells me you are Croatian, raised among Albanians."

"Yes, Kadin."

"I am from Ulcinj, in the land of Montenegrins," she revealed. "So many of us—like you and me—all of us slaves from Rumelia who have risen to positions of power within the Ottoman Empire, such as Ibrahim, and the sultan's themselves, all born to former slaves, who continue the practice of impregnating female slaves. I think it is interesting how the leadership of this Turkish Empire becomes less and less Turkish with the birth of each sehzade." She flashed a sardonic grin. "Perhaps one day the Turks will awaken and realize it is they who are the real slaves."

Mahidevran played with the large jewel bracelet wrapped about her wrist. "Of course, not all of us come from Rumelia," she remarked snidely. "That witch Roxelana, who Suleyman and his court refer to as Hurrem—she is from the Ukraine!" Haris noticed how a wrathful expression temporarily stole the beauty from her face. "I'm sorry—forgive my rudeness. We are not on good terms—she and I." She paused to take a deep breath. "Tell me Haris, why do you think the sultan chose you to train my son?"

"For military experience."

Mahidevran moved toward the throne after climbing the platform steps, and dropped down into the chair. "I presume you are a good soldier?"

"This is what I have been told," Haris replied. "However, I was also told how I think too much, and I believe maybe this was the reason for my selection."

Mahidevran did not reply, but Haris could see how she studied him with intensity.

"The sultan wished for Mustafa to learn to feel compassion as a military leader, just as much as it was his desire to have the sehzade schooled in the art of warfare," Haris explained.

"Hmm . . . compassion?" Mahidevran replied with a tone of suspicion. "Well, it doesn't surprise me. Suleyman could certainly exhibit compassion, as well as passion on occasion. Unfortunately, I am no longer the recipient of such emotions from the sultan. But there was a time when I was his world." She paused, rising from the chair. "Haris, there are moments when I regret having given birth to my son. He has been born into a grave situation which grows more dangerous with each passing year."

"What danger do you speak of, Kadin?"

"His destiny," she announced. "I love my son very dearly—more than anything in the world, and I will do everything within my power to protect him. Never forget that."

"Kadin, I have nothing but deep respect and admiration for Mustafa. I have sworn to protect him."

"I'm sorry, Haris. You do appear to be very sincere with your words." A frown wrinkled her face. "But I have lived in this world of betrayal and deceit for a long time. It has left me tainted, laden with an empty heart. Thus, I trust no one! As a mother who has been able to raise only one sehzade, I am at a great disadvantage over the witch Hurrem, who I'm convinced has used black magic to coerce Suleyman into siring four sons with his seeds!"

"As I have reminded the sehzade on occasion, as the oldest son, he is first in line for the throne," Haris said. "His appointment as the Beylerbey of Manisa is evidence of his position at the top. As you are aware, many past sehzades have trained in this place before becoming sultan, including Suleyman."

"Yes, I am aware," Mahidevran said. "I gave birth to Mustafa in this place." She scoffed. "First in line, you say—first in line to be murdered then!" Mahidevran looked away from Haris as though she harbored a secret, and began a slow pace near to the wall of the chamber with her back to him. "I struck her," she called out.

"Kadin?" Haris asked, unsure of the meaning of her words.

Mahidevran stopped and spun toward Haris. "Hurrem! I slapped the bitch across the face, and called her sold meat! But I did not pull out her hair or scratch her face as she contends!"

Haris did not respond, but began to ponder his last conversation with Rustem.

"I think another reason we are here in Manisa is because Hurrem convinced the sultan to exile me!" she exclaimed. "I am hopeful Suleyman is not punishing his son for my actions, and that Mustafa's appointment here is truly for his advancement! But Hurrem and Rustem are plotting against my son! I am sure of it!"

"Rustem?"

"Yes, the two of them are very close and they sneak around like two jackals," she described. "Rustem reports every move made within the Enderun to Hurrem—he is her spy."

"Forgive me for doubting you, Mahidevran Kadin, but how do you know this?"

She produced a wide grin. "I have my spies too, Haris. That is another item you should not forget."

Haris was left speechless, again.

Mahidevran's snide grin evolved into a warm smile. "Enough talk of dark plots. We are here together Haris, and I expect that you will keep your word to protect my son. I think I shall like you. It has been a pleasure to finally have met you in person."

"As it has been my pleasure as well, Mahidevran Kadin," Haris replied with a bow.

"Oh—and Haris, we have never had this conversation," Mahidevran warned in a soft voice. "It is only between us. I do not want Mustafa to think he was not his father's first choice, as it would shatter his confidence. Is this understood?"

"Yes, Mahidevran Kadin."

"I think you would do well to find a woman, Haris," Mahidevran blurted, surprising him. "Someone with whom you could occupy your time and energy, so as to avoid dirty palace intrigue."

CHAPTER

TWENTY-ONE

Clad in a robe of canary yellow, Badra sat quietly among the colonnades, set beneath the central dome of a small outdoor garden pavilion. She tried to enjoy the pleasant weather, but the variety of emotions being juggled by her psyche would not permit it; for she had not received correspondence from Haris before leaving Constantinople and wondered if he knew of her situation. Suddenly, the sound of footsteps worked to clear her head, as she noticed a robed man wearing conical shaped headgear pacing leisurely in her direction. As the figure drew closer, the maiden could distinguish Sehzade Mustafa. Slowly she rose from her seat, wanting to step away from the pavilion; although fear of offending the beylerbey would not allow her feet to move. She made sure the black veil covering her face remained secure, and slowly bowed her head as he approached.

Badra felt her heart beating furiously, when to her surprise, Mustafa stopped before her.

"What is your name?" he asked.

"Badra," she replied softly, with her eyes still focused on the tile pavement.

"You are Austrian?"

"Yes, Your Royal Highness."

"The blonde hair gives it away. You are very beautiful. Remove your veil."

Badra slowly unfastened the veil from her flat cap.

"You may look at me."

Badra lifted her head so that Mustafa could gaze upon her. He smiled, before reaching up and placing a blue scarf on top of her left shoulder. "Do you know the location of my apartment?"

To Badra, the weight of the soft scarf upon her shoulder felt like a thousand pounds, as she knew the meaning of its placement. "Yes, Your Royal Highness," she replied meekly.

"At dusk this evening, you will come to my apartment. There will be a guard outside of my door, and he will know to let you inside," Mustafa explained. "Be sure to bathe before your arrival." He stepped beyond her, continuing his stroll.

Badra breathed heavily, as her eyes filled with tears.

* * *

Dusk had set the western horizon of the valley afire, throwing long shadows around the palace compound, as Badra found her way from the harem to the sehzade's apartment. As she proceeded down a long, narrow corridor, she recognized a Janissary guard posing rigidly outside of a large wooden door. Dressed in a silk blue robe with flat hat and black veil, Badra nervously scrutinized her own outfit, slowly approaching the door without any verbal exchange with the guard. The Janissary pushed opened the door, permitting her entry.

When Badra had stepped completely inside the room, the guard pulled the door closed behind her. She stood silently, gazing at the decorative tiled walls, as well as the tall fireplace with gilded hood. Three stained glass windows were set on one wall of the apartment, and Badra noticed how the shutter of one of the windows was opened, providing a view of a reflecting pool and gardens lying beneath it. At the far end of the room set a large circular bed made with gold silk sheets. However, Badra's immediate attention was drawn to an alcove carved within a wall to her right, set behind a beaded doorway, where candlelight revealed the silhouette of a man.

"Are you frightened, Badra?" a man's voice whispered.

Badra removed her veil. "No, Your Royal Highness." She reached for the circular buckle at the end of the belt wrapped around her waist, and nervously began to play with its leaf shaped design.

"You appear fidgety," the voice said.

Badra sighed, realizing that she could not keep her anxiety from showing. "Your Royal Highness, forgive me, but this is the first I've been called upon. I understand why I am here, as I have been tutored for this intimate moment for some time. But I must be honest with you when I say although I am physically prepared, emotionally I am not," she revealed, her voice trembling. "My role and my desire to provide for you a pleasurable experience is genuine. But I'm afraid my heart presents a hindrance to this. Forgive me, Your Royal Highness, for I do so very much wish to gratify you . . . but what is pleasure, if the body is not in tune with the mind?"

Badra found herself breathing heavily, before the moment of silence was broken by the voice. "Your mind and your heart—do they ache for someone else?"

She bowed her head and swallowed hard. "Yes, Your Royal Highness," she replied, with a response weakened by guilt.

"How can there be another when you have been sheltered inside the sultan's harem for over three years?"

Badra hesitated, deciding to avoid the question. "Your Royal Highness, I feel that I just need more time before I can lie down with you. I am flattered that you have selected me today, but

I wish to give you my entire being, so that the experience will exceed your expectations! Only then will it be truly wonderful—"

"And mutual," the voice interrupted.

Badra was left speechless by the response, when suddenly the candlelight extinguished. She watched the shadowy figure part the beads of the alcove, and step before the opened window. The day's final beams of sunlight revealed his face.

Badra could not believe her eyes. "Haris!" she called out, before rushing forward and falling into his arms.

The two shared a long embrace. "I have imagined us holding one another every night in my dreams!" he remarked.

"In my dreams as well!" Badra released herself from his embrace, stepping back to gaze upon his face. "For so long I have only been able to see a glimpse of your face from behind the window grill, leaving me with only segments of your features like pieces from a puzzle! But now I see the complete profile!"

"And—?"

"I am disappointed," she jested, before producing a wide smile and embracing him again. "Oh Haris, I was petrified of having to go to bed with the sehzade!" Suddenly, she released herself from his arms again. "Where is the sehzade? Isn't this his apartment?"

"It is. I believe he is outside admiring his gardens this evening."

"But he's expecting me! I spoke with him this afternoon! He placed his scarf on my shoulder!"

Haris grinned. "This was his idea."

"What? His idea? I don't understand?"

"He is the Beylerbey of Manisa and I am his first vizier. But most importantly, I am his friend," Haris explained. "You are his gift to me. I mean . . . it is certainly true that I requested you, and he bequeathed you to me—"

"*Gift*? I am his *gift* to you?" she repeated—the smile replaced with an angry grimace. "And as your gift, what is it that you expect me to do for you? Cook, clean, pleasure you sexually? Perhaps all three?"

Haris was surprised by her response. "I chose you so you would not have to face that moment you have dreaded of being selected to share the sultan's, or sehzade's bed!"

"Why me? What did you think—that you and I are in love?"

Her words pierced Haris. "Our letters—they are flirtatious! They reveal our secrets, our dreams! Isn't that what lovers do?" he asked.

"Haris we are friends—close friends! I will give you that! But to be passed around like an object—that is not love! It is demeaning! It is exactly the type of treatment I abhor about palace life!" Badra lamented. "Haris, you've become one of them!"

Haris' shock turned to disappointment. "What are we left to do then?"

"I will return to the harem!"

"But the harem is your prison?"

"What is the difference if I am a prisoner in a palace, or within a man's home?"

"I would not treat you like a prisoner!"

"Haris—" Badra's tone grew softer, as she took hold of his hands. "I am sorry if I have wounded you by sharing my feelings. I do think I could love you, but I do not want to be caged and forced to learn to love someone. I need love to find me, and not for me to concede to a lover's pursuit."

Haris studied her carefully, overcome with disillusion quickly morphing into sympathy. He pulled his hands from her. "Then you are free to go! In the customs and traditions of the Ottoman world you are still my gift, and my decision is to set you free!"

"Set me free?" Badra repeated with a look of astonishment. "Free to go where?"

"Home—home to Vienna! Come, we've wasted enough time within the sehzade's apartment," he said sternly, walking past her toward the door.

"Haris," Badra called out, stopping him. "I'm sorry my reaction is not what you expected. This was a very clever and romantic way of bringing us face to face. I commend you and the sehzade for your creativity. You are very sweet and very dear to me. But you are also part of this Ottoman world in which we find ourselves, and it is their treatment of women that I resent."

"And you will find better treatment from Austrian men?" Haris scoffed. "It may not be called by the same name, but whether as a maiden inside of a palace, or as the housewife of a farmer, either way of life reduces a woman to a position of slavery! You are not rejecting what you see as a barbarous tradition . . . you are rejecting me!" Haris turned away quickly.

* * *

Badra spent a restless night of trying to come to terms with her insensitivity in dealing with Haris, before falling asleep only to awaken to the realization the passage of nightfall had done nothing to make her feel better. The morning began with a message requesting she join the sehzade in the Audience Chamber, leaving her to wonder if the summons was merely another ruse concocted by Haris and Mustafa.

* * *

Within the Audience Chamber, Badra found Mustafa alone, seated on the throne. She took a deep breath and paced toward him, stopping and bowing just before the raised platform.

"Remove your veil," Mustafa commanded.

Badra complied, and raised her head toward him.

"Haris tells me you were not amused yesterday with our efforts to bring the two of you together."

"On the contrary, Your Royal Highness, I remarked to him how clever I found the effort."

"But you rejected his desire for you. You were my gift to my friend. How do you think this makes me feel?"

"I am truly sorry, Your Royal Highness."

"Just who do you think you are to have rejected him?" Mustafa pressed, his voice now raised in anger. "Do you think you are a princess, perhaps? Let me remind you that you are a member of the harem! You are a slave! Your rejection is an insult to me, and as a sehzade I do not take kindly to being made a fool!"

"Forgive me, Your Royal Highness."

"If I did not know Haris like I do, I would think that such a man's acceptance of being rejected by a woman of the harem was the sign of a weak man." Mustafa leaned forward on the throne. "Haris is not weak. His fault may be that his heart is too big, but it is not a sign of weakness. The day we left Constantinople for Manisa, he told me about you. Do you know the sultan offered him a choice of one woman from a selection of thirty, and he turned my father down because you were not among the choices? Instead, he selected a horse!" The sehzade chuckled, but Badra recognized it as a reaction of disbelief. "And when he discovered you had been chosen to be among my harem in Manisa, he was elated. I asked him what was so special about you, and he told me he was attracted to your mind, as well as your body."

Badra began to weep.

"Personally, I think you have made a mistake! Haris insisted that I not punish you—but I think your actions deserve punishment."

Badra gasped.

"I am granting your request to be free of Haris as well as free of the harem, and I think you may find, in time, it will be your punishment," Mustafa warned. "Within a day or two you shall receive a document signed by me guaranteeing you safe passage and transportation from Manisa. In six days, Ottoman galleys will set sail from Izmir across the Aegean for Thessaloniki. You will be a passenger aboard one of those ships. From Thessaloniki you will be escorted to the Austrian border, and afterward you will be on your own."

Badra resumed her sobbing.

"I hope you find what it is you are searching for, Austrian woman," Mustafa added. "You are dismissed."

Badra bowed her head, and began to slowly turn away from Mustafa, when he called out. "He risked his life for you!"

Badra spun back towards the throne.

"I know about the secret correspondence between the two of you within the harem at the Yeni Saray! Haris told me of this! It was quite foolish and dangerous for both you and him! Yet, you question his love for you?

"Haris has taught me many things over the past four years, but I did not recognize until now what he has taught me about love. When a man finds the courage to be forthright in expressing his adoration for a woman, at the risk of losing everything, including his life . . . then this is true love."

* * *

Over the next five days, Haris tended to his duties as though Badra did not exist. Neither did he inquire of her whereabouts, or speak to anyone about her in public, including Mustafa. In private, he carried a heavy heart, wounded by her sudden rejection.

Late in the afternoon on the day before Badra was scheduled

to set sail to Thessaloniki, Haris rode Alabaster outside of the palace walls beyond the outskirts of Manisa, guiding the animal up a steep, tree lined road leading to a clearing beneath a mountain peak. He fastened the reins of his horse to the branch of a tree, and marched to the center of the clearing. Plopping down into the tall grass on his back, Haris found himself gazing upward at the strange rock formation looming over him, before shutting his eyes and falling off to sleep.

After a short spell, he was awakened abruptly by the clopping of horse's hooves, and noticed Alabaster remained tied to the tree branch; although he could see a horse-drawn carriage approaching. When the cart rolled to a stop, Haris watched as the rider dismounted and assisted a woman from out of the carriage. Immediately she set her feet in motion, advancing toward him with her shoulder length blonde locks bouncing as she walked. Haris sighed, and fell backward to the ground with Badra's approach.

When her shadow blocked the warmth of the sunlight against his face, Haris opened his eyes to view the maiden standing above him. "How is it you were able to leave the harem?" he asked.

"The sehzade gave me permission."

Haris sat up. "And I suppose he also told you where to find me?"

"He did. When I saw the white mare, I thought she might be yours. I asked my escort to remain back some distance, so that we may speak alone." She glanced back at Alabaster. "Is she the horse you chose over the women in the sultan's harem?"

Haris refrained from answering the question. Rather he huffed, and once again fell backward onto the grass.

Badra took a deep breath, and glanced around the clearing, when she caught sight of the base of the stone rising to a great height behind them. Her vision was cast upward, drawn to the unique peak. Placing her hand above her eyes as she gazed into the sun, she studied the formation with interest. "The stone—it appears to be shaped like the face of a woman."

Haris groaned. "She is known as the Lady of Niobe. The name is a product of an ancient Greek legend."

"Please tell it to me."

Haris frowned.

"Please," she persisted.

Haris sat upright once again. "Legend has it that Niobe was a Greek queen married to a king with the name of Amphion. At one time, he supposedly ruled over the city of Tantalus, which once existed at the foothills of these mountains. Niobe gave birth to fourteen children—seven boys and seven girls. Legend also has it that at the same time, there lived a woman named Leto, who was a consort of the god Zeus. She gave birth to two of his children, Apollo and Artemis. Leto became so consumed with jealousy having borne only two children, as opposed to Niobe's fourteen, she instructed her two sons to kill all of Niobe's children, which they did. Niobe was thought to be so distraught over the deaths of her children that Zeus turned her into stone, in the hopes it would soothe her pain."

"And the stone is Niobe?" Badra asked, looking back up at the rock formation.

"If you believe Greek mythology, yes."

"Well, I don't."

"I don't either," Haris admitted. "But I find it very interesting to have such a particular legend in this place."

Badra brought her attention back to Haris. "Why?"

"Because Manisa is the city for training sehzades. Sehzades with jealous, scheming mothers—all consorts of sultans—who challenge one another in their attempt to influence the positioning of their son as the next sultan. It often results in fratricide."

"What is fratricide?"

"The killing of siblings until one survivor is left standing to rule the empire."

"How barbaric." Badra turned her attention to the stone formation again. "She looks sad."

"The stone formation is known as Weeping Rock because when it rains, water pours from her eye."

"How do you know all of this?"

"I read. When I learned we were moving from Constantinople to Manisa, I decided to learn whatever I could about the area."

"You are very smart."

"Have you followed me here today to throw compliments at me before saying goodbye?" Haris huffed. "If so, will it be goodbye in Turkish, or in German?"

Badra ran her tongue across parched lips and focused her eyes to the ground. "Like the Lady of Niobe experiences when it rains, I've cried every night since I rejected your romantic overture." She paused, slowly lifting penitent eyes toward Haris. "Mentally, I was troubled in preparation for going to bed with the sehzade that night. Your appearance from behind the sehzade's beaded curtain, your words of compassion, your firm embrace—it all came so suddenly for me! I found my fear transforming into spontaneous joy, as if I had awakened from a dream! But our embrace, the touching of our flesh told me it was real! And then the reality became even more so, when you categorized me as a *gift*! At that moment, the many passionate words we had exchanged within all of our letters seemed to evaporate as does rain droplets beneath a burning sun! It did not help me that all of this came on the heels of your appointment as the sehzade's vizier! It left me asking myself how I could have been so fooled—fooled by someone who swept me away with his bravado and uprightness! You had made me believe my situation within the harem was not hopeless! But in referring to me as a *gift,* my first thought was how power changed you!"

"Badra, I am still the same—"

"Please, let me continue," she interrupted. "But I was wrong. I do believe you are still the same man who wrote me those words! Words I longed for during the grueling weeks between receiving each new letter! Words I would read secretly by moonlight in the middle of the night over and over again, as though the ink might disappear from the page before I could digest the meaning! Words offering hope for a future, together away from the palace!" She paused, as tears began to well up in her eyes. "Haris, I did not come here to say goodbye . . . I came here today to tell you that I love you!"

Haris rose to his feet, and grabbed Badra at her sides, pulling her firmly into him. Without hesitation, their lips found one another's, and pressed together for a passionate kiss, before Haris broke the union.

"Then you are staying in Manisa?" he asked her.

Badra's watery eyes sparkled in the sunlight, as she produced a coy grin. "If it pleases you? After all, you did select me —"

Haris sighed. "You are wrong. I did not select you." The corners of his mouth began to rise. "Love selected us."

CHAPTER
TWENTY-TWO

Manisa - January, 1534

Inasmuch as Manisa's palace had for ten months, become a training base for Mustafa in the art of governing, for Haris and Badra it became the location for a fairy tale romance. Since the moment Badra announced her change of heart in desiring to remain there, she and Haris had become one of the palace's favorite couples. The two lovers used common sense and discretion in trying not to flaunt their amorous relationship; but when seen within each other's presence, the affection they displayed for one another was clearly evident.

Early one morning, the couple, excited by the return of sunshine after a week of daily rainfall, decided fresh air away from the confines of the palace would do them both well. The elusive winter sun's reappearance sparked an eagerness to get away to what had become one of their favorite outdoor locations— Weeping Rock.

When arriving at the location, the two lovers instructed their Janissary escorts to remain a half mile down the hillside away from the peak of the mountain, in order for them to be alone. Badra exited the carriage that transported her, and the two set off on foot, with Haris pulling Alabaster's lead line. When certain they were out of sight of the Janissaries, Haris and Badra mounted the mare, acting like mischievous children in defying the Ottoman rule prohibiting women from riding a horse.

Upon reaching the clearing, set within the shadow of the mountain peak, they dismounted and secured Alabaster, before strolling hand in hand through the tall wet grass soaking the bottom of their clothing. They stopped when arriving at a spot directly beneath the unique rock formation that had become their familiar beacon.

Badra raised her head to view the stone. "Since rainfall gives the Lady of Niobe tears, I am sure she cries much throughout the winter."

"I'm certain it's true," Haris replied, clad in a white conical headgear reflecting his status as vizier. "We are free from the palace, today. Would you desire to speak in German or Turkish?"

"*Deutsch*," she said.

"Very well," Haris responded in German, bringing a smile to Badra's face.

She scanned the tree line bordering the clearing. "The raindrops on the tree leaves glistening in the sun are so pretty."

"Yes. The weather here in southern Anatolia is wonderful year round. Even the winter rain is not so much of a nuisance."

"It is better than snow," she said. "But lately, I have been missing Austrian winters."

Haris smiled. "It was snowing in Austria, the first day I set eyes on you."

"How do you remember?"

"How could I forget?"

Badra returned the smile and leaned into Haris, who responded by planting a soft kiss on her lips. She sighed, gently pulling away from him, before turning to glance over the valley stretched out below. The scenic view revealed the sprawling houses and linear streets of Manisa, appearing from a great distance like the subject of Ottoman miniature art. "It is very beautiful here. I like it much better than Constantinople."

"Constantinople has its beauty too, but this place is more sedate—far removed from the hectic pace within the Ottoman capitol," Haris described.

She spun toward him. "I must admit, that my sudden freedom here fills me with guilt, because I am viewed as your *gift*. I feel out of place, as if no one in the palace knows exactly where I am to fit in. I'm like a boarder inside a large house whose rent is free of charge. Most of the women of the harem seem to be envious of my ability to come and go as I please, and when Mahidevran passes me, it is with suspicious eyes."

Haris sighed. "You are my future bride, and as we have discussed, it is not yet time for marriage. At present, I need to be focused on Mustafa and the administration of government here in Manisa." He paused to gently run the back of his hand against her soft face. "Besides, we need to know my future with Mustafa is secure. If Mustafa is not selected as sultan, then I must return to the status of a Janissary. It is forbidden for the Janissary to marry until the age of forty. As harsh as it may sound to you, if I'm a vizier, you may be my wife, but as a Janissary, you are my consort."

She frowned. "Well, I imagine consort is a step up from *gift*."

Haris produced a smirk. "I'm sorry, but it is the way things are done."

"I know Haris, I've told you before how I abhor this way of life. If I didn't love you, I couldn't tolerate it, but I understand." She smiled. "Do you think he will be sultan one day?"

"Yes, I do—if Mustafa keeps his head. He must be patient."

"And you shall be his grand vizier!"

"If it comes to be, then you, my dear, will be the wife of a grand vizier!"

Badra leaned into Haris, and pecked a kiss on his cheek, before bringing her hand to his face. "Your skin is so smooth."

"It is unlawful for a Janissary to wear a beard." Haris explained, massaging his chin. "The law does not restrict a vizier from growing one, but I have become so accustomed to shaving that I have no desire for facial hair."

"The corbaci wears a mustache," Badra said. "He is a Janissary."

"The mustache is permissible."

She turned back to glance again at the valley. "I can see the palace domes and the minarets. How long do you think we will have to remain here in Manisa?"

"I'm not sure," he said. "It may depend upon events in Constantinople. I fear the serenity in which we find ourselves today is the calm before the storm."

She spun back toward him. "What storm?"

"Everything is much too perfect now, and from what I've seen as a member of the Enderun, it is apparent that the sultan's reign thrives on challenges. Whether it may come in the form of a threat from a foreign adversary, or as intrigue from behind the palace walls, I believe Suleyman hungers to be tested on occasion. It is a means of control for him."

"Well, if a storm must come, I hope it passes quickly." She stared at his circular headgear rising from his scalp nearly half a foot into the air, causing her to produce a witty leer which Haris felt compelled to address.

"What is it?" he inquired.

"Your hat does not suit you." Badra grinned. "I found the hat with wooden spoon sewn to it, much more becoming of you."

"You refer to the Janissary's bork."

"Is that what it's called—bork?" she asked. "And what is the purpose of sewing a spoon to one's hat?"

Haris laughed. "You are very inquisitive today. It is a good question though, and it is the first thing a young Janissary is taught."

"And what is that?"

"Well, if you must know, it is no surprise how food has played an important role in traditional Turkish gatherings. This custom goes back centuries," Haris said. "Think about it, one of the few times of the day when the entire family can come together and bond, is around a meal. It is during this moment when much is shared and discussed between family members. In the same way, the Janissary corps is viewed as a family, and so the structure of the corps is organized around the kitchen."

"You're serious, aren't you?"

Haris laughed. "Of course I am. The entire corps is known as the *ocak*."

"What does that mean?"

"*Ocak* means hearth," Haris explained. "The hearth is one of the most important features of a kitchen. In fact, the emblem of the whole corps is a *kazan* of *shorba*."

"*Shorba* means soup," Badra said.

"Very good. Yes, it does, and *kazan* means cauldron."

"A cauldron of soup," Badra deciphered whimsically. "How interesting."

Haris continued. "The corbaci is one of the highest ranking Janissary officers and the word means soup men. Even the insignia sewn to a corbaci's dolama is related to food, for it is that of a large ladle. It is also true in the field of battle, important meetings of the corps are often held around a cauldron. And I have heard when displeased with the sultan, Janissaries have been known to overturn the cauldron as a symbol of their discontent."

"So, the Janissary corps is all about food."

"No, it is all about family," Haris corrected. "And what it takes to bring a family together—including a family of soldiers."

Badra plucked a piece of tall grass from the ground and brushed it gently against her cheek. "In one of your letters, you explained to me how after being taken from your home in Rumelia, you lived with a Turkish family."

Haris laughed. "We are changing the subject now, I see."

"I wish to know everything about you."

Haris grinned. "Well, when I was a boy, I was not taken by force." He paused as his expression grew more serious. "My father paid for my slavery with silver coins. But yes, from Rumelia I was brought to Adana, in southern Anatolia. The family who placed me under their roof uses the name Haytac, which means friend."

"Have you seen or written to them since you left their home to be a Janissary?"

Haris frowned. "I have not, and it is something I do regret."

"Well, you should find the time to do so."

Haris sighed before rattling off questions of his own, believing his query might work to change the subject. "What about you? What is your story? Where are you parents? Do you think they are concerned for your well-being? Do you have brothers and sisters?"

"Why, Haris, I am flattered that you wish to know much about my past." Badra produced a quizzical grin. "Just because I asked this of you, does not mean you need to ask it of me."

Haris grinned. "Please, I am truly interested in your story."

"Well, I have one brother, we are twins. My mother died of sickness when my brother and I were very young, and I remember how my father told us it was the smallpox that killed her. I do not remember my mother," she said, with little emotion in her voice. "My father raised us. He was a farmer in the village of Frankenhausen, in the County of Schwarzburg. He was killed during the Peasant's Rebellion. My father wished to stay out of the conflict between farmers and the nobility, refusing to take up arms, but when the army of the nobility arrived in our village, they took mercy on none, massacring thousands."

His grin had faded. "Such tragedy in your life. I'm sorry. I would never have known that you harbor such misfortune and despair. It is hidden very well."

Badra forced a smile, continuing. "Together my brother and I fled eastward, finding refuge in Vienna. We were finally building a new life together when the Ottomans came. My brother decided to stay and fight them against my wishes, while I fled the city with a great many others. The group I moved with was captured by the Turks in the forest. I do not know what became of my brother, and I pray to God every night that he survived the siege."

"I am sorry."

"You needn't be sorry." Badra laid her hand to the side of his face.

"But I was part of the siege that separated you from your brother."

"There were countless lives forever affected that day. I'm sure my story is just one of many," Badra said. "You were a soldier following orders, conditioned to fight other soldiers. There was little thought given to the innocent ones, whose arrival amid the chaos is as sudden as a burst of colors in a dark forest. The preparation for war is filled with darkness, with little consideration given to the appearance of a sudden rainbow. And like the rainbow, it is not long before those colors fade."

Haris studied Badra's disposition with admiration. "You are strong, like the rock above us."

Badra glanced upward at the rock formation. "I think the Lady of Niobe was not so fond of my story. She still looks sad."

"She lost fourteen children. I think it will take some time before she can recover from such tragedy." Haris reached up, and gently grabbed a lock of Badra's hair, feeling the softness of the strands against his fingers.

"And what about you, Haris?" she asked. "Do you have siblings?"

Haris lifted his hand from her hair. "I have a younger brother and sister. What memory I have of them is in pieces. We were very close, often playing behind our home, on the hills and cliffs overlooking the Adriatic. It was a time of innocence I once thought would never end." Haris looked away from her.

"You have not heard from them or your parents?"

He brought his attention back to her beguiling eyes. "Years ago, a messenger brought me a letter just before marching off to war with Hungary. It was from my brother. He told me he had been ordained a Catholic priest and also reported how my father had died."

"I'm sorry." She traced her finger tips over the back of his hand. "I remember you telling me you were Croatian."

Haris smiled. "I was born in a small coastal village, called Nin. When I was very young, warfare between the Venetians and Ottomans had consumed the village." The smile faded from his face. "My parents fled southeast to escape the violence, settling in the remote village of Lezhe to live among Albanians. Years later, the Ottomans added Lezhe to their growing empire."

"And then the devshirme came to Lezhe?"

"Yes." Haris resumed his smile. "Now I am here being interrogated by you."

"Enough talk of the past," Badra announced. "What is important is the here and now. In mentioning children, isn't the news Fatma is soon to give birth, exciting?"

"Yes, I am happy for Mustafa. It begins a new chapter of life for him." Haris folded both arms across his chest, and produced a snide grin. "He wasted little time in finding a consort."

"She is a beautiful woman, and a good person. I have known her since my arrival to Constantinople."

"It will be interesting to see what Mustafa has learned from his father when it involves consorts," he said. "Will he be satisfied with just one, or will the cycle of competition among mothers and their sons continue?"

"As I said, Fatma is a kind person, but I do not see love in her eyes."

"Hmm—then Mustafa may be following in his father's footsteps. You once told me how your role within the harem was to entertain the sultan with your voice."

"Yes, this is true."

"Well, why have you never sung for me?" Haris queried whimsically.

"Ha! You would like for me to sing to you now?"

"As you continue to remind me, you are my gift." He winked at her. "Thus, I believe it only proper that you should do this for me."

Badra bowed sarcastically toward Haris. "As you wish, Vizier Haris. I shall sing you an old ballad my father once taught me." She cleared her throat and closed her eyes. Suddenly her lips parted, emitting a melodic tune carried by a heavenly voice that filled Haris with admiration.

"And the maiden was going to the matins one day...
Time is made long for me.
She went the way where the high mountains lay...
Yet I know that sorrow lies heavy..."

Suddenly, Badra's tune was interrupted by the sound of clopping hooves—not from a single horse, but from many. They looked to the path and watched a group of riders come into view, quickly distinguishing Mustafa as the lead rider.

"There is a problem," Haris mumbled.

The sehzade steered his horse off of the path, and continued galloping toward the couple. As he approached, Mustafa slowed his steed, stopping the animal a few rods before them.

"Sehzade, is there something wrong?" Haris asked, now speaking Turkish.

"The Queen Mother is dead," Mustafa announced bravely. "A messenger from Constantinople arrived to the palace this morning with the news."

"I am sorry," Haris offered. "Surely we belong to God and to Him we shall return."

Badra bowed her head. "It is very sad news, Your Royal Highness."

"My mother and I are preparing to leave for Constantinople in the morning to attend her funeral," Mustafa explained. "Haris, as my first vizier, I am leaving you in charge of Manisa until my return. I suggest the two of you return to the palace immediately."

CHAPTER

TWENTY-THREE

On the day following Mustafa's departure to Constantinople, Haris awakened with the sunrise, beginning the morning by bathing in his private hammam. He stood waste deep within the tepid water of the marble tub, near to where the ornamental fountain gushed from out of the wall. Cleansing his body with a sponge, he submerged beneath the water, resurfacing within the steamy mist to behold Badra suddenly standing above him at the water's edge. "How did you get in here?" he asked, recognizing how her shapely figure was accentuated by the crimson silk gown she wore.

"I told the guard I had something urgent to tell you."

Haris was surprised. "He permitted you entry without first coming to me? I must speak with Kamil about the security in this place."

"The guard knows of our relationship. He trusts me," she said with a smile.

"What urgent message do you bring me?"

She batted her long eyelashes. "I love you."

Haris' bewildered glare transcended into an amusing grin. "That is the nicest thing I've heard all day."

"And the day is just beginning." Badra began to slowly slip the straps of her dress from her shoulders allowing the silk gown to fall to her ankles. Stepping from out of her sandals, she kicked the dress aside, and proceeded to remove her undergarments, until she stood before Haris naked.

He found it impossible to look away from her beautiful curves, sculpted of porcelain skin bespeaking of purity, innocence, and modesty—three virtues of which, upon viewing Badra in her nakedness, he became eager to put to the test.

Gracefully, the lovely maiden descended the gray marble steps of the bath with tantalizing patience, until stepping onto the floor of the tub and submerging beneath the warm water. Instantly, she reemerged standing with her body exposed to the air from the waist up. She shook the water from her ears as her wet, long golden locks dripped, running straight down her neck with breasts supple and perky. All the while, sunlight streaming through the glass from the top of the honeycomb shaped ceiling worked to fill Haris' imagination with the belief he beheld a goddess encapsulated within a supernatural aura.

"Do you mind that I share your bath?" she asked, now switching to her native German tongue, which he found oddly stimulating.

"That is the second nicest thing someone has said to me today," he replied in German.

She moved closer to him and reached up, delicately tracing her fingers over his well-defined chest, before lifting her emerald eyes to his. "I desire you," she whispered provocatively.

Haris took a deep breath. "That is the third nicest—"

Before he could finish, Badra rushed to join her lips with his, and with the aid of a tight embrace they kissed feverishly. Haris' passion was quickly aroused, as the lovers explored one another's bodies with a deep yearning, making love within the bath water until both were spent.

* * *

Later that morning, Haris was interrupted by a chamberlain with information that Mustafa's consort was in labor with the doctor by her side. A few minutes later, he arrived at her apartment just as Jucef ben Ezmael was exiting it. The doctor, with both shirt sleeves rolled up to his elbows, approached Haris, while drying his saturated hands with a piece of cloth.

Jucef nodded. "Vizier Haris."

"Jucef, please tell me we have a new member in the palace this day?"

Before Jucef could respond, Badra appeared from behind Haris running down the corridor. "Fatma has given birth?" she asked, breathing heavily as she stopped before the two men.

"As I was just about to inform the vizier, yes, we do indeed have a new member of the palace." Jucef smiled. "He is a healthy boy, and both he and his mother are doing well."

"It is a shame that Mustafa missed the birth of his son," Haris remarked.

Jucef did not reply; although Haris could see the doctor's smile transform into a suggestive smirk, implying that such a thing was not uncommon among the royal family.

"Has Fatma named the boy yet?" Badra inquired. "I know she and Mustafa had selected a name for a boy and one for a girl, but it was kept secret."

"He is named Suleyman," Jucef revealed.

"Suleyman? Mustafa named him after his father?" Haris questioned. "I find that interesting."

"Vizier Haris, do not be surprised what a sehzade will do to win his father's favor," Jucef said.

"May I see her?" Badra asked.

"Of course, my lady," Jucef permitted. "I'm certain she will welcome your presence."

* * *

The following afternoon, Haris was enjoying an opportunity to ride Alabaster inside one of the corrals of the imperial stable, when his exercise was interrupted by a Janissary guard who informed him of the arrival of a group of unexpected visitors to the palace. To Haris' surprise, the six men represented the Republic of Venice, and their presence constituted an unannounced diplomatic mission for which he was unprepared. He decided to speak with the diplomats out of respect for their long distance voyage, eager to learn the nature of their mission.

After stabling Alabaster, Haris hurried off in the direction of the domed chamber of the Imperial Council; although first he would find his way into the Tower of Justice, just as the delegation arrived at the gate. He realized how behind the grilled windows set at the base of the tower he would be able to discretely assess his visitors.

From his vantage point, Haris watched as the six men passed through the gate; but what he observed next, baffled him. As the visitors strolled across the courtyard, they stopped briefly at the appearance of a woman who emerged from an alley way. All six men respectively removed their hats and bowed in the direction of the woman, while one of them stepped free from the company to have a brief conversation with her. The highly unusual display between a male and female within the confines of the third courtyard had been made even more bizarre by the fact that Haris recognized the woman as Badra.

In sizing up the members of the diplomatic group, Haris could see how most wore berets, and were fitted with large waistcoats that hung beneath plaited overcoats exhibiting wide, puffy sleeves made from colored silks. Yet, he noticed how the attire of the man who conversed with Badra differed from the rest in how he donned a black halo shaped hat, along with a dark slashed doublet.

Badra's conversation with the gentleman was brief, but she spoke directly to him, and Haris recognized that she kept her distance, all the while twisting her neck as though she feared being seen. When they had finished, she turned quickly away from the man, moving hurriedly in the opposite direction.

Haris was both mystified and annoyed by Badra's actions. He left the Tower of Justice through a secret doorway that brought him inside the domed chamber of the Imperial Council where he took a seat on a cushioned bench. Absent his conical headgear and lacking a more dignified kaftan, Haris hoped his plain clothes would not be mistaken as offensive.

Suddenly, a chamberlain appeared, announcing the presence of the Venetian delegation. The group filed through the entranceway, and proceeded across the marble floor in the direction of Haris. As they paced, Haris noticed how the Europeans appeared impressed by the colorful painted domed ceiling, while admiring the beautifully scripted Islamic verses that adorned the tile walls.

The group stopped just before the wooden railing in front of Haris, and in unison bowed toward the vizier, before one of the men stepped from the delegation to address him. "Vizier Haris," the man called out in Turkish. "I am the translator. We are a delegation from the Republic of Venice, representing the Signoria of Venice—the governing body of our country. Our spokesman is an esteemed member of the Minor Council. I present to you, Signor Marco Cancharello."

At the mention of the group leader's name, a small bronze-skinned man with a large, wide nose stepped forward, bowing in the direction of Haris. As he spoke in his native Venetian tongue, the translator relayed his words to Haris in Turkish.

"Honorable Vizier Haris, my lord the Doge Andrea Gritti sends his greetings on behalf of all the subjects of Venice."

"Thank you," Haris replied. "The timing of your visit is most unfortunate, considering the Sehzade Mustafa has been abruptly called back to Constantinople to attend the funeral of the Valide Sultan, Ayse Hafsa."

"Our sincere condolences in regards to the death of the Queen Mother."

"I also apologize that I am not appropriately dressed for your state arrival, as I found myself riding when I learned of your presence at the palace," Haris explained.

"It is our apology we have arrived without giving advanced notice," Cancharello countered. "Please understand how it was the desire of the doge to honor Manisa's new beylerbey as quickly as possible, as both a gesture of respect, as well as with the hope that a new era of benevolence and peace may begin between our two peoples."

"Should not the sultan be the recipient of such discussion between our peoples, rather than the sehzade?" Haris queried.

"As you have pointed out, the sultan has recently buried his mother," Cancharello reasoned. "The doge recognizes how sultans, like doges, are often besieged by issues at home and abroad, which places limitations on their accessibility. Sometimes the most effective means of allowing your message to be heard requires taking the road less traveled. It is our hope building a constructive relationship with the sehzade may provide us with an avenue to Constantinople." Cancharello paused to nod.

"We have heard how Sehzade Mustafa is well thought of by the Ottoman Janissaries," Cancharello continued. "Stories of his feats on the battlefield have not gone unnoticed. Whether they are fact or fiction, the mere idea the Janissaries speak of a leader in such favorable terms is noteworthy."

Haris was surprised to hear of the praise heaped on Mustafa; but even more surprised by the talk of creating dialogue between Venice and Constantinople. "There already exists peace between our two countries. Why should you suddenly be concerned about an Ottoman threat to Venice?" he pressed, as the translation of his words produced a buzz among the delegation.

"I understand that as a new vizier for the sehzade, you may not be privy to many details of Ottoman military planning and foreign politics," Cancharello blurted. "However, it is clear to all Europeans, as well as to those within Suleyman's inner circle, that your sultan is bored with times of peace. Suleyman has had a thirst for warfare since his conquest of Belgrade, more than a decade ago."

Haris frowned, taken aback by what he deemed was the Venetian's arrogance. "I was a member of the Janissary corps, and fought bravely alongside the sultan at the battle of Mohacs, as well as on both Vienna campaigns. Signor Cancharello, suddenly you seem to forget as first vizier for Sehzade Mustafa, I am a member of the Enderun, and do have knowledge of world events. I am also aware of whom the sultan views as his friends, as well as who he sees as his enemies."

"Forgive me, Vizier Haris," Cancharello offered. "My words were ill-advised. Then you must realize Venice is concerned with the increased presence of Ottoman warships in the Adriatic, as well as with rumors of an impending alliance between your country and France. The Treaty of Constantinople, signed between King Ferdinand of Austria and your sultan in July, now holds Austria ransom at the cost of thirty thousand guldens each year. Venice, hopes to avoid such a conundrum."

Haris did not respond, feeling slightly embarrassed that he was unaware of many of the details spewing from the Venetian. He was certain Mustafa lacked such knowledge as well.

"Perhaps now is not the time for such a discussion," Cancharello suggested. He turned toward another member of the group, who handed him a wooden box which he presented to Haris, placing it down in front of the railing. "The doge wishes that Sehzade Mustafa may accept his gift."

Haris reached down and opened the lid to the box. Using both hands, he pulled a golden gilt ewer out from inside, admiring the elongated spout, fixed opposite a handle in the shape of a winged lion.

"The winged lion is the symbol of Saint Mark, the patron saint of Venice," Cancharello described. "It is the hope of the doge, that when the sehzade may draw liquid to drink from the ewer, he will remember the generosity of the people of my country."

"I know the sehzade will appreciate the gift. I proudly accept it on his behalf," Haris said.

"I can see we have taken up too much of the vizier's time. I believe it is best now for us to leave," Cancharello announced. "Please convey our greetings and blessings to Sehzade Mustafa, and may your God protect you." He bowed his head—an act quickly replicated by the other five men.

"You are forgetting as a Janissary, I was once a Christian, Signor Cancharello. I know the Christian God and the God of Muhammad are one and the same," Haris explained.

Cancharello produced a smug smile. "If kings and sultans truly believed what you say, there would be no wars."

"Kings and sultans fight not over religion, but for the want of power," Haris corrected. "The fact you are present before me today tells me this . . . for isn't the real reason you are here in Manisa an attempt by Venice to assess whether or not the sehzade is a person with whom you can deal?"

Cancharello's smile faded. "It was to assess how much of the Sultan Sulyeman's character has been passed down to his eldest son. If Mustafa is not like his father, then I assume his destiny will be short-lived," he said boldly. "The history of betrayal and bloodshed within the sultan's family bears witness to what I speak. It is the strong and cunning who survive." He paused with a grin. "With that being said, I bid you *Ciao,* Vizier Haris." The other group members repeated the Venetian goodbye, with the exception of the man in the halo hat, who blurted, "*Tschuss.*"

"Wait!" Haris yelled out, rising to his feet. The translator did not need to translate the command, as the inflection within Haris' voice forced all to stop, and spin back toward the vizier. "You! With the halo hat! You speak German!" Haris spoke, now himself conversing in the German tongue.

The man nodded.

"What is your connection with the Venetian delegation?"

"I am Austrian, and we find ourselves as friends," the man replied. "Much the same as most Hungarians are now conveniently friends with the Turks, as a result of the Treaty of Constantinople."

"Within the theater of war, I have experienced how friendship can be easily purchased—but it is fleeting," Haris remarked. "Today's ally is very often tomorrow's enemy."

"What you say is true, Vizier Haris. That is why delegations, such as ours, are important. We need to know with whom we can trust. A steady wind can suddenly change direction."

"Then spying against an ally is like a lateen sail, the device which allows the ship to sail against the wind," Haris countered.

The Austrian appeared flustered by the comment. "I'm not sure I know of what you speak?"

Haris continued to stare at the Austrian, until the man looked away from him. "God's peace, be upon you," Haris said. His blessing brought an end to the audience, persuading the delegation to resume their movements toward the exit.

* * *

Sometime later, after Haris was informed of the delegation's complete departure from the palace, he sought out Badra, finding her pacing alone in a corridor just beyond Fatma's apartment.

"Hello, my love," Badra greeted, smiling. "I was just checking in on Fatma. She and her son are doing very well."

"That is good news," Haris replied, although the look upon his face remained serious. "Badra, I need to ask you something."

"Of course. What is it?"

"I've just come from an audience with a Venetian delegation. There was an Austrian among them. Do you know him?"

Badra appeared confused. "No . . . how would I—"

"You had words with him," Haris interrupted. "I saw you speak to him in the courtyard. What did he have to say to you?"

Badra took a deep breath. "He guessed I was Austrian by the color of my hair, and asked me if it were true," she relayed timidly. "I told him he was correct, and described how I was taken prisoner at Vienna several years ago."

Haris studied her face judiciously. "You appeared to be upset. Did he offend you?"

Badra swallowed hard. "No. His German speech and his appearance only reminded me of Austria and of my brother." She frowned. "Why do you interrogate me? What are you thinking?"

"Nothing . . . nothing at all." He forced a smile, before placing his arms around her waist, pulling her against him to share a kiss.

CHAPTER

TWENTY-FOUR

Yavuz Selim Mosque, Constantinople – February, 1534

Beneath the marble and granite colonnaded portico gracing the outside entrance of the domed Yavuz Selim Mosque, a group of Janissaries mingled around a stationary horse-drawn carriage. Suddenly, a great number of sipahis appeared on horseback, trotting through the street adjacent to the mosque. As the horsemen drew near, the Janissaries recognized the lead rider wearing conical headgear as the sultan, and hurried into a rigid military pose.

Each Janissary bowed his head low as Suleyman dismounted his horse with assistance. "I assume Hurrem Kadin is inside?" the sultan asked.

"Yes, Your Royal Majesty," a Janissary replied. "She remains at her morning prayers."

"Very well then, I shall wait for her in the gardens behind the mosque near to the tombs of my father and mother. When Hurrem Kadin is finished with her prayers, instruct her to meet me there. Her carriage is not to move from this spot until she has met with me."

"Yes, Your Royal Majesty."

Suleyman, accompanied by four sipahis, paced along the tiled porch outside of the octagonal building, until arriving at the gardens. Two domed brick mausoleum's dominated the botanical area, and he took a seat upon a stone bench opposite the tombs. With his eyes closed, Suleyman prayed silently.

A short time later, the sultan's invocation was interrupted by a soft voice. "Do you pray for your parents?"

Suleyman opened his eyes to gaze upon Hurrem. "I pray for all of us," he replied. "When I come here, it reminds me of how I wish to commission the construction of my final resting place. I realize I am still young, but only Allah knows when it may be a man's time."

"Will it be *our* final resting place?"

Suleyman smiled, before dismissing the Janissaries. He rose from the bench and approached Hurrem. "My love, why have you continued to avoid me? I am the sultan of the greatest empire on Earth. When I summon my subjects, they obey. But you— you ignore my requests with contempt, as though I am no more important than a common stable hand. Mahidevran is in Manisa, so she cannot be your excuse this time."

Hurrem removed her veil. "I've told you repeatedly how I desire to be much more than just one of your subjects. I am your lover, and the mother of your children. More importantly, I am a converted Muslim, which I have been now for some time. I switched my faith and chose Islam because of you, Suleyman. I know traditionally, the sultan's consorts must be Christian slaves. Well, now that I am no longer a Christian, in the words of our prophet, I can no longer be regarded as a slave. Thus, if you desire to share your bed with me, then make me your wife as our faith decrees."

Suleyman grimaced and sighed. "I have been flattered for some time by your desire to convert to Islam, but my love, no sultan has ever married."

"Then be the first," she declared. "I love you more than life itself, and I want very much to be your wife. We are united in

246

heart and passion, Muhibbi. But to truly be as one, it is necessary for us to be together—man and wife."

Suleyman looked at Hurrem with desirable eyes. "You are my elixir."

"Then make it so that you are never without it."

Suleyman turned away from her and paced a short distance before stopping and spinning. "Yes, it is time! This has gone on long enough! You shall be my wife! In the name of my love for you—here before the tombs of my parents—I announce the time has come to change the Ottoman tradition of sultans foregoing marriage! Hurrem, my world, my darling—be my wife!" Suleyman reached out for her with both arms.

Hurrem rushed toward him, falling in between his arms and wrapping hers around his waist. She buried herself in his chest. "I love you!" she exclaimed, raising her head so they could unite in a kiss. When their lips parted, Hurrem backed away from Suleyman and he could see tears streaming from her eyes.

"You cry tears of joy?" he asked.

"Yes . . . yes and no."

"What do you mean no? What is the matter?"

"I am very happy you have decided to break tradition and marry me, this I cannot deny. However, even with marriage, it pains me to think we must continue to live apart, in two different palaces on either side of Constantinople."

Suleyman folded his arms across his chest and looked beyond the garden wall. He viewed the majestic Golden Horn located below the grounds of the mosque, but his thoughts wrestled with Hurrem's request. "My precious gem, you test my resolve."

"If I am your wife, and we do not live together within the same palace, then I am really only a wife in name! Consorts reside with other consorts, wives live with their husbands!"

"My delicate rose, traditions are like the pillars of a palace. If one pillar must be brought down, there are others left to support the dome, allowing for smooth and gradual change." Suleyman took hold of her hand. "However, if too many pillars are removed at the same time, the dome will come crashing down, leaving the palace in ruins. For now, let us bring down the pillar foreboding a sultan to marry, and keep the dome intact. In time, we shall explore the idea of living together under the same roof."

Hurrem slowly leaned back into Suleyman's embrace. "You are wise, my Muhibbi. Maybe you are right, and now is not the time for such discussion. We are to be married, for this I am grateful. We shall address the other in the future—the near future?"

"Yes, the near future," Suleyman agreed. "In the interim, we shall marry in the month of May. It will be a grand wedding— one of its kind, befitting an emperor and his empress. All the kingdoms of Europe will be amazed by the celebration, as they will truly bear witness to the fact that the love between us has no equal anywhere on Earth."

Sea of Marmara off the coast of northern Anatolia – May, 1534

After having set sail from the port of Izmir the day before, the wooden oars cut through the choppy sea water, rocking the Ottoman galley as it moved in an easterly direction, carrying its cargo of royal passengers. With Constantinople as its destination, and the presence of fair weather assisting the voyage, the ship's crew anticipated arriving in the port of the Ottoman capitol by dawn the following day.

As the sun rapidly set in the western horizon, painting the stern of the vessel golden, Haris stood port side. He steadied his balance by clutching a piece of thick rope tied to a mast, as the warm sea breeze ruffled his hair. For the moment, his thoughts were with Badra, who had been left behind in Manisa, while he, Kamil, and Mustafa, accompanied by a dozen Janissaries of the sehzade's silahdar, traveled with invitations to the royal wedding of Suleyman and Hurrem.

Haris knew Badra would not be alone in Manisa, for Fatma remained home as well to tend to her infant son. Mahidevran also declined the wedding invite, using her grandchild as an excuse; although it was suspected that the great bitterness she harbored toward Hurrem, probably constituted the true reason for her reluctance to attend the nuptials.

"There's something calming about being on water." Mustafa had stepped up beside Haris, catching him by surprise. "Yet, at the same time, we find ourselves in a wooden vessel, floating on the surface of a sea with depths beyond our comprehension—still men are drawn to it, despite knowing how the slightest change in the weather could place our ship in great peril."

"I think it may be because men enjoy the thrill of gambling, ever confident they can beat the game of chance," Haris replied.

Mustafa spun around to behold the bottom sphere of the sun dip beneath the watery horizon. "I wonder what game of chance we are playing—you and I?"

"What do you mean?"

"I mean, what are my chances of being appointed the heir to my father's empire?" Mustafa turned to address Haris directly. "Now that the sultan has decided to break with centuries of Ottoman tradition and take a wife, I feel the odds of becoming his successor are stacking quickly against me. Hurrem's sons outnumber me four to one, and once she becomes the sultan's wife, she will have even greater influence over my father."

"The stepping stone to the sultan's throne is Manisa. You, and not your brothers, are its beylerbey," Haris reminded him.

"You are correct about Manisa as a training ground for the next sultan. However, with my father, tradition doesn't seem to matter any longer. What is so tasking about Manisa, anyway? It is not located on the front line of any foreign adversary, and aside from the Venetian delegation which arrived in my absence, what other leaders would care to travel to a town of little strategic importance? Manisa's population is at peace, living in a city quietly nestled away in the foothills of mountains."

Mustafa raised his head to view the main sail extended with its captured wind, before bringing his attention back to Haris. "When I attended the Queen Mother's funeral, for the first time I sensed something had changed between my father and I. Granted, he was never really a parent to me, as it was my mother who raised me. Yet, while growing up, in those few times that the sultan and I did spend alone together, there was a look of pride upon his face when he gazed at me. I did not see such a look when last in Constantinople. Rather, I saw apathy, as though I've become a nuisance. In fact, when I told him of the birth of my son, and revealed I had chosen to name my boy after him, he replied how the empire is not big enough for two Suleyman's. Of course, he followed it with laughter, as though he was jesting. But I recall what the English writer Chaucer once wrote: 'Many a true word is spoken in jest'."

"I'm sorry, Sehzade."

"My father has nothing to fear from me," Mustafa said. "I do not want his throne while he is alive. But with Hurrem as his wife, I fear she will transform my stepbrothers into a pack of hungry wolves in competition for the sultanate."

"Should that be the case, then we shall fight them together, and vanquish them all!"

Mustafa seemed surprised. "What happened to the teacher

who once talked of patience and goodwill—explaining how I could one day end the madness of fratricide with the stroke of a pen, and not the sword?"

"That message still rings true, Sehzade." Haris stared into Mustafa's eyes. "But often there are those times when the sword is needed to precede the pen. Remember, the first lesson I taught you—it was to trust no one."

Constantinople

As Suleyman had promised Hurrem, their marriage ceremony and subsequent celebration proved to be one of the most grandiose spectacles of the sultan's reign. After a sacred ceremony, which was held following a Friday morning prayer service within the palace of the Yeni Saray, the festivities commenced with a flurry of activity. To coincide with the number of verses within the first *sura* of the Quran, Constantinople became the focal point of seven days of celebration, which witnessed the draping of all the city's balconies in garland, while at dusk the urban streets glowed from lanterns on every first floor windowsill and were left burning until sunrise the following day. Tournaments were held daily in the Hippodrome involving skills competition between archers, horseback riders, and men demonstrating feats of strength, while military parades erupted each day in the streets featuring exotic animals—elephants, giraffes, and African lions—hailing from all corners of the empire.

On the fourth day of the celebration, Haris and Mustafa, who boarded within the Yeni Saray, decided to explore the Audience Chamber, which had become a temporary storeroom for the great many wedding gifts. Many of the presents were splendid works of art forged in gold and silver, containing pearls and precious gems, while the creativity shown within other pieces reflected intricate and resplendent handcrafted items designed to represent specific regions of the sultan's empire. As the two men perused the chamber, gawking at the varied items, they were interrupted by the Grand Vizier Ibrahim.

Ibrahim bowed to the sehzade, and bid hello to Haris.

"Grand Vizier, I've heard much praise for your military victories against the Safavid army of Tahmasp. Congratulations," Mustafa said.

"Thank you, Sehzade. I've actually only returned from the East last week in time for the sultan's glorious wedding," Ibrahim explained. "Ottoman forces recaptured the city of Bitlis, and have gone on to occupy Baghdad and Tabriz as well."

"Perhaps Tahmasp has learned his lesson?" Mustafa asked.

"Unfortunately, I don't think he has. Your father and I have recently discussed the possibility of leading a larger army into the region in the near future, as the threat to Ottoman sovereignty remains alive."

"God willing, you shall prevail," Mustafa offered.

"Yes, God willing," Ibrahim repeated. "Speaking of God, since you're here, I would like to share with the two of you, a rather interesting wedding gift," he said, and began pacing to a far corner of the chamber, followed by both men. After poring over a number of gifts, the grand vizier located a small wooden box, carefully lifting it from a table.

"The sanjak-bey of the Sanjak of Dasmascus presented this gift," Ibrahim described. Slowly he opened the box, reaching down inside to pull back a silk, red linen, revealing a narrow object which appeared to be about one half foot in length and only a few inches wide.

"It is a piece of wood," Mustafa described.

Haris gazed at its rough and blackened surface. "A very old piece of wood."

"Jerusalem lies within the Sanjak of Damascus. This object was found in the holy city. The sanjak-bey claims it is a Christian holy relic—a piece of the *True Cross*," Ibrahim said.

"The cross on which the Jew Jesus was crucified?" Mustafa asked.

Ibrahim nodded.

"Why would someone present the Caliph of the Islamic world a Christian relic as a wedding gift?" Haris asked.

"Such relics are prized by the sultan," Ibrahim replied. "It is the sultan's belief that the more Christian relics he can possess, the more the Europeans will take him seriously. They can also be used as an effective means in which to bargain with Christian kingdoms, should such methods be necessary. And do not think the covenant of such religious items is rare within the realm of the sultan. There's a room within the Yeni Saray known as the Destimal Chamber, which is filled with a great many holy objects. Faith tells us all of these items are what they claim to be."

Ibrahim closed the box and gently set it down. "Suleyman is also the guardian of many Islamic relics that have been passed down to him by previous sultans. *The Sacred Trusts*, as they are known, contain a piece of Muhammad's tooth, a hair from the prophet's beard, as well as the banner Muhammad carried when our prophet laid siege to Mecca."

"I was unaware of such items," Mustafa professed.

"It is not something discussed openly or very often," Ibrahim disclosed. "As the caliph of our faith, the sultan himself carries the only key to the room—no one else is permitted entry without the sultan's permission."

"Thank you for sharing, Grand Vizier," Mustafa said.

Ibrahim bowed. "God willing, as the future sultan, it was only a matter of time before you became privy to these sacred treasures."

CHAPTER

TWENTY-FIVE

Despite the Ottoman army's liberation of both Tabriz and Baghdad from Safavid military rule, by the spring of 1534 the brazen Safavid Shah Tahmasp had led his troops back into both cities by the summer, threatening stability along the Ottoman eastern border.

In June of 1534, Suleyman said goodbye to his bride, and with his Grand Vizier Ibrahim at his side, led an army of over one hundred thousand men eastward against the army of Tahmasp. The dispute between the two empires had its roots with the Safavid dynasty's refusal to recognize Suleyman as the caliph of the Muslim world, coupled with the spread of the Shia branch of Islam, which had resulted in the alleged forced conversion of many among Persia's Sunni Muslim population. Suleyman viewed Tahmasp's efforts to increase the size of the Safavid empire as a threat to his Sunni subjects living within Anatolia, and lands west of the Euphrates River.

By August, Suleyman's army had reached the city of Tabriz and subdued the rebellious population, before turning southward toward Baghdad, which fell to the Ottomans by the end of November. The sultan would remain with his army in Baghdad; although he became greatly distressed when he learned that Tahmasp's forces had reconquered Tabriz by early February, 1535.

Manisa – April, 1535

Mustafa received reports bimonthly from Constantinople messengers regarding the state of the empire. As a result of the information, the sehzade was kept aware of the progress of his father's campaign in the east, and understood how the warm, dry climate of the Persian Plateau differed greatly from that of southeastern Europe. Mustafa realized that unlike the campaigns against Vienna, seasonal changes in the weather did not permit Suleyman's army from advancing in the winter months, thus there was no telling when the sultan would be returning to Constantinople.

On a bright, pleasant April morning, Mustafa and Haris paced leisurely about the stunning gardens within the Manisa palace, discussing whatever subject came to mind.

"Fatma is with child again," Mustafa revealed.

"That is excellent news, Sehzade!" Haris exclaimed. "Praise be to God."

"Thank you, Haris. Yes, we are excited, and our boy Suleyman is doing well."

"Will you marry Fatma?"

Mustafa's eyes widened. "As the sultan has married Hurrem? I don't think so. It is not because I desire to sleep with many women. Rather, it is because I fear losing my identity. With marriage, two become as one, and although my father may not recognize it, Hurrem has become the sultan's conscience and his perspective. As Mahidevran continues to warn, such a situation is self-destructive for a person like my father."

"It may be true for the sultan, but how can you be sure the same would apply to you?"

Mustafa sighed. "The older I get, the more I realize that in many ways, I am indeed my father's son."

"Forgive me, Sehzade, but I think you're wrong."

"But why should I not aspire to be like the sultan?" Mustafa asked. "He is viewed as a great leader by all the kings of Europe, and his subjects from across the empire sing his praises."

"It is because you are aware of what goes on behind the palace walls."

"I know it only because Mahidevran tells me such things," Mustafa blurted. "I love her, for she is my mother. But I recognize the pain and bitterness she holds toward the sultan. Maybe she is blinded by her heartache?"

Haris did not offer a response, but only continued his relaxed pace alongside Mustafa.

"And what about you, Haris? When will you marry Badra?"

"I'm not sure. I promised her I would, and God willing I desire to keep that promise. Now is not the time," he explained. "Of course, she never allows me to forget my promise."

"Then you should marry her soon, before your promise turns to dust. That is of course—if you love her."

"I do love her. Our time here together in Manisa has allowed our relationship to blossom. And for this, I have you to thank."

Mustafa smiled. "I am happy for you, my friend. Manisa is so beautiful. The palace is comfortable and peaceful. It is like a paradise here. I should be happy my duties as the beylerbey of this place are not stressful, but—"

"But you're not?" Haris interrupted.

"No. The truth is I am bored, and disappointed the sultan did not invite me to campaign with him against the Safavid. Have I fallen out of favor with him?"

"I understand your stepbrothers were not asked to campaign either."

"They are too young," Mustafa said. "But I am not, and have

proven my military worth at Berndorf. I feel trapped here in Manisa—trapped and helpless, as though I wait for the sultan to decide my fate."

"When the sultan's campaign against Tahmasp has ended, I'm sure he will return to focusing on molding the future of his empire—and that future is you."

"*When* the sultan returns," Mustafa stated. Haris sensed a tone of doubt within his voice. "Unlike his campaigns in Europe, now the sultan's army fights against a foe in a warmer climate. He may not be back to Constantinople for another year. Haris, I've recently learned my father has ordered his army back to Tabriz to wrestle it from Tahmasp."

"We cannot control such things."

"But we can take advantage of it." Mustafa stopped abruptly to face Haris. "I wish to do something daring, Haris."

"What did you have in mind?"

"Jerusalem! I would very much like to see Jerusalem!" Mustafa announced. "I have been thinking about this since Constantinople, when you and I were shown my father's collection of religious artifacts. Jerusalem is one of the three holiest cities of our faith, and exists as the most historic of all places. Lying as it does within the borders of the Ottoman Empire makes Jerusalem accessible."

"But why do you want to see it now?"

"Because I can," Mustafa replied. "With the sultan now marching toward Tabriz, it may be many months before he will return to Constantinople. Thus, I will not be missed. Mahidevran can certainly manage the palace in my absence, and should my actions be questioned, I will argue that as the future sultan, I felt it necessary and desirable to personally set eyes on one of the most important cities of the empire. It will be viewed as a learning experience undertaken by a sultan's son with high aspirations."

Haris felt offended. "Sehzade, you mentioned Mahidevran can manage the palace while you're away. What about me?"

"Why Haris—I would never undertake such an adventure without my best friend!" Mustafa smiled. "What do you think?"

"It sounds possible." Haris sighed. "But what if the sultan questions the cost of the resources used to bring you to and from Jerusalem, especially at a time when the empire is at war? As a sehzade, you will need an entourage of soldiers and servants to accompany you."

"I will travel in disguise. It will be my goal to move among Jerusalem's population as a commoner, so as to experience the true character of the city. In this way, I will not be exposed to a charade because I am the son of a sultan," Mustafa explained. "There will be no entourage, only you and me, and two other loyal servants—all of us in disguise. Four seems like a number that would not attract too much attention. Who would you select to join us?"

"I would choose Kamil and Serkan," Haris offered. "Kamil knows the road to Jerusalem, for he has made the hajj, and passed through the city on his way to Mecca. Serkan has already proven his worth as a warrior." He sighed. "The journey may be dangerous."

"Then it is done!" Mustafa exclaimed.

Haris could see the excitement in Mustafa's face, realizing it was useless to try to reason with him. "When did you have in mind for such a journey to commence?"

"It depends on the sultan." Mustafa reached down and grabbed the stem of a flower, pulling it from the bed. "He will probably not reach Tabriz until the middle of summer, and if he reconquers the city, it is his nature to stay among the vanquished for about six months before returning to Constantinople." Mustafa stepped over to a reflecting pool, staring at his reflection on the surface of the water. "We must wait for news of his campaign. If he fails, then I will look like a traitor deserting my post during time of war. If he succeeds, I think November may be the perfect time. The sultan will be basking in his victory, and the empire will be basking in a time of peace." Mustafa tossed the flower into the pool, creating ripples distorting his reflection.

Manisa - early November, 1535

Over consecutive months, the messenger from Constantinople continued delivering positive news to Mustafa on the Ottoman war against the Safavids. Suleyman had reconquered Tabriz in July and while occupying the city, no other rebellions had broken out in cities controlled by the Ottomans. It appeared Tahmasp had grown weary of fighting. When the latest messenger to Manisa reinforced the sultan's success, Mustafa announced to Haris how the trip to Jerusalem would commence within a week.

The morning after the announcement, Haris, Badra and six Janissaries of the silahdar set out for the port city of Izmir—a journey that would take the casual rider nearly two hours to complete. Haris and Badra rode together inside the small, four wheeled horse-drawn carriage with the Janissaries each mounted on horseback.

As they neared the outskirts of Izmir, the road began a gradual descent into a small fishing village nestled around a wide, sheltered gulf on the northern coast of the Urla Peninsula. They made their way down the road and into the port city, riding over dirt streets set beside a long wooden pier, as squawking, soaring seagulls announced their presence.

After stopping the carriage, Haris and Badra, accompanied by four soldiers, began a stroll along the pier in the direction of the bustling Agora marketplace, which set along the water's edge. Although the Janissaries who guarded the couple were clad in dolamas and borks easily identifiable as belonging to the sultan's elite corps, Haris and Badra dressed rather modestly for the purpose of blending into the port city's crowd.

As they entered the marketplace, Haris observed a man moving briskly along the pier, carrying a large burlap sack thrown over his shoulder. The sack appeared to contain something heavy, as shown by the grimace on the man's face; although he worked hard to avoid eye contact with pedestrians who crossed his path. While watching his movements, Haris became suddenly distracted by Badra, who stopped and gasped when strolling past a narrow passage in between two buildings. Haris followed her eyes to observe two men positioned midway down the alley. One man sat on the ground with his back pressed against the wall, holding his palm to the side of his head, while the other stood above him clutching an object in his hand.

"Is that a knife he holds?" Badra asked aloud. "Has he attacked that man?"

"Remain here!" Haris ran down the alley toward the two men, followed by two of the Janissaries.

When the man clutching the knife saw the three men coming toward him, he turned and dashed down the opposite end of the alley, disappearing around a corner.

"My son! My son!" the man on the ground called out.

"Are you injured?" Haris asked.

"A bump on the head is all! But my son—he was kidnapped by pirates! Please stop them before they set sail!"

"We saw only one man run away from you!" one of the Janissaries explained. "We did not see a boy!"

Haris remembered the man with the sack thrown over his shoulder and turning quickly, sprinted toward Badra, pausing only briefly to instruct the Janissaries to remain with her.

Emerging from the alley, he scanned the multitude of single mast ships moored to the pier, before recognizing a sprinting man come to a stop along the pier near to a small craft. The man quickly climbed into the hull of the boat just before another man finished untying mooring lines. As they attempted to push the craft away from the dock with their oars, Haris increased his stride and leapt from the pier, landing on his knees inside the stern of the vessel.

The two men were stunned momentarily, but once the violent rocking of the boat subsided, one of the men lifted a sword from the hull, while the other grabbed a large knife. Haris looked to his feet, where he found a fish net and a wooden oar. He lifted both, grasping an object within each hand.

Suddenly, one of the men charged Haris, attempting to run him with his sword. Just before contact, Haris turned his body sideways, avoided the blade, and shoved the handle end of the oar into the man's torso. He clubbed the side of his head with the paddle, knocking him off the boat. As the man disappeared beneath the water's surface, Haris turned just as the second man charged him wielding the knife. He tossed the net over the man's weapon, pulling the assailant's knife away from him, before bashing the paddle against his head, sending him overboard on the port side.

Haris jumped down into the hull of the vessel and worked fast to untie the drawstring at the end of the burlap sack. As he began pulling the burlap sack down, a frightened young boy appeared.

"Are you all right?" Haris asked. "I'm here to help you!"

The boy nodded, and pulled himself free from the sack. Haris turned his attention back to the pirates treading in the water.

"Can you swim?" Haris called out, to which neither man replied. "I'll assume no response means that you can swim! I am the vizier of Manisa! You are both charged with kidnapping this boy, and if found guilty, in accordance with Ottoman law you will be beheaded! I imagine that as soon as you reach the shoreline, you will be arrested! However, if you begin swimming now in a northwesterly direction, with much luck you may arrive in the Greek islands within a few weeks! That is, if the sharks don't feast on you first!"

Haris guided the boat back toward the dock, where a Janissary helped secure the ropes to the pier's mooring. Badra and the boy's father stood nearby, watching as Haris assisted the boy from the boat and onto the pier, before he ran into his father's outstretched arms.

The tall, thin fisherman with salt and pepper hair bowed toward Haris. "I am honored to be in the presence of the vizier of Manisa! My name is Duman." He patted the top of the boy's head. "This is my son, Onur. May Allah bless you a thousand times for rescuing him!"

"You said those men were pirates?" Haris asked.

"Yes, from Seferihisar. It is a fishing village on the southern coast of the peninsula. On occasion they have been known to kidnap young boys from the ports up and down the Aegean, seeking to add to their fiendish crew. Usually it is boys fishing alone at night that meet with a dubious fate. But today's actions by the pirates were particularly brazen."

"I must say I am surprised that such criminal activity within the Ottoman Empire goes unpunished," Haris said.

"Most locals would believe it is because—" Duman suddenly paused.

"What is it?" Haris asked.

"I'm sorry, Vizier. I should know better to speak of such things," Duman explained with his head bowed. "You have saved my son, and that is what is important. It is inconsiderate of me to spend time dwelling on the grumbling of locals."

"As the first vizier of Manisa, I have the beylerbey's ear," Haris said. "I assure you that he is quite interested in the opinions of his subjects."

Duman slowly raised his head, running his tongue across his sundried lips. "The Sanjak of Sugla is under the jurisdiction of the red bearded Barbarossa—a former pirate himself—whose presence in these parts is legendary. Many people think Barbarossa may show reluctance to cleanse Seferihisar of its piracy, because he shares a past with their profession."

Haris nodded his approval. "I appreciate your candor, Duman. I promise that I shall speak to the sehzade of this matter with discretion."

Duman placed his arm upon his son's shoulder.

"Badra was most fortunate to notice you in distress," Haris said. "Had we waited any longer, your son may have been lost."

"Yes . . . yes," Duman agreed, embracing his son tightly. "Thank you, my lady." He brought his attention back to Haris. "Vizier, may I ask what brings you to Izmir?"

"The sea. We decided to step away from the palace today, and take in the sights, sounds, as well as the fresh air of Izmir."

"Very good. It is a fine day for sailing," Duman said. "Do you have a boat?"

"I usually have an Ottoman fleet at my disposal," Haris said with a smile. "However, there is no galley in port today."

"Then you will sail in my boat!" Duman offered with excitement.

"Duman, that is very generous of you, but unnecessary," Haris explained. "We had no intention of sailing today, only to visit the market, and taste the cuisine here in Izmir."

"But to truly experience the beauty and heart of Izmir, you must be on the water!" Duman persisted. "Go—select your food and bring it back with you to the pier. I will prepare my boat for sailing and meet you here. You saved my son! It is the very least I can do to honor your bravery! To say no to this would offend me!"

"Well then, how could I decline," Haris replied with a smile, before addressing his Janissaries. "Take the pirate's fishing boat back out and fetch those two water rats from the sea. Arrest them and turn them over to the local authorities."

* * *

Within the market, Haris and Badra examined a great number of carts displaying a variety of fresh fish and vegetables, before selecting a bowl of zerde rice made from saffron, and a boyuz pastry filled with spinach. Once their hunger had been addressed, they returned to the pier to meet the enthusiastic fisherman.

Duman's fishing boat was of average size, equipped with several oars, along with one main mast allowing it to be easily sailed in fair weather with a two man crew. The fisherman and his son assisted Badra onto the vessel, before Haris jumped on board.

"My lady and Vizier," Duman addressed. "Do you like my boat?"

"It is very welcoming—as is its captain," Badra said. "I had never before been on a boat until we sailed with the Ottoman fleet from Constantinople."

Duman laughed. "She cannot compare to an Ottoman galley, this is true. But do not underestimate her, for I have sailed her to the Adriatic and back on many occasions. She is a sturdy and fine vessel." He smiled, before bowing. "Enough talk, please sit and enjoy!"

Duman and his son worked diligently at untying the mooring lines of the vessel, and although the boy appeared to be very young, he impressed Haris and Badra with his sailing skills. The wooden boat looked dull, while reeking of fresh fish, but like two starry-eyed children themselves, Haris and Badra refused to balk at the conditions. Instead they settled in comfortably beneath a canvas canopy, set up at the stern of the vessel to provide relief from the relentless rays of the sun.

It was not very long before the large sail caught a breath of wind, propelling the vessel across the surface of the turquoise water. As they welcomed the warm sea breeze against their faces, Badra took the opportunity to remove her veil, while unbuttoning her outer robe. She shed the long garment, revealing a dark blue robe beneath it, and shook her long blonde hair to cool the perspiration around her neck. Haris noticed that Duman had taken an interest in Badra's appearance, catching the fisherman ogling over her for a moment, before casting his eyes back to the sea.

"It would appear our captain is fancying the beauty," Haris remarked softly to Badra.

"Well, he was correct!" Badra peered up and down the seaboard. "What a magnificent view of the coastline we have from this boat! It's gorgeous!"

"It is not the view of the coastline I'm referring to." Haris offered a coy grin. "I caught him looking at you, my love—the most beautiful addition to this coastline any resident of Izmir has seen in some time."

Badra blushed as she fell into Haris' arms, before sharing a passionate kiss.

"Thank you for bringing me here today. It was a lovely gesture," she said.

Haris smiled at her before looking away. "Badra, although we are surrounded by the grandeur of this coastline, there is no setting on earth equipped with enough splendidness to soften the words I must tell you today—"

"I know you are leaving, Haris," Badra interrupted. "Fatma told me yesterday."

He flashed a surprised expression. "And you are not saddened?"

"Of course I am saddened. But I know you are the first vizier of Manisa, and your allegiance lies with the sehzade."

"But my heart lies with you."

Badra smiled, bringing her hand up to Haris' face. "As it should," she said. "Fatma tells me you are going to Jerusalem."

"Yes, Mustafa feels the need to spread his wings. He is annoyed that his father has gone off on campaign without him."

"When do you leave?"

"Next week."

"How long will you be gone?"

"I'm not sure . . . months I would assume."

She turned away from him to watch a soaring pelican suddenly plunge head first into the surface of the water, emerging with a fish in between its beak. "I will miss you."

Haris reached out and grabbed her gently by the wrist, turning her toward him. Placing both hands on her waist, he stared deeply into her striking emerald eyes. "While I am away, take time to gaze at the moon my love, and know that when you are looking at it, I shall be looking at it with you."

CHAPTER

TWENTY-SIX

One late November morning, Mustafa, Haris, Kamil, and Serkan left the palace in Manisa on horseback. Their planned route was to venture southeast across the Anatolian Plateau to the Turkish port town of Dortyol. From there they would proceed south along the Mediterranean coastline to the village of Akka, and then traverse southeast again to the town of Nazareth, before veering due south to Jerusalem.

Abiding by Mustafa's wishes, the four travelers were forbidden to wear clothing that might reveal a political or military connection to the Ottoman Empire. Instead they dressed as commoners, clad in breeches concealed by long robes covered by vests and simple turbans. The only exception to this decree was the arquebuses they carried, as well as the wearing of woolen dolamas at the beginning of the journey to shield them from the blustery winter wind, while crossing the higher elevation of the plateau.

Adana, Anatolia – December, 1535

On the seventeenth day, the travelers welcomed much milder temperatures after having navigated natural passes through the Taurus Mountains, emerging to behold a large expanse of flat, fertile land lying to the southeast of the mountain's slopes. Centered within the plain was the large village of Adana composed of merchant houses, a mosque, and a marketplace organized around buildings set along dirt streets that intersected one another. Just beyond the village, miles of agricultural farms were visible, dividing the fertile plains into symmetrical rows of cotton, wheat, and date palms, surrounding the town like petals around the stamen of a daisy.

It was late in the afternoon when the four horsemen arrived, and for Haris, the view especially excited him; for he had convinced Mustafa that stopping within the village should be a priority. At Badra's urging, Haris agreed to seek out the Turkish couple who volunteered to raise him over a seven year period as part of his Janissary indoctrination. After thirteen years since last they had contact, he too felt the time had come to reconcile with his surrogate parents.

Haris led the group in avoiding the main streets of Adana, taking the back roads in search of the cotton farm belonging to Ahmet of the house of Haytac—a route which he remembered as if it were only yesterday.

Dusk descended over the plains when Haris brought the group to a dirt road stretching for several hundred rods, ending at a modest two-story home built of sun-dried brick. As the four horsemen rode toward the house, a dozen Turkish workers moved past them in the opposite direction, pausing briefly to gaze with curious expressions at the men with arquebuses strapped around their backs, and swords sheathed at their sides.

When they arrived at the front door of the home, the riders noticed a balding, portly gentlemen appear from out of a second, smaller brick building set away from the house, closer to the fields of cotton. The man had a thick mustache hiding his upper lip, while appearing confused in his approach toward the strangers. Filled with excitement, Haris dismounted Alabaster just as the old man reached him.

"Merhaba," the man greeted. Haris noticed how the farmer eyed the four armed strangers with uneasiness.

"*Baba*," Haris said.

The man's mouth gaped, as though he were trying hard to remember the last time someone had referred to him as father. He focused deeply on Haris' bearded face, paying close attention to his eyes. "Haris? Is it really you?"

Haris stepped forward hugging the man, as they kissed one another's cheeks. "I cannot believe my eyes!" the man exclaimed.

Suddenly, they were interrupted by a middle-aged woman with long, salt and pepper hair who stepped gingerly from the front door of the house, carrying a piece of cloth in her hand. "Ahmet, is there something wrong?"

"*Ana*," Haris called out, freezing the woman's approach.

Slowly she resumed her steps with eyes cast in his direction. "Haris?" She peered closer. "Haris? Praise Be to Allah, it is you!" She rushed toward him, embracing him.

Wrapped within a firm hug, the woman lifted her head to kiss his cheek. "We've heard wonderful things of you!" the woman said. "We have learned how you have risen to the position of vizier of Manisa! We are so proud!"

"Yes, Haris. We were overjoyed by news of your appointment!" the man praised.

"How do you know of this? Adana is far from Manisa," Haris asked.

"Our neighbor who lives down the road is a goat herder. His wife is the sister of Jucef ben Ezmael," the man revealed.

Haris smiled. "The doctor—why of course."

"When he writes to her, we learn of life in Manisa," the woman revealed.

Haris turned to look back at his three travel companions who were still resting atop their steeds. "Friends, I would like to introduce to you Ahmet and Zahra, of the house of Haytac—my Turkish *baba* and *ana*."

"Welcome!" the couple greeted in unison.

"My companions are Serkan, Kamil, and Mustafa," Haris continued, as each man nodded toward the couple at the mention of his name. "Serkan is an esteemed member of the silahdar which protects the sehzade. Kamil is the silahdar agha—"

The couple looked at one another with raised eyebrows.

Haris raised his head toward Mustafa. "And Mustafa. He is the Beylerbey of Manisa, the Royal Highness Sehzade Mustafa, first son of Sultan Suleyman."

The couple's faces produced a look of shear dread. "Allah!" Ahmet exclaimed, bowing his head. Zahra dropped to the ground on both knees, covering the top of her head with the linen.

Mustafa laughed. "Please . . . please, kind people, we are not here on a diplomatic mission. I wish to be treated as a humble guest."

"Forgive me, Sehzade Mustafa!" Zahra blurted with her head bowed toward the ground. "I should be wearing a veil outdoors, and most especially in your presence! But out here in the country . . . out here, we are so far removed from the ways of the city—"

"Do not fret, Zahra," Mustafa interrupted. "I am not wearing the royal *yusufi* on my head, or the kaftan of a sehzade. Forego the formalities, and please be at ease."

Haris helped Zahra to her feet. "We are passing through Adana, and had hoped you could put us up for the evening."

"Why of course!" Ahmet exclaimed. "We are honored!"

"And please do not go to any extra effort for me," Mustafa remarked. "Wherever I can lie my head will be adequate."

"Please! You may secure your horses in the stable around the back of the house! I have just sent the laborers home for the day, and my wife was in the process of preparing the evening meal!" Ahmet explained.

"Yes, please wash up and join us for dinner!" Zahra pointed toward the house. "I have prepared enough food for all! I'm certain of it!"

* * *

The travelers dined on a hearty meal of lamb and rice, accompanied by side dishes of eggplant, beans, onions, zucchini, and tomatoes, while sharing stories from Manisa. Ahmet and Zahra reveled in such interesting conversation, while Haris studied their enthralled expressions—certain that such talk had not graced the inside of the Haytac home for some time. Afterward, Zahra did her best to find them comfortable locations around the house, and before long they turned in for the evening. The familiarity of his old home was for Haris surreal, and worked to afford him the first restful night of sleep he had experienced since the journey began.

* * *

The following morning, crowing roosters and the cackle of chickens announced the first glimmer of sunlight on the horizon, awakening Haris. He found his way to the kitchen at the back of the house where he located his mother preparing a breakfast of eggs and vegetables. As he approached her, he grinned at the sight of a purple hijab wrapped around the top of her head and neck.

"What is that grin of yours, Haris? Do you mock your ana?" Zahra asked playfully. "I felt naked without it in the presence of the sehzade yesterday. I shall not make the same mistake today."

Haris kissed her on the cheek, before pouring himself coffee. "You needn't worry about Mustafa."

"You favor the future sultan, don't you?" Zahra asked. "Oh, my!" she exclaimed. "I just realized the future sultan is staying in our home!"

"He's a good man."

"He's a young man," she countered. "How did the two of you meet?"

"The sultan asked me to train him to be a warrior."

"A warrior?" Zahra repeated. "Always so much fighting and bloodshed." She shook her head, using a wooden spoon to stir the eggs in a pan she held over a fire. "With your unshaven faces, the four of you look more like gypsies than soldiers."

"We have been traveling across the countryside for over two weeks, camping outdoors."

"Why is a sehzade traveling on horseback with only three men, and living off the land?" She began stirring the eggs with more vigor. "Has there been a revolution? Is he running from something? Are you in danger?"

Haris laughed. "No Ana, it is nothing like that at all. It is merely the desire of the sehzade to remain discreet."

Zahra huffed. "I remember how it took over a year for you to call us ana and baba."

"It was hard for me then, knowing my birth father paid to send me far away to a stranger's home."

"That is all behind you now," Zahra consoled. "Tell me, the four of you—where is your destination?"

"I'm afraid I cannot reveal what you ask without the sehzade's permission."

Zahra grinned. "I understand . . . Vizier Haris." She paused in stirring the eggs to look longingly at him. "You've done well for yourself since leaving our home."

A wave of emotion stirred Haris, as he sensed the pride in her words. "Ana . . . I'm sorry I haven't written to you and baba. It was thoughtless of me. I would not be the man I am today if it were not for the love and care I received from the two of you. It has taken me too long to recognize this. Please forgive me."

Zahra set the pan of eggs down and stepped toward Haris, bringing the palm of her hand to his bearded face. "You were young when you left. Young men are full of bravado, fury, and pride. But you returned to us, as I knew someday you would."

"I am relieved by your forgiveness."

"It is not forgiveness, it is love."

He bent over and kissed her softly on the cheek. "I have something more to tell you." He pulled away from her, securing her attention with his eyes. "I am to be married sometime next year."

Zahra exploded with joy, beaming, and clapping her hands. "It is wonderful news! Who is she?"

"Her name is Badra, and she has stolen my heart!" Haris described. "She is charming and beautiful. I have told her everything about the two of you, as well as of my time spent here in Adana. I had been plagued with guilt for not writing to you for so long, but it was she who encouraged our group to stop here while on our journey, to seek you out!"

"Then we must celebrate this wonderful news!"

"Thank you Ana, but we haven't the time. We must be on the road again soon," Haris explained. "When all is settled after my return, I will send for the two of you, and have you brought to Manisa."

Zahra embraced him tightly. "I am so happy for you!"

"I shall go and wake the others," Haris said.

"Mustafa is already awake. He is outside with Ahmet." She pointed to a square opening in the wall, featuring wooden shutters. "Your baba likes to begin the day with a walk at sunrise with his *subha*. They are walking and praying together."

Haris stepped over to the opening in the wall and threw open the shutters. He could see the two men pacing leisurely aside one another, with Ahmet clutching the Islamic prayer beads. "I hope Mustafa is not giving away the secrets of his kingdom." Haris opened the back door and stepped outside, immediately catching the two men's attention.

"Good morning, Haris," Mustafa greeted.

"It's a beautiful morning," Haris replied.

The two men stopped before Haris, as Mustafa turned toward Ahmet. "Thank you Ahmet for allowing me to share your walk, as well as your piety."

Ahmet bowed.

"Ana is preparing breakfast. It should be ready shortly," Haris revealed.

"Then I shall go and wash. We should be leaving immediately after breakfast to be sure we are gone before Ahmet's field hands begin arriving," Mustafa declared. He patted Haris on the shoulder in passing him, moving toward the house.

"Come, Haris. I need to assess what amount of work awaits me today," Ahmet said. He began stepping toward the smaller building set behind the house. "Then we will have a few minutes alone to talk."

When they reached the building, Ahmet unlocked the door and led Haris into a spacious one room area. The stale air inside the dark room struck both men squarely in the face before Ahmet threw open the shutters on several square openings. Immediately a soft breeze entered, accompanied by rays of the morning sun, cleansing and brightening the room.

Haris noticed how more than half of the room was full of harvested cotton, piled up twice the height of an average man. He approached two work benches, each featuring a small wooden apparatus composed of a wheel with teeth cut out of the wheel's edge. Setting above the wheel was a narrow cylinder carved with ridges attached to a handle. Playfully, Haris grabbed the handle and turned the wheel. "I see you have two worm wheels now."

"Yes, I purchased the newest one in the Adana marketplace several years ago," Ahmet explained. "I was fortunate. It is not often one comes across such a device. They say it was made in the land of the Mughals, just as my original one. Now, with both ana and me working the worm wheels, we can clean seed from nearly twenty-five pounds of cotton a day."

Haris nodded his approval.

"Tell me Haris, did your ana and I—did we prepare you well for your admittance into the Janissary corps? You know of what I speak—your education in Islam, and providing for you a good home?"

"Of course, Baba. Only a few moments ago I was thanking ana for the love and devotion that both of you have bestowed upon me."

"I'm glad you told her of this." Ahmet stepped to the other side of the room. "A woman needs to hear such things."

"And you should hear it too, Baba."

Ahmet smiled. "Because Zahra could not bear children, Allah saw to it that you would be the son we could never have."

"I owe both of you more than you can know."

Ahmet turned to look at Haris. "Well, you are the vizier now, so I will expect monthly payments." He laughed. "The sehzade— he seems to be an independent one."

"How do you mean?"

Ahmet began a deliberate stroll in the direction of Haris. "Just the fact that a man of such importance would be traveling across the plateau with only three other men and not an army, seems irresponsible," he said. "I do sense there is virtue within him, but his actions seem ill-conceived. If you and I were to undertake a similar journey it would most likely prove uneventful. Who we are, and where we come from blend easily with the simplicity of the world around us. But Mustafa is like a diamond in the rough, and as is the case with most precious stones, they often end up being handled by unscrupulous characters."

"I have pledged to protect him."

Ahmet stopped at the table and rested both palms on top of it. "And no doubt you will honor that pledge—but be careful my son, because the sehzade remains an untamed horse who others may believe needs to be broken, and if not broken, then freed. You must ask yourself, if Mustafa is found to be unbreakable, then what becomes his freedom?"

Haris studied the quizzical look on Ahmet's face—a look he had seen a thousand times before. "This conversation brings back so many memories of the countless times you filled me with your words of wisdom."

Ahmet smiled, lifting his hands from the table, and folding his arms across his chest. "As a vizier, you undoubtedly move in close quarters with the royal family. Without asking you to spill any secrets of the sultan's world, what has surprised you most?"

Haris thought for a moment. "It would have to be the influence of the peoples from across the Aegean on the empire's growth." Haris resumed playing with the worm wheel. "Mustafa's mother opened my eyes to the reality of just how many individuals holding high governmental posts are not Turkish, but like me, they have their origins in Rumelia."

Ahmet grinned, nodding. "There are several local farmers who own Shepherd hounds. When each animal comes in contact with another, as they so often do, they play with each other." He hesitated, before raising the index finger of his right hand. "But there is another farmer who lives among us that has a Dalmatian for his pet. When the Dalmatian encounters any of the other Shepherd hounds, both animals react with hostility. Now why is this, you may ask, for they are all hounds?" He lowered his hand. "These hounds are very much like men—men who live peacefully among their own kind. Yet the same men feel threatened by those who do not look, speak, or pray like him. Like the hounds, men react this way because strength lies in numbers, and because belonging to a similar group means survival."

"Then why permit outsiders to join the group?"

Ahmet grinned. "Many centuries ago, my people, the Turks, invaded these lands we now call home. Eventually, from the clan led by Osman, an Ottoman kingdom was established. As the kingdom grew into an empire, it became inevitable that the Turkish borders would expand, bringing non-Turkish peoples inside the empire. As the sultanate passed through history, it became wise to include non-Turkish peoples into the government as a way of strengthening the empire's bonds with non-Turks. In this way, they reasoned they could prevent rebellion in places such as Rumelia. But how do they go about acquiring non-Turks?"

"The devshirme—they enslave them," Haris answered.

"Yes, and the Turkish people remain content because they are labeled as free."

"The sultan told me something similar to what you speak of," Haris remembered.

Ahmet's eyebrows rose. "You have had an audience with the sultan?"

"Twice, now."

"That is impressive," Ahmet said. "But what I'm certain the sultan did not tell you, was that, yes, bringing non-Turkish peoples into the Ottoman government is certainly a practice necessary to prevent rebellion, but not so much a revolt from the outside, as much as a way of discouraging revolt from among the Turks themselves, who they see as the greatest threat to the stability of their empire." Ahmet produced a coy grin. "Just as Osman overthrew the Turks led by Seljuk, there is always the chance of another Turkish clan challenging the present throne. All empires have their beginning and their end, and the end for many has its origins from within. Mark my words Haris, the Ottoman Empire is strong and prosperous today, but should someday the Turkish people desire to have greater control of the sultanate, it will spell the end."

"Your wisdom speaks loudly, Baba."

"Haris, my advice for you is to hold your allegiance not to the sultan, but to your soul."

"Thank you, Baba. Your words are heard."

"And when you and your friends arrive at your destination, be sure to treat the holy city with reverence and respect, for in return, God will treat you likewise," Ahmet advised.

Haris was surprised. "Did Mustafa reveal to you the city of our destination?"

Ahmet chuckled. "No, only that you will proceed in a southerly direction. What is there that lies south of Adana other than mountains, desert, and the sea? It is Jerusalem. You are certainly not the first to pass through Adana on the way to Jerusalem, and you shall not be the last. However, be careful, for the journey south of here will grow much more dangerous as you near the holy city. It is as though the closer one gets to the house of God, the more demons he must pass through."

CHAPTER
TWENTY-SEVEN

Four days after leaving Adana, the sehzade and his companions found themselves riding through a fertile, unpopulated gorge cut by the waters of the narrow Orontes River, when they came upon a relic from the past. The ancient, rundown stone fortress set strategically atop the rocky knoll, standing silent yet telling, like a weathered stela protruding from the highest ground within a cemetery. As the four horsemen passed the archaic structure, Kamil took a moment to identify it. "Bagras Castle," he called out.

From his saddle, Mustafa turned toward Kamil. "You've been here before?"

"Only in my dreams, Sehzade," Kamil replied.

"Your dreams must be vivid?" Mustafa jested. The four horsemen moved past the ruin, with Mustafa's horse trotting in between those carrying Haris and Kamil, while Serkan assumed the position as the rearguard.

As they rode, Kamil began to scratch his beard.

"Corbaci, you do not like your new face?" Serkan called out, before laughing.

Kamil turned slightly, looking back at him with a grin. "It is prettier than yours!"

Serkan scoffed. "But see how the vizier does not complain. As he no longer is a Janissary, such a fashion may suit him!"

Haris chuckled. "You're wrong Serkan. If my beard is anything like yours, then it looks like last year's bird's nest!"

The men shared in laughter before Kamil interrupted. "We are nearing what remains of the ancient city of Antioch. My mother's family has their roots here, and as a boy, I was raised on many wonderful stories of this place."

"Your mother was born here?" Haris asked.

"No," Kamil replied. "My mother and father were born and raised in Rumelia—in the Greek land of Thrace. Generations of my mother's family once lived in Antioch. My mother, despite never setting foot here, told me stories that had been passed down by word of mouth describing this ancient city. Her family descends from the Oghuz, a Turkish tribe which migrated to this place many centuries ago. They adopted the Christian faith, but when the Mamluks invaded, my ancestors avoided persecution by fleeing the area. They journeyed across Anatolia, and when reaching the Aegean coastline, they set sail for Thrace. My mother was born there and met my father, whose family had been in Thrace since the Turks conquered it almost two hundred years before. His family worshipped Jesus and migrated across the Aegean from Ephesus. Thus, I was raised a Christian."

"And then the timarli came to your village?" Haris asked.

"Yes, to collect for the devshirme," Kamil replied. "That is how I, a Christian Turk, became a member of the sultan's Janissary corps, and later a convert to Islam. I feel blessed, for it is as God has willed, although Allah continues to challenge me," he added, grinning.

"In my education, I have heard many stories of Antioch," Mustafa recalled.

Kamil nodded. "Its location sets at the crossroads of history, having been conquered and reconquered throughout the ages by

281

every major army that rose in power across the Mediterranean world, including the Turks. What remain of the ancient city are only ruins. The Turks built the city of Antakya not far from here to replace it."

Haris glanced back at the rearguard. "Serkan, where are you from?"

Serkan smiled proudly. "I am from Monastir in the land of Macedonia. Like this place, there are ancient ruins strewn about my homeland. Unlike the corbaci, it is not the old that I remember, only the new. There is a great bazaar in Monastir with over eighty shops—most of them in the trade of selling tiles. The bazaar is protected by four large iron gates, and every day it is alive with the sights and sounds of people bartering, or sharing the latest news. My parents took me there often, so it holds a special memory for me."

"How old were you when taken for the devshirme?" Kamil asked.

"I believe I was twelve when the Turks came and took me from my parents. I recall how the soldiers marched me past the Greek Christian Church in my village, and I remember praying for God to intervene." Serkan recounted the details, displaying little emotion. "It was the last time I saw my family . . . but as a member of the Janissaries, my eyes have been opened to the true faith. Allah, be Praised!"

* * *

Over the next five days, the four men followed the Orontes River until arriving in the Beqaa Valley of Mount Lebanon. Here they moved through an environment altering dramatically across short distances, from fertile fields, to rocky terrain and thick forests, before giving way to fertile fields once again. The wintry air blew cold in the mountains, and after leaving their dolamas behind in Adana, the men now protected themselves with plain woolen garments, while replacing their turbans with a heavy, woolen cloth held on by a black rope cord.

Donning dark facial hair, with skin colored by the sun and wind, the bearded group of men migrated farther south—each leg of their quest appearing to take them further back in time as they passed through the ancient cities of Safed, Nazareth, Afula, Jenin, and Nablus. It was if the four horsemen were burrowing through each layer of the earth, trying to reach its core.

* * *

On the morning of the eighth day since Antioch, the four men, who had been riding since the break of dawn, watched as the sunrise behind them slowly lifted the darkness ahead, revealing a scenic view of rolling topography.

Kamil brought the group to a halt. "We have been passing through the Kidron Valley," he explained, before pointing to a high, gently sloping hill. "To the north lies Mount Scopus." He switched the direction of his arm. "And to the west lies the Mount of Olives. On the opposite side of the valley from the Mount of Olives, will be Jerusalem."

"Then we are close," Mustafa said.

"Yes, Sehzade," Kamil said. "We must find a place to bury our firearms. I suspect the only people inside the city who may enjoy the luxury of carrying an arquebus would be Ottoman soldiers, Sehzade," Kamil explained.

"We would stand out in the crowd and ruin our cover," Haris said, looking about. "I don't see any settlements in these parts."

Serkan pointed in the direction of a lone, lofty tree with flaking reddish bark, and a dome-shaped crown. "Over there may be a good place to bury them, at the base of that sycamore. We would have no problem finding the location on our return. The tree can be seen from a great distance."

The men agreed and rode toward the tree, working fast to dig a hole and wrap their firearms in cloth, before burying the weapons beneath the shadows of the spreading branches. When finished riding their horses back and forth across the soil to hide any evidence of a burial site, they set a course in the direction for the Mount of Olives, armed now with only sabers, daggers, and Haris' bow and arrows.

Within a few hours, they stopped along a ridge overlooking a narrow dirt road. On the opposite side of the road they noticed how the slope of the hill was staggered with pockets of small trees featuring twisted trunks that supported leafed out branches, sprouting silvery green leaves and white feathery flowers. "Olive trees," Kamil identified.

"Look," Haris said. He pointed to a man walking along the road beneath them, moving in a westerly direction. The gray bearded man, clad in a fringed woolen garment hanging from his head and draped around his shoulders, led a one humped camel by a rope.

"He wears the tallit—he is a Jew," Kamil described.

They continued to watch the man shuffle along with slightly arched posture and a wobbly gait, noting how he paused on occasion to reposition any one of a number of bulging sacks that had been strewn across the back of the camel. Momentarily, he stepped away from his animal to look back at the road behind him. Suddenly, Haris and his companions could hear the thunder of galloping horse's hooves, when from out of a cloud of dust stirred up by the charging horses there appeared three riders dressed in long white tunics, wearing red and white head cloths.

"Are they Druze?" Mustafa asked.

"No, Sehzade," Kamil corrected. "They are Bedouin. Their kind is a nuisance in this area, notorious for raiding caravans of pilgrims traveling toward Mecca."

Rapidly, the three men overcame the old man and his camel, with one of the riders quickly dismounting. The Bedouin circled the camel on foot, inspecting the animal before approaching the elderly man, and evoking a conversation. The old man reluctantly moved toward the beast, and tapped on the animal's side with a thin stick, causing the camel to drop slowly onto all fours. The Bedouin said something more to the old man, who responded adamantly as if pleading, before the stranger shoved him to the ground. Another Bedouin dismounted, and the two of them worked at moving several sacks from the back of the camel to the back of the rider-less horse, before one of the men mounted the camel. The animal rose up, and the Bedouin used the reins to turn the camel in the opposite direction. The Bedouin, who had assisted in moving the sacks to the horse, mounted his steed and grabbed the reins to his accomplice's horse. The despondent Jew could only watch as all three tribesmen headed off in the direction from which they came.

Serkan turned toward Mustafa. "They've stolen his camel, as well as the old man's goods!"

"What shall we do, Sehzade?" Kamil asked.

Mustafa glanced around at all three men. "We must stop this theft!"

"Very good," Haris replied. "Sehzade, I suggest that you stay here and tend to the old man. The three of us will go and recover the camel and the stolen goods."

Mustafa nodded, and watched as the three horsemen set their steeds into full gallop, before he steered his horse down the hillside.

Haris, Kamil, and Serkan continued to ride along the ridge above the road, keeping a careful distance from the edge of the cliff to remain out of sight. After traveling some one hundred rods or more ahead of the Bedouin, they stopped their horses.

Haris dismounted and tied the lead line of Alabaster to a nearby tree before returning to the ridge, where he located a large boulder overlooking a bend in the road. He pulled his bow over his head. "This will be an ideal spot."

"What are you planning?" Kamil asked.

"The two of you will go down to the road and wait for the Bedouin. They should appear just around the bend of that hill," Haris explained. "Try to negotiate the return of the camel, and with the first sign of trouble, I will take them out with arrows."

Both men nodded, and rode off down the hillside. Soon they were in position, seated stationary on their horses, facing the bend. Suddenly, from around the hillside, the winding road revealed the thieves—but only two of the three. One Bedouin continued to ride the camel, while the other rode alongside of him, still guiding the rider-less horse.

From atop the ridge, Haris fixed an arrow on the bowstring. *Where is the third Bedouin?*

Both Bedouin continued their approach, stopping within ten rods of Kamil and Serkan, as the one on horseback flashed a large smile. "*As-salaam Alaikum.*"

Kamil responded in Arabic, "And God's peace, be upon you."

"You are strangers in this region," the Bedouin guessed.

Kamil glanced quickly at Serkan, and then back at the Bedouin. "You have borrowed our friend's camel. He wishes for you to return it now."

The two Bedouin looked at one another with astonishment,

before laughing aloud. "I'm afraid you are mistaken, friend. The old man gave me the camel. It is mine."

Kamil took a deep breath. "First, you are not our friends. And secondly, I am trying to keep you alive. All you must do is dismount the camel and move on. We do not seek trouble."

Once again the Bedouin burst into laughter, when suddenly the man on the camel unsheathed his saber and kicked the sides of the animal. The camel, with its rider waving the blade above his head, charged toward Kamil and Serkan. Kamil quickly withdrew his kilij, but before they could engage one another, the saber fell from the Bedouin's hand, and he slumped forward, with an arrow piercing his back. The dead man plummeted from the back of the camel, as the second Bedouin withdrew his saber and charged his horse toward Serkan.

Haris moved from behind the boulder to procure a better angle from which to fire, and set another arrow against the bowstring. He listened to his pounding heartbeat grow louder, before he realized it was the sound of a galloping steed. Spinning quickly to his rear, he found the third Bedouin charging toward him, closing rapidly. Haris awkwardly aimed his arrow and fired. The arrow struck the Bedouin in his face, passing through his eyeball. His body fell from the horse just as Haris rolled out of the path of the charging stallion.

Haris scurried to his knees, peering down at the road to observe Serkan battling the Bedouin on horseback. Both men guided their horses in circles, while swinging their swords at one another. Haris fixed another arrow to the bowstring, but refrained from letting it fly in fear of striking Serkan. Suddenly, Kamil moved his horse closer to the dueling men and swung his blade, slicing it deep into the Bedouin's right side. The Bedouin screamed, dropping his sword as blood spilled from his mouth, before tumbling from his horse onto the ground.

Haris quickly mounted his horse and descended the hill to meet his comrades. "I'm sorry, Serkan!" he exclaimed. "I was suddenly surprised by the third Bedouin!"

"No worries, my friend! It is reassuring to know that the silahdar agha chief can still wield his kilij!" Serkan quipped.

Kamil dropped from his horse, and secured the camel, which barked with agitation. "Easy, girl!" He seized its reins and waited for the animal to calm, before inspecting the contents of the bags strewn across its back. Reaching inside one of the sacks, he withdrew a handful of black, tiny round fruit. "Olives!"

"Yes, but I believe it was the camel the Bedouin were after," Haris concluded. He gazed out at the landscape, which revealed a trail of dust behind the dead Bedouin's fleeing horses.

"Perhaps it was the camel, but now we've killed three Bedouin," Kamil lamented. "This is not a good thing. They will be missed and when their bodies are found, their fellow tribesmen will seek vengeance. Allah challenges us this day!"

Serkan noticed shadows at his feet, and lifted his head to the skies. "Look!" He pointed at two vultures circling overhead. "Already the birds are assembling to feed on the dead!"

"It won't be long until their presence reveals something is wrong here," Kamil said.

"We must hurry," Haris decided. "Serkan and I will clean up this mess. Kamil, you take the camel, return to the sehzade, and wait for us there."

"Very well, but first, Haris tell me—what are we doing here?" Kamil asked with a bewildered look. "I am in no position to question the sehzade, so I will question you. Why are we here on the doorstep of Jerusalem?"

"Yes, it is a question I too have asked myself," Serkan added.

Haris gathered his thoughts. "I don't know. When the sehzade and I were in Constantinople, we were shown religious artifacts, some from Jerusalem. Perhaps, we are witnessing a boy becoming a man. He found his courage on the battlefield at Berndorf, and maybe now he seeks spiritual growth by journeying to the holy city."

"The sultan himself has never been to Jerusalem," Kamil revealed.

"Maybe this is a way for the sehzade to gain the recognition from his father that he craves," Haris wondered aloud.

"How long does the sehzade plan to stay in Jerusalem?" Serkan asked.

"I'm not sure—maybe a few days at the most?"

"Then you must ask him," Kamil insisted. "Of the three of us, you are the only one who is in a position to inquire such things."

"I promise I shall ask." Haris glanced down at the two dead Bedouin. "What is most important at the moment is returning to the sehzade before our actions on this road are discovered."

Kamil mounted his horse.

"Oh, and Kamil," Haris called out. "We should all be careful not to address Mustafa with any titles in the presence of the Jew. It is important we keep his identity secret."

Kamil nodded, grabbed the reins of the camel, and led the animal down the road in the direction of the Mount of Olives.

Haris pulled the arrow from the back of the Bedouin he had struck down, and used the other Bedouin's saber to stab the wound area made by the arrow.

"What are you doing?" Serkan asked.

"I am trying to make it appear as though the death blow came as a result of the Bedouin sword, and not an arrow." Next, Haris removed the saber from the hands of the arrow victim, and plunged the point of its blade into the open wound in the side of the other Bedouin. "Now it may appear that both men killed one another in a duel."

They scurried to the top of the hill and buried the third Bedouin in a shallow grave, before mounting their horses and setting off to meet the others, finding the sehzade and Kamil conversing with the very animated elderly man.

"He speaks Arabic?" Haris asked, looking closer at the withered face of the old man, highlighted with bushy gray eyebrows, and a distinguished nose protruding outward like a weather vane.

"As well as Hebrew," Mustafa said. "His name is Amos. He was bringing the olives to Jerusalem. They are in the midst of their Hanukkah celebration. He wants so badly to repay us for recovering his camel and goods, but insists that he is too poor. Instead of money, he has offered to show us around Jerusalem."

"We will need a guide around this great city," Haris agreed.

Serkan looked to the sky. "I believe it is the will of God that we came to the aid of this man."

CHAPTER

TWENTY-EIGHT

The four Ottomans, moving alongside Amos the Jew, continued on a path ascending the Mount of Olives, when they began to notice a great many caves blemishing the stark hillside, as if they had climbed a giant termite hill. Amos pointed out how they were Jewish burial caves, easily carved from the limestone chalk. The pockmarked landscape held their fascination while the road continued its gradual rise, until they found themselves at the crest of the hill. Here they stopped to behold the inspirational scene below them.

Kamil held out his arm. "'Set your face toward Jerusalem'— the center of the world!"

The five men gazed down upon a square, walled medieval enclosure, built around a great many stone dwellings laid out close to one another, separated arbitrarily by narrow streets. Within the northeastern sector of the enclosure, the condensed city unfolded below and beyond a large, flat, white stone platform centered by a multi-colored octagonal building that supported a large dome. One of four minarets occupied each corner of the platform, and the dome's ivory tile shimmered in the afternoon sun, giving it the appearance of a giant pearl suspended above an island set in the corner of the ancient city.

"How do you mean—center of the world?" Mustafa asked.

"Jerusalem is home to three great faiths," Kamil explained. "Each one tracing its roots to the prophet Abraham."

"Yes—yes of course," Mustafa replied.

Haris nudged the sides of Alabaster with his heels, sending the horse in motion. "The Dome of the Rock appears as stunning as they say."

"As it should." Kamil brought a tone of reverence to his voice. "It is the spot where Muhammad ascended into heaven, and is one of Islam's holiest shrines."

They resumed their approach toward Jerusalem, recognizing a number of other smaller domes and church steeples which were scattered around the city, towering above the coalescent arrangement of buildings.

"I must admit, the city is not what I expected," Mustafa announced. "There appear to be huge gaps in sections of the wall that surrounds it, as though the structure is in a state of disrepair. I imagined Jerusalem to be more . . . majestic."

Kamil interpreted Mustafa's opinion to Amos, as the Jew could not understand Turkish. The Jew nodded and quickly replied in Arabic. "Like the average person, the outer appearance is not as important as what it is that cannot be seen. Jerusalem's stone and mortar harbor the soul of mankind."

From the peak of the Mount of Olives, the road descended toward the city, bringing the men outside of a large, rectangular, stone gate set in the eastern wall of Jerusalem. The gateway consisted of two wide, arched doorways with decorated facades set at an angle, making it impossible to enter directly without performing a ninety-degree turn.

Amos sensed the group's curiosity with the gate. "This is the Golden Gate, one of six gates in the city wall. It is the oldest of all gates. They call the southern part of the gate, the Gate of Mercy, and the northern part, the Gate of Repentance. The gate was built angled to slow attackers on horseback from charging through." He bowed his head in the direction of the Gate of Mercy, and recited a prayer in Hebrew, before again addressing the men in Arabic. "The Gate of Mercy once provided direct access to the Jewish temple before it was destroyed by the Romans. Where the temple once stood is now known as the Temple Mount. To the faithful of Islam, it is called al-Haram al-Sharif, for it is the location of the Dome of the Rock and the al-Aqsa mosque—two sites very holy to Muslims. This is also the gate on which it is believed the Jew Jesus passed through, riding on a donkey."

Haris stroked Alabaster's mane. "Indeed, the center of the world. We are at its entrance."

Amos looked up at Haris. "My friend, it is not unusual for young men to wander about Jerusalem with swords sheathed. However, your bow and quiver may bring unwanted attention."

Haris frowned. "Yes—I believe you're correct."

Amos pulled the tallit over his head, approaching Haris. "Place this on." He handed the garment to Haris. "It will conceal your weapon."

Haris nodded and slipped the garment over his head.

After dismounting their horses, and joining Amos on foot, each man followed the old Jew in leading his animal through the gate. Once inside, they immediately came upon a stable, which Amos recommended, as it was owned and operated by a close friend. The men stabled their animals, and helped Amos remove the sacks of olives from the back of his camel. As there were five sacks, each man carried one, and they set out on foot toward the Temple Mount.

In a few minutes, they had come upon a white marble staircase consisting of nearly two dozen steps leading to the hallowed platform. As they began to climb, Mustafa stopped to gaze upon a hole set in the side of the earthen mound supporting the Temple Mount's foundation. Haris noticed Mustafa's preoccupation with the opening, which appeared wide enough to permit a large hound to pass through.

"Is that a drainage pipe?" Mustafa asked.

Amos stopped his climbing and turned toward Mustafa. "It is what remains of an ancient aqueduct no longer in use. Solomon had the aqueducts constructed to bring water from the Hebron Mountains—some distance from Jerusalem." Amos paused to reposition the sack of olives in his arms. "Such aqueducts brought fresh water inside the city to be used to clean the threshing floors of the Temple after animals had been sacrificed."

The men resumed their climb, and upon reaching the top of the stairs, beheld a large stone courtyard whose size Haris guessed was at least thirty acres. Situated directly across from the stairs, they cast their eyes upon the Dome of the Rock, with its vibrant marble and mosaics adorning the octagon base supporting the dome.

"From my Islamic schooling, I know the Prophet ascended into heaven from the large stone that rests inside the structure," Mustafa said. "But why did Muhammad choose this particular stone?"

Haris glanced around at the others, guessing each seemed hesitant to answer the question, fearing they might offend Mustafa's lack of knowledge; for, as possibly the future caliph of the Islamic world, it was information he should know. Haris took a breath and smiled. "Ah—but I'm sure you remember how this is the rock on which it is believed Abraham attempted to sacrifice his son to God."

Mustafa nodded confidently. "Yes . . . of course. I had forgotten."

The men moved on past the holy site, listening to the distant chant of muezzins from their perches atop the minarets, calling the Muslim faithful to prayer. Suddenly their procession merged with scores of Muslims flocking in the direction of a second domed building—this one gray, with its dome centered amid a rectangular design.

"Behold the al-Aqsa Mosque," Amos described. "It is built on the site where a Christian church once stood, dating back to the time of the Byzantine Emperor Justinian."

"The mosque now commemorates where Muhammad experienced the 'night journey'," Kamil explained.

Haris began to notice how passing individuals stared disdainfully at him. "Am I the only one feeling out of place?"

"It is the tallit you wear," Amos said. "There are Muslims who take offense to Jews walking across the Temple Mount." He sighed, lowering his head. "It is no secret to me that the four of you are Muslim. So, I must ask for your forgiveness, for as a Jew I too am treading across this Islamic holy place."

"We are not those Muslims," Haris said.

"Sez—I mean . . . Mustafa," Kamil stammered, catching himself. "Considering we behold one of the holiest places in our faith, would it be your wish to pray inside the mosque?"

Mustafa stared at the mosque's impressive façade, which consisted of over a dozen stone arches. "We are fortunate to have Amos at our disposal at this time, so under his guidance, I believe it would be prudent to become acquainted with the city first. Once we have successfully seen what Jerusalem has to offer, we may thank Allah for our journey, as well as for His blessing, and we will be sure to pray within the mosque upon our departure."

Kamil nodded, before throwing a quick glance in Haris' direction.

"Mustafa, have you given thought to how long we are to stay in the holy city?" Haris asked.

"No more than a few days, unless of course, Allah has other plans," Mustafa replied, turning toward Amos. "Let us move on."

The Jew smiled, and resumed his steps, leading them across the platform to another series of stairs descending the Temple Mount. From there they traversed a narrow thoroughfare which Amos described as the Street of the Chain, gradually ascending in a southwesterly direction. They traveled on the street for only a short distance, before turning southeast in an alleyway, which at its end, brought them into a large plaza. At the far end of the plaza stood an ancient wall towering over sixty feet, with a length almost three times its height. Dozens of men, wearing *yarmulkes*—the dark skull cap gracing the crown of their heads— could be seen standing close to the wall, facing the stone structure while praying aloud.

"It is the Western Wall," Amos announced—excitement filling his voice. "This is the most sacred structure to the Jews. We are standing in the Jewish Quarter. The city is divided into four sections—the Muslim, Jewish, Christian, and Armenian Quarters. The Western Wall is all that remains of the Temple of Solomon."

After gazing at the great wall for a few minutes, Amos led them back down the alleyway and out into street. They followed it in a southwesterly direction away from the Temple Mount, passing homes decorated with carved honeycomb patterns of stonework hanging over the doorways. Soon they came upon a domed synagogue, situated below street level.

"Why is the temple lower than the street?" Mustafa asked.

"This is known as the Great Synagogue," Amos said. "At the time of its construction, Jews and Christians were forbidden from building anything higher than the Muslim structures."

The five men continued to move across the city, meandering through the twisting network of paths intersecting several bazaars along Al-Wad Street, where they stumbled across merchants specializing in yogurt, coffee, cheese, butter, and roasted nuts, as well as cafes selling hummus and kebab. When they laid eyes upon a bell tower, Amos revealed how they had reached the Christian Quarter in the western section of Jerusalem. The large bell tower set attached to a massive stone church with its two main domes supporting Christian crosses.

"Now you are looking upon Jerusalem's most sacred place of worship for Christians," Amos described. "This is the Church of the Holy Sepulcher. It is supposedly built on the site where Jesus was crucified and buried. So, it holds very special significance to the Christian faithful."

The description of the church, along with its connection to Jesus stirred Haris, as it conjured up memories of his birth parents and Christian upbringing as a child. He wondered about his traveling partners—particularly Kamil and Serkan—who, like him, were raised on Christianity before being taken from their homes. *Did they share in his nostalgia? Were they thinking of their youth? Could they feel the spiritual connection between Jerusalem's quarters, despite man's attempt to segregate the city?* Haris realized there was no time to ponder such questions, as Amos led them to the northern side of the church, where they entered another congested bazaar. The busy market, pulsating with throngs of people, was set near to, and running along the inner western wall of the city. Haris concluded that of all the dilapidated sections of wall surrounding Jerusalem, this particular portion seemed the worst. Large breaches in the structure, reduced to mounds of rubble, afforded a clear view of the brown, rolling topography beyond the city.

Finally, Amos brought the four men to a modest shop wedged in between one owned by a butcher, with its hanging display of raw legs of lamb, and one the property of a grocer, which showcased baskets of fruits and vegetables. As the men waited beneath a canopy sheltering the assemblage of baskets of olives, set among ceramic vases of olive oil, they watched as Amos was greeted by an older woman and two younger males. Immediately they overwhelmed him with questions, and Haris noticed how the three appeared relieved by Amos' presence, before tossing suspicious glares.

"They are asking the Jew if we are soldiers," Kamil explained.

Haris glanced down at the kilij sheathed at his side. "Even without uniforms, we must look the part."

With a large smile and a wave of his hand, Amos invited the men to approach the storefront. They complied, and deposited the bags of olives in a corner of the shop. Haris could tell that the old woman wanted to reward them with food, as she moved quickly toward the back of the establishment.

Suddenly, screams filled the market air, and Haris turned to see horses leaping over the stone rubble where the wall lay in ruin. The red and white cloth headgear of the riders identified them as Bedouin and he counted six of them. The bandits waved swords above their heads, while leading their thundering steeds on a reckless rampage of the market place, scattering the terrified populace with the fury of a sudden sandstorm.

Three of the Bedouin rode their horses back and forth through the market, flipping food carts, knocking poles out from underneath tents, trampling individuals who could not escape their marauding charge, and with swinging swords, threatening others who dared risk intervening. The other three Bedouin jumped from their horses, clutching sacks, and began to gather whatever goods they could find. They did not discriminate in their theft, stuffing the bags with as many items as each sack could hold.

Serkan unsheathed his sword. "We need to help these defenseless people!"

Kamil followed Serkan's lead and raised his kilij. "Then we shall!"

The two men rushed out into the chaotic scene unfolding before them.

Haris remained behind, turning toward Amos. "Can I get to the roof?"

Amos nodded, beckoning Haris to follow him to the back of the shop.

Haris turned toward Mustafa. "Follow me!" Both men caught up to Amos, who showed them a stone stairwell rising two flights to the flat rooftop above the street. They hurried up the stairs until finding a position overlooking the melee beneath them.

Mustafa pointed below. "There they are!"

Haris could see Kamil and Serkan—each engaged in a sword fight with two of the bandits—while another Bedouin on horseback galloped toward the dueling men. Haris pulled the tallit over his head, tossing it aside. He fixed an arrow to his bow, aimed, and fired. The arrow struck its target, piercing the man's side, and dropping him from his horse. Quickly, Haris gathered another arrow from the quiver and repeated the act, taking out a second rider. By now, Serkan had seriously wounded the Bedouin with whom he dueled, while Kamil's opponent and the other two Bedouin halted their actions, realizing that they were being ambushed from the rooftop. The two marauders on foot dropped their sacks, mounted their steeds, and all three Bedouin fled the market area through the breach in the wall, vanishing just as suddenly as they had appeared.

Recognizing the threat had diminished, the crowd in the marketplace began to besiege Kamil and Serkan with a display of gratitude, before suddenly being halted by the sound of a gunshot, forcing the bystanders to quickly recede back into their shops. Four men dressed in traditional Arab garb, with white headgear, moved swiftly on foot toward the center of the bazaar—each armed with an arquebus. As Kamil and Serkan tried to flee, the men yelled for them to stop and drop their swords or be shot. Both men did as they were told and when the Arabs caught up to them, they bound their wrists together and led them away.

Haris and Mustafa hurriedly descended the stairs, confronting Amos.

"Who were those men that took our friends?" Haris asked.

"They are the Jarm, an Arab tribe that acts as the police force of Jerusalem," Amos explained.

"Jerusalem is located within the Sanjak of Damascus," Mustafa said. "Where are the Janissaries assigned to here? Who is the sanjak-bey?"

"No Janissaries are assigned here," Amos replied. "The Ottomans recognize Jerusalem as a city of prayer and not one of politics. The emir of the Jarm has been given the responsibility of administering the law."

"The market was attacked by Bedouin!" Mustafa exclaimed. "People were killed! Goods were stolen! Laws were broken! Yet, our friends are taken away as criminals?"

Amos remained silent.

"Where will they be taken?" Haris asked.

"The emir is located in the northeastern section of Jerusalem, within the Muslim Quarter," Amos described. "You will find his location near to Herod's Gate."

Haris removed his quiver, handing it and the bow to Amos. "Keep an eye on these until we return."

Haris and Mustafa set out on foot, returning to the Muslim Quarter, locating a two-story, narrow building. It set across from a stone wall tower, equipped with a small, wicket gate. Here they witnessed a number of Arabs with arquebuses slung over their shoulders, gathered around the outside of the building.

"Well, I think we are in the right place," Mustafa said.

Haris pointed to a small stable across from the gate, where a large camel held its big-lipped snout, dripping with saliva, over a wooden palisade. Haris and Kamil approached the stable, taking up positions on either side of the animal.

"What now?" Mustafa asked.

Haris scanned the area before him. "We wait for opportunity to show itself."

Mustafa huffed.

Haris could sense the sehzade's frustration. "You have pirates to deal with," he blurted.

"What?"

"When Badra and I were in Izmir, we rescued a fisherman's son from being kidnapped by pirates." Haris sighed. "The fisherman said they inhabit Seferihisar."

Mustafa looked confused.

"Yes, I had never heard of it either," Haris said. "If I remember correctly, the fisherman said it is a village located on the southern coast of the Urla Peninsula."

"Why are you telling me this now?"

"It's as good a time as any, and because our current situation reminds me how there are disreputable men in positions of power throughout every corner of the empire." Haris winced at the camel's breath. "Look at us now. Here we stand outside the seat of Jerusalem's government, and something smells corrupt."

"Perhaps it is the camel you smell?"

Haris grinned, nodding toward Mustafa. "The pirates seem to be protected by Barbarossa—a former pirate himself."

"The Kapudan Pasha? He is in charge of the Ottoman navy," Mustafa said. "As a boy, I heard my father speak of him often. His victories across the Mediterranean are truly legendary. But if marauders are preying upon the people of Izmir, he needs to be questioned about this."

"The more pressing question at the moment is how do we get inside that building to free our friends, without being arrested ourselves?" Haris asked.

"Perhaps we should march into the building, and I will declare my true identity as the sehzade."

"Something tells me they won't believe you." Haris petted the camel before it snorted. "And even if they did, without any Janissaries about, whom could we trust? Look at what we have witnessed within the marketplace. Jerusalem is a sacred island in the middle of a sea swimming with its own pirates. I suspect the ransom for an Ottoman sehzade may be very attractive."

Mustafa frowned. "I find it strange and disheartening how my position as sehzade is only evident by the clothing I wear. Beneath this disguise, I am viewed as no better than the Arab who stables his camel."

Haris could see disappointment in Mustafa's face, and longed to find words of encouragement; but he could find none. He knew Mustafa was correct.

"Haris, despite my complaint, I think it is good we have come to Jerusalem dressed this way." Mustafa grinned. "It has opened my eyes to the vulnerability of royalty."

"I would suspect the remedy is found with humility and awareness. I believe you possess both, Sehzade." At that moment the camel spit, bringing laughter to them both, when suddenly Haris noticed a group of uniformed men passing through Herod's gate. "Look! We may be in luck! Their uniforms—they are Janissaries!"

Mustafa gaped. "And the officer leading them carries a ceremonial staff with three feathers!"

"Then he is a pasha, probably the Sanjak-bey of Damascus! Perhaps the cavalry has finally arrived!"

"Yes, and he looks familiar to me!" Mustafa held out is arm, inspecting his own attire. "Perhaps now it is time to cast aside my disguise, and gain freedom for our friends."

"Very wise decision, Sehzade. Let's seek out an audience with the sanjak-bey."

Haris and Mustafa gained entrance to the building by identifying themselves as accomplices of the detained foreigners. After expressing a desire to speak with their imprisoned friends, they quickly found themselves disarmed at gunpoint, before being escorted up a stairwell to a room on the second floor.

Inside the room, Haris and Mustafa were prodded to approach a heavy set Arab, with somber appearance. The rotund man feasted on a handful of dates, while reclining atop several large pillows. He displayed a pudgy, brown face, framed on three sides by his head cloth, and bordered by a thin, scraggly beard that lined his square chin and jaw. He glared condescendingly at Haris and Mustafa, as one of the guards dropped kilijs on the floor beside him.

Without lifting his head, the Arab raised his eyes to Haris and Mustafa. "I am the Emir Al-Ahmed bin Farooq." He spoke deliberately, as though his consumption of the dates took precedence.

"And I suppose you are going to tell me that you've come to Jerusalem on a religious pilgrimage? Where are you from and what is your business here?"

Haris and Mustafa glanced at one another, before Mustafa spoke. "I am the Beylerbey of Manisa, the Sehzade Mustafa!"

Farooq sat back and his eyes widened, before he broke into laughter.

Mustafa continued. "I demand to speak with the Sanjak-bey of Damascus! We followed him inside this building!"

Farooq tossed a date into his mouth. "I must commend you—Mustafa, is it? For you have brought levity to what has already been a very dull day."

Mustafa frowned. "I assure you Emir, by treating us as your prisoners you are making a very grave mistake! I demand that you release us all immediately!"

"You demand?" Farooq scoffed. "On the contrary, the punishment for impersonating a member of the royal family is beheading." He chewed on a date before glaring closely at Haris. "You—with the fair complexion, you appear to be European. And I'm going to assume that his royal highness here is Turkish. It is an odd pairing indeed. Now what would the two of you be doing, traveling together in Jerusalem? You have already caused enough trouble by killing three Bedouin. Maybe you have some nefarious interest in the al-Aqsa Mosque or Dome of the Rock?" He belched before continuing. "Well, we have unpleasant ways of extracting the truth from the likes of men such as you."

Haris and Mustafa glanced at one another with frustration.

Farooq addressed the guards. "Take the imposter and his friend away! Throw them into the cell with the other two! There they may entertain one another with more imaginative stories about sharing royal titles!"

The guards grabbed a hold of Haris and Mustafa, when suddenly the sanjak-bey emerged through a beaded doorway at the far end of the room, accompanied by his Janissaries.

Mustafa stared at the lanky, Ottoman leader with clean shaven face—the exception being a dark, thin mustache that formed a semicircle over his upper lip. "Deli . . . Husrev!" the Sehzade exclaimed. "Deli Husrev Pasha! That is who you are! I remember now!"

The sanjak-bey appeared surprised. "What do we have here?"

"These two are accomplices of the men we have locked up," Farooq explained, rising to his feet. "They murdered the Bedouin this afternoon in the Christian Quarter."

"The Bedouin attacked the marketplace!" Haris exclaimed. "We were aiding the people there!"

Mustafa continued to focus on the sanjak-bey. "Pasha, we met in Constantinople two years before! Actually, you and I first met at Koszeg when you joined the Austrian campaign that year, although we did not speak!"

"This one claims he is the Sehzade Mustafa!" Farooq barked, laughing.

Mustafa sneered at Farooq, before bringing his attention back to Husrev. "Pasha, we met again and spoke in Constantinople in November that year, when my father celebrated his return after the successful campaign!"

"Your father?" Husrev asked.

"Sultan Suleyman!"

"This charade has gone on long enough!" Farooq yelled. "Take them away!"

"Wait!" Husrev looked deeply into Mustafa's eyes. "What did we speak of, when in Constantinople?"

"We spoke of Jerusalem!" Mustafa breathed heavily. "You had just been appointed Sanjak-bey of Damascus! You told me how it was your wish the sultan would provide more resources to the city of Jerusalem!"

Haris could sense how Husrev's curiosity was piqued by Mustafa's claim, but he did not yet appear entirely convinced. Haris reached out and placed his hand on Mustafa's arm. "Sehzade! Tell him of the wedding gift!"

Mustafa thought for a moment. "Yes! We saw the wedding gift you presented to the sultan! It was a piece of the True Cross!"

Husrev gasped and took a step back from Mustafa, bowing his head low. "Your Royal Highness!"

"What?" Farooq questioned. "He speaks the truth?"

"His Royal Highness is who he says he is!" Husrev raised his head in the direction of Farooq. "You stupid baboon! Release all four of these men!"

The guards immediately lifted their hands from Haris and Mustafa, as Farooq dropped to his knees, prostrating himself at Mustafa's feet. "Forgive me, Your Royal Highness! A thousand times I am a fool!"

Mustafa huffed. "Yes, you are a fool! Now rise to your feet and stop your whimpering!"

Farooq clumsily picked himself up off the floor, and stood silently with his head bowed.

"Your Royal Highness, your attire—it is, well . . . it is unbecoming of your lofty status." Husrev bowed again. "May I inquire to what brings you to Jerusalem?"

"It is not important why I am here." Mustafa turned toward Farooq. "We witnessed a Bedouin raid on the city today, and we defended the city! Why, would you arrest us?"

Farooq swallowed hard, still with his head bowed. "Forgive me Your Royal Highness, but my men reported how you were armed, carrying swords and I was told bow and arrows! It is reported how you defended the city with the skill of soldiers—soldiers out of uniform! Such men carrying arms easily stand out in Jerusalem, calling into question their motives for being in the holy city!"

Husrev cleared his throat. "If I may interject, Your Royal Highness, we have information there may be a threat to the al-Haram al-Sharif. This threat has caused suspicions to run high, especially with the Christian observance of the birth of their so-called Messiah and Hanukkah overlapping this year. We find ourselves in the midst of Hanukkah now, and the Christian's sacred day will occur in two days."

"What type of threat?" Mustafa asked.

"Hanukkah is celebrated to commemorate the rededication of the Second Temple in Jerusalem at the time of the Maccabean Revolt." Husrev was interrupted by the appearance of Kamil and Serkan entering the room. He waited for the four men to acknowledge one another with nods before continuing. "The revolt occurred at a period in ancient history before the Roman Empire ruled this region."

"It is a time when the Seleucid Empire ruled Jerusalem," Haris interjected. "Part of the reason for the revolt was because of the Jews refusal to worship Greek gods."

"Yes," Husrev acknowledged. "And then later the Romans would become the new rulers of Jerusalem, and would destroy the Second Temple."

"And what about this threat you speak of?" Mustafa asked, raising his voice.

"As you are aware, Your Royal Highness, Muslims have been the caretakers of Jerusalem for almost one thousand years," Husrev said. "The Dome of the Rock and al-Aqsa Mosque are built on the site where the Jewish temple once stood. There are

Jews who believe that their own messiah shall only appear when the temple is rebuilt."

"And so, to rebuild the temple, would mean the destruction of the mosque," Mustafa concluded.

"Yes, Your Royal Highness," Husrev said.

Mustafa flashed a look of disbelief. "You're saying there is a Jewish plot to destroy the mosque?"

"There are rumors of such a plot," Husrev revealed. "We have reason to believe there may be a Jewish group working from inside Jerusalem, whose goal is to destroy the mosque as a way to bring about the coming of their messiah."

Mustafa scratched the back of his neck with his hand. "What does this have to do with the birth of Jesus?"

Husrev rubbed his palm nervously against the top of his staff. "Our information tells us they are being aided by European Christians—fanatics themselves—who believe the destruction of the mosque, as well as the rebuilding of the temple, will signal the return of their Messiah Jesus, and usher in judgment day."

All eyes were drawn to Mustafa. "How do you know of this?"

"Informants."

"Do you have names?"

Husrev cleared his throat. "One name has surfaced—Stephen."

"Stephen?" Mustafa frowned. "It is a Greek name, I believe."

The room fell silent.

Mustafa paced across the room, pausing to lift his head. "Why have you not asked for assistance from the sultan in this matter?"

"To be honest, Your Royal Highness, such threats against al-Haram al-Sharif are not new, but nevertheless we take each one seriously. We've known about the recent threat for some time now, and that is why I am in Jerusalem today. It would take a great deal of manpower and much luck to bring down the mosque. We've dealt with such threats before, and will continue to deal with them." Husrev produced a smile that turned his thin mustache upward. "No need to bother the busy sultan in such matters."

Mustafa scoffed. "Yet, how many other innocents have fell victim to your suspicions as we nearly did?"

Both Husrev and Farooq said nothing, bowing their heads.

"But what is done, is done," Mustafa said. "I think it is time for us to leave you to continue your work in seeking the source of your threat."

"Your Royal Highness, if I may ask, where is your army to protect you while you visit Jerusalem?" Husrev asked.

Mustafa waved his arm in the direction of Haris, Kamil, and Serkan. "There is my army."

"Three men?"

"Rest assured, my three friends are worth their weight in gold."

"Your Royal Highness," Farooq addressed, raising his head. "May I ask how long you plan to be a guest of our city?"

"So, now I am a guest and not a prisoner?" Mustafa scoffed. "I'm not certain how long."

"Your Royal Highness, I shall be here on location throughout Hanukkah, or until the threat to al-Harem al-Sharif has been alleviated," Husrev explained. "I will be more than honored to extend to the Sehzade the finest lodgings in the city, as well as to provide you with a number of Janissaries, should you need them during the remainder of your stay."

"No. I wish to remain anonymous. I am in good hands." Mustafa nodded toward Haris. "But it is good to know you will be in Jerusalem, should I require your services."

"Of course, Your Royal Highness," Husrev said, before bowing. "And when you are ready to leave, let me offer Your Royal

Highness passage aboard an Ottoman galley that can be ready to set sail from the port of Jaffa, upon your request."

Mustafa nodded.

"Very good," Husrev said, bowing again.

Mustafa sighed. "It is a shame that such a reverent place as Jerusalem need fear such despicable plots."

Husrev lifted his head. "Yes, Your Royal Highness. It would seem to reason demons would fear to tread the streets where angels surely roam."

Mustafa frowned. "But one should never underestimate demons, for they are not easily identified."

CHAPTER

TWENTY-NINE

By the time evening fell over Jerusalem, Mustafa and his entourage had found humble lodgings at an inn within the Christian Quarter located near to Amos' shop. Despite Husrev's pledge to keep their identity secret, they realized it would not be long before word of their presence within the city spread throughout the four quarters. This assumption convinced Mustafa to announce that they would pray at the al-Aqsa Mosque the following day, before leaving Jerusalem the morning after.

At daybreak, the four men rose and dined on a light breakfast, before heading out to say goodbye to Amos. Upon arriving at the tiny establishment, they were greeted by the friendly Jew, standing beneath the canopy outside of his shop. "It gives me great comfort to know that you are all free!" Amos brought the palms of his hands together in a gesture of prayer. "We feared the worst after hearing how all of you were under arrest. How did you manage to gain your freedom so quickly?"

Haris flashed a coy grin in the direction of Mustafa. "We are friends with the sultan's son, Sehzade Mustafa."

Amos' eyes widened. "*Oy ve!* Please tell the sehzade how he must come to visit Jerusalem one day."

Mustafa smiled. "My friend, we are on our way to the al-Aqsa Mosque to pray before we leave Jerusalem."

"Leaving so soon? Well, it just so happens that I am headed in that direction to pray at the Wall. Would it be too much trouble if this old Jew accompanied you?"

Mustafa chuckled. "Of course not."

"Please allow me a moment to grab my yarmulke." Amos looked at Haris. "And you cannot forget your weapon."

"Ah—the bow and arrows," Haris said.

The old man disappeared in the back of his establishment, as Haris stepped away from his friends. He walked out from beneath the canopy into the bustling street to feel the morning sun on his face, and smell the sweet aroma of baked bread. Suddenly, he was approached by two fair skinned men dressed as Arabs, who stopped in front of the shop, and stared in his direction.

One of the men addressed him. "*Parlez-vous Francais?*"

Haris shook his head.

The man tried again. "*Englais?*"

He shook his head once more. "Rumelia," Haris said.

The man studied the curved sheath hanging from Haris' side. "*Qu'il est Ottoman,*" one man said to the other. Quickly they turned away from Haris, stepping back into the busy street.

Haris was joined in the street by his friends. "Those two men who just passed, they are French," he said. "Frenchmen dressed as Arabs. Remember yesterday, how Husrev mentioned he suspected the rumored plot against al-Haram al-Sharif involved Europeans?"

All four men turned their attention to the two strangers moving down the street away from the store. As they watched, one of the men turned his head slightly, looking back at Haris.

"They're moving with purpose now," Kamil said.

Haris nodded. "I think we should follow them, but not too closely."

Just then Amos appeared, donning the skull cap, carrying a

bow and quiver, along with a tallit. He handed the weapon and garment to Haris. "Keep the tallit, my friend."

Haris thanked Amos, slid the bow and quiver over his shoulders, and pulled the tallit over his head, before the five men set out in the direction of the Jewish Quarter. As they walked along the narrow street, Haris caught sight of the two strangers and tried to hurry the group so as not to lose them; however, Amos' sluggish pace, and the shifting throngs of pedestrians, proved as tasking as sailing a sloop against the current.

Haris turned toward Mustafa. "At this pace, we will lose those men. I will take Kamil and move closer to them. We will meet up with you and Serkan at the Wall."

Mustafa nodded, sending Haris and Kamil running ahead to close the gap with the men. The Frenchmen's route led into the Jewish Quarter, where Haris and Kamil continued to follow them within the shadows of the Western Wall.

Still within eyesight, Haris watched the two men pass beyond the Western Wall, proceeding toward a gate cut from Jerusalem's city wall, which was situated east of where the sacred structure ended. At the gate, the Frenchmen met a third, much shorter, stockier man dressed in a hooded brown tunic tied at the waist with a thin rope.

As Haris and Kamil drew closer, the third man's face came into view. "I know that man—the one dressed as a monk!" Haris exclaimed. "The left side of his face is scarred from his eye to his lower lip! He was the sapper Parshan and I followed in our retreat from Vienna!" They watched as the three men passed through the gate. "Come! Let's climb the steps to the rampart! We will be able to see where they're headed from atop the wall!"

Haris and Kamil hurried toward a stone stairway set to the side of the gate that ascended to the rampart, offering a bird's eye view of the surrounding area. The vantage point fired Haris' imagination with images of armor-clad Crusaders positioned on the wall in defense of Jerusalem, cringing at the site of Saladin's advancing army, as it prepared to lay siege to the city.

From their perch, Haris and Kamil scanned the throngs of people mingling below and outside the city wall, until Kamil recognized the three men, who were now leading a donkey pulling a cart. "There they are! They're moving in the direction of those hills across from the gate!"

"There is something in the back of the cart, but it is covered with cloth!" Haris said.

They watched the men pull the donkey in a direction away from the city wall halfway up the hill, where they stopped, and disappeared behind a large pile of stones.

"We must climb that hill," Haris said.

"Yes, but first we need to locate Mustafa and Serkan."

From the rampart, Haris and Kamil performed an about face, searching the area of faithful pedestrians below who gathered in front of the Western Wall, watching the crowd move fitfully like a cast of crabs along a beach. Suddenly, Haris spotted their three friends standing steadfast, perusing the crowd. Quickly, they descended the stairs, moving in the direction of the men, before Mustafa recognized them.

"The Europeans—where did they go?" Mustafa asked.

"Through the city gate," Haris replied.

"That is the Dung Gate," Amos described. "In the days of the Temple, thousands of animals were sacrificed during religious ceremonies. The animal waste was removed through the Dung Gate and deposited in the Kidron Valley across the way. The hillside is known as the City of David because it is believed King David is buried there."

"There appears to be the foundation of an old building on the hillside," Kamil said. "It is only ruins now."

Amos wiped perspiration from his brow. "It is the remains of a Christian church destroyed by the Crusaders. They destroyed it so it would not fall into the hands of Saladin. The hillside is a popular burial site, especially for Jerusalem's Christians, for Christianity's first martyr is thought to be buried there."

"Who would that be?" Mustafa asked.

"Sadly, he was killed by Jews shortly after Jesus' death. He was called Stephen."

Haris and Mustafa exchanged a look of astonishment at the mention of the name.

Amos noted their surprised faces. "Stephen is considered a saint by the Christians. His feast day is celebrated December twenty-six."

"The day after tomorrow!" Haris exclaimed. "Stephen is the name Husrev said is thought to be connected with the plot!"

"Plot?" Amos asked.

The four men realized how they had reached a juncture where discussing any more information within Amos' earshot, risked his safety. With heartfelt praise, they thanked him and decided to bid farewell, leaving him with his prayers at the Wall.

After exiting the Dung Gate, they followed a narrow path winding up the hillside across from Jerusalem. As they traveled, they passed near to a rectangular area of stone rubble revealing a flat stone floor segmented into large squares, with weeds growing up in between the sections. Crude wooden crosses were implanted sporadically in an area of the hillside to the far end of the floor, convincing Haris and the others they had stumbled upon the excavation site of the church that once marked the location of Stephen's tomb.

The four men stopped their advance at the excavation site, where they could see the stranger's donkey and cart setting near another large pile of stone rubble, about two hundred rods ahead.

Serkan glanced about. "Look around. As Amos told us, there are other burial sites here. Perhaps those men are doing nothing more than burying someone."

"If they're not, and are engaged in something illegal, then they are going to become very nervous should they see us approach," Kamil said.

"Maybe we would be wise to leave well enough alone," Serkan guessed. "They may be only smugglers hiding their goods on the hill. It is for the emir to worry about, and not us."

Haris wiped his sleeve against his brow. "But if they are not smugglers, and they succeed in destroying the mosque, Jerusalem will see religious warfare that will make the Crusades seem like a lover's spat."

"How could they possibly threaten the mosque from here?" Serkan turned and faced Jerusalem. "Look how far we are from the city walls."

The debate fell silent as all eyes turned toward Mustafa. "I could never forgive myself knowing I had the opportunity to prevent a great tragedy, as would be the destruction of one of Islam's holiest sites. 'There is nothing but God'." Mustafa looked directly at Haris. "It is in our interest, and in the interest of Jerusalem that we investigate the activity of those men."

"Your wish is our command, Sehzade," Kamil announced. "How do you suggest we move upon them without being noticed?"

"We bury our dead friend," Haris interjected.

"Dead friend?" Serkan asked.

"The Frenchman has already seen my face," Haris replied.

"So, my identity must remain hidden. You will cart my body up the hill to bury me. It will allow us to get close enough to these men, so that if we must engage them, they will not panic before we strike."

"Allah challenges us this day," Kamil uttered.

* * *

After renting a donkey and cart, Mustafa, Kamil, and Serkan, found themselves retracing their footsteps. Kamil guided the donkey by its lead line, while Serkan and Mustafa, paced along either side of the animal. Inside the back of the cart, Haris lay on his back, covered with a large cloth.

As they drew near to the location of the mysterious activity, Kamil could see one man standing beside a cart, carefully watching their approach with a suspicious glare. "Sehzade, what are we to say to him when we stop the cart?"

"I will ask if we may borrow an extra shovel."

"What if he speaks only French?"

"I speak French. My father is obsessed with French customs at court."

Kamil smiled. "During my schooling as a young Janissary, I remember reading *Chanson de Roland*, although it had been translated into Turkish."

"Yes—the story involving the great Frankish king, Charlemagne. His feats of bravery have echoed throughout the ages."

"Sehzade, I must tell you how much I admire your bravery."

"Actually Kamil, between you and me, I am frightened to death."

A few minutes later, they arrived at the site, bringing the donkey and the cart to a stop, which provoked the lone man to yell out to them in French.

Mustafa took a breath and looked at Kamil, before addressing the man in his native tongue. "My good man, we are burying our friend further on up the hill, and we could make use of another shovel. Would you have an extra one we may borrow?"

The man turned to glance into the entrance of the burial cave, before spinning back toward Mustafa. "I'm sorry to hear about your friend's death." He began a slow approach toward the cart. "May I ask how he died?"

"His heart suddenly stopped beating. I believe the journey proved too much for him," Mustafa replied.

The man leaned over the side of the cart to inspect the bulging contour of the cloth covering Haris to his ankles. "He must have been a very important man."

Mustafa remained silent for a moment before uttering, "Only a simple man."

The man turned toward Mustafa with an odious glare. "Because it is uncommon to bury a dead man while he still wears his boots!" he exclaimed, quickly unsheathing his sword.

The Frenchman swung his blade at Mustafa, who had removed his kilij just in time to block the strike. Undeterred, the Frenchmen continued to slash his blade violently, while Mustafa matched his strokes with retreating steps until falling backward after tripping over a large stone.

Haris, hearing the commotion, threw off the cloth, and leapt from the cart, landing onto the back of the Frenchman. His attack forced both men to crash hard to the ground. Haris released his grip on the man and rolled away, as the Frenchman struggled to his feet and raised his sword. Suddenly, Serkan appeared from around the side of the cart, and plunged his kilij into the man's back. The Frenchman gasped, as his body stiffened, before falling to the ground.

Before Haris could pull himself off the ground, he heard the clashing of steel and looked to see Kamil engaged in a sword duel with another man, who had appeared suddenly from out of the entrance of the burial cave. Both men dueled with aggressive strikes matched by counter strikes that Haris found resembled the meticulous choreographed movements of a ballet.

Haris, Serkan, and Mustafa drew closer as the two men feverishly sliced away at one another; but as Kamil fell back from an aggressive lunge by his opponent, the two men suddenly found themselves face to face, pressing against one another with swords locked. Mustafa seized the moment to charge and stab Kamil's opponent from behind. The assailant dropped his sword, falling forward to the ground.

Breathing heavily, Kamil nodded at Mustafa. "Thank you Sehzade, but I could have finished him!"

"I believe you!" Mustafa said, before lowering his gaze to the corpse. "So, that is how it feels to kill a man!"

"And what is it that you feel, Sehzade?" Kamil asked.

"I feel hollowness!"

Haris stepped up from behind. "Then don't ever forget that feeling." He reached down and retrieved the dead man's two-edged sword, examining it closely. "We were correct about the identity of these men. This is a European sword."

Serkan explored the Frenchmen's cart. "It is empty!"

Haris moved toward the opening of the burial cave. "Well, obviously these men believed they were protecting something important enough for which to risk their lives!"

Kamil reached out and grabbed Haris' arm. "Remember the sapper! He's probably inside!"

"Shall we see?" With his outstretched kilij leading the way, Haris stooped to clear the top of the cavern, warily passing through the opening, followed by his three companions.

Haris found the cave absent of anyone, and took notice how it was not very deep, but littered with more piles of stones, along with four rectangular limestone boxes. "Ossuaries." He slid open the lid to one of the boxes and reviewed its contents. "Bones of the dead."

Kamil noticed a hole in the northern side of the cave near the floor. "It looks to be manmade, and the cave floor has markings leading to the ossuaries, as though the boxes had been dragged across the floor."

"They may have been using the ossuaries to conceal the hole," Serkan said.

Haris returned the kilij to its sheath. "I'm guessing we will find a tunnel beyond this opening, and along with it, the sapper. Let's leave the cave and hide the bodies in the back of one of the carts." He turned toward Mustafa. "Sehzade, I suggest you remain with the carts to keep an eye out for any other unsavory characters who may wander this way. Kamil, Serkan, and I will explore what lies beyond the hole."

"Haris, those men were French," Kamil said. "If a tunnel does exist beyond the hole, then there may be more Frenchmen. The Sehzade is the only one of us who speaks their language."

Mustafa looked at Haris. "Kamil is right. I will go with you."

"Then Serkan, you will stand guard outside the cave," Haris decided.

Outside of the cave, the four men lifted the bodies of the two Frenchmen into the cart, covering them with the cloth, while Haris removed his tallit and grabbed his bow and quiver.

Haris, Mustafa, and Serkan returned inside the cave and approached the hole. After slinging the bow and quiver over his shoulders, Haris dropped down and began crawling through the opening, followed by Mustafa and Kamil. They crawled for about six feet until the hole opened into a wider tunnel permitting each man to stand.

Haris noticed the tunnel sloped away from the hole, and was partially illuminated by a flickering light hanging from the wall, located some distance down the passageway. "It looks as though they have been digging here for some time." His attention was drawn to a bulky object setting in the shadows only a few feet from them. "A barrel! This is what they were hauling in the cart!" He approached the wooden object, examining its staves bound together by iron hoops, and carefully pulled open the plug of its bung hole. A black powder began to pour from the opening. "Gunpowder!" Haris quickly replaced the plug. "They're assembling explosives!"

"But the tunnel looks to be a straight passageway running due north," Kamil said. "Jerusalem lies to the west of this hill. What could be their target?"

"Let's find out," Haris said.

Kamil shook his head. "Allah challenges us this day!"

Vigilantly, the three men proceeded down the tunnel, passing the burning torch affixed to the stone wall, traveling for what Haris estimated was about one hundred feet, before seeing a large pile of stone set on one side of the cavern. Just beyond the stone appeared another opening. Haris moved slowly toward the large cavity and cautiously leaned his head through the opening, finding another narrow tunnel running in an east and west direction with a higher ceiling. He stepped into the passageway with Kamil and Mustafa close behind.

Haris placed his hand against the wall, feeling the smooth, cold stone. "Cut from solid rock." He looked down at his feet where a rill of water moved along a slender channel in a westerly direction. "This is an ancient aqueduct."

"Could this be Solomon's aqueduct?" Mustafa asked.

Kamil gaped. "Whoever it is we follow has found Solomon's aqueduct, which runs beneath Jerusalem—probably as far as the temple threshing floor."

"Which is now the location of the al-Haram al-Sharif!" Mustafa exclaimed, before taking a few steps. "Look!" He pointed to an object setting in the aqueduct's channel. "It's a wheelbarrow! What do you think those men are planning?"

Haris sighed. "My guess is that they're moving barrels of gunpowder to the end of the aqueduct, beneath the mosque."

"They're going to blow it up!" Mustafa realized.

Haris stepped up to the wheelbarrow, finding a few stones inside. With a concerned look, he tossed the stones away and turned toward Mustafa. "Sehzade, perhaps we should return to Jerusalem and seek the aid of Husrev and his Janissaries."

"Haris, should those at the end of this tunnel discover their friends have mysteriously vanished from the cave's entrance, they may decide to ignite the fuse today! I believe we need to act now! Allah has chosen us for this moment! This is why we are here—I'm sure of it!"

"You may be correct. But I'm afraid we are leading you into a dangerous situation. Maybe you should go back and stay with Serkan."

"You forget how I found myself in just as much danger at Berndorf!"

Haris sighed. "You were surrounded by a greater army at Berndorf. We have no idea how many of the enemy lie ahead."

"Then it is better to have three rather than two!" Mustafa held out his fist. "I remember what you told me at Berndorf—to be strong, for we are in this together!"

Haris grinned, placing his fist on top of Mustafa's. "Together!"

Haris grabbed the handles of the wheel barrow, and the three men began moving quietly through the dank, stale tunnel that was dimly lit by torchlight at intervals along the way. Haris guessed they had traveled for over thirty minutes before they could distinguish the silhouettes of two figures in the distance, moving toward them. He stopped and set the wheelbarrow down. "Sehzade, move behind me," Haris said. "Kamil, grab the handles and when I say go, begin wheeling the cart!" Haris slid his bow from his shoulder and retrieved an arrow from the quiver. "Go!"

Haris took up position behind Kamil, fixing the arrow to his bow. Suddenly, one of the two men in the distance began yelling in French.

"He is asking us where we have been," Mustafa translated.

"Tell them we were delayed, but all is secure," Haris said.

The two groups of men continued to move closer to one another as Mustafa relayed the message.

Haris raised the bow and arrow, pointing it in the direction of the approaching men. He leaned into Kamil. "Stop the wheelbarrow! Drop to your knees!"

Kamil did as he was told, and Haris launched an arrow that whistled through the tunnel before striking one of the men in the chest. As the man fell backward, his partner turned to run, just as a second arrow pierced his back, dropping him face down into the channel.

The tunnel fell silent as Haris, Mustafa, and Kamil resumed their pace toward the bodies. Upon reaching them, Haris recognized how one man was dressed in Arab garb, while the other was bearded and wearing a tallit. "One was French—the other a Jew!"

They continued on past the slain men, walking for another twenty minutes, before halting at the sight of a stone wall rising waist high and stretching the tunnel's width.

Mustafa turned toward Haris with a confused expression. "They're building a wall?"

Haris nodded. "Yes. That's why there was a pile of stone in the opening leading to the aqueduct. They're not only using the wheel barrow to haul in black powder, but they're bringing in stone to build a wall. It is a method Ottoman sappers use when preparing a tunnel with explosives. They can safely light the fuse from behind this wall, and protect themselves from the blast." Haris looked beyond the wall to see a much wider section of the tunnel filled with a number of barrels stacked on top of one another, positioned some fifty rods away. "Look! There must be two dozen barrels!"

Suddenly, a number of figures ambling near the barrels came into view. "And about a half dozen men!" Kamil remarked.

Haris looked at Mustafa. "Well, there are three of us. I would say the odds are in our favor!" Haris unsheathed his kilij, which spurred Kamil and Mustafa to do the same.

Mustafa nodded. "How many can you take out with your arrows?"

"I could take out all of them, if I had enough arrows!" Haris slipped the bow over his shoulder. "But I've only one remaining!"

"May God have mercy on us!" Kamil exclaimed, before the three men stepped over the wall.

At first, the brisk movements of the three men went undetected, but when they had closed within fifteen rods, their presence was discovered, causing a flurry of excitement among the group. One bearded man clad in a tallit tried to skirt the attackers by planting himself along the wall, but was quickly struck down by a blow from Kamil's kilij. Suddenly, swords were drawn, and the men engaged one another fiercely, filling the previous silence of the tunnel with sounds of clashing steel.

Both Kamil and Mustafa found themselves dueling separate combatants, while alone Haris confronted two armed men, studying both opponents as if their faces could reveal their next move. The taller of the two wore a thin mustache parted at the divot in the center above the lip, while another man draped with a tallit, had the lower half of his face hidden beneath a bushy beard.

Within the gaze of the bearded one, Haris could sense hesitation and fear in his wide-eyed stare, while his taller opponent remained expressionless, bespeaking of a resolute, disciplined warrior. Haris felt convinced the taller man would provide the greatest challenge, and then with a squint, the mustache lifted, and clenched teeth shone, before the blade of the opponent's sword graced Haris' garment. This was followed instantly by another slash of the sword, which Haris defended, before the bearded man entered the fray, attempting to deliver a blow from his own blade.

Haris moved back and forth, countering the dual strikes, which came successively and sometimes simultaneously. With the bearded man attacking from the side, Haris decided to allow his left to be exposed, and began slashing away at the taller man on his right, when suddenly the bearded man overextended his reach, lunging and stabbing his sword at Haris. From out of the corner of his eye, Haris reacted to the move, springing backward to avoid the stab. He grabbed the man's tallit, and pulled the bearded man in front of him, just as the taller attacker delivered a blow, unintentionally spearing his fellow conspirator's stomach. Haris wasted no time in thrusting his kilij downward, slicing off the taller attacker's arm at the elbow. The wounded man stood steadfast, in shock from the loss of blood, as Haris tossed the bearded man's lifeless body aside, before running his blade through the taller man's chest.

Haris breathed heavily, and from across the tunnel could see his friends battling their opponents, when suddenly he spotted the sapper running from the fray toward the stone wall. He withdrew the lone arrow from his quiver and fixed it to his bow. As he pulled on the bowstring—aiming the arrow in the direction of the fleeing sapper—a flash caught his eye and he could see a burning flame moving quickly along the floor near to the tunnel's opposite wall in the direction of the barrels. "The match cord!"

Haris reasoned he was positioned too far from the burning fuse to snuff it out in time. Adding to his dread, he noticed that although his friends were located closer to the fuse, they were both preoccupied dueling with combatants.

Kamil's skill with the blade began to weigh down on his opponent, affording him an opportunity to deliver a death blow to his opponent's midsection. After freeing his blade from his victim's stomach, he turned to witness Mustafa's sword being knocked from his hand. "Charlemagne!" Kamil called out. Mustafa's foe swung his attention to Kamil, who began rushing toward the swordsman. The sehzade seized the moment to charge the unsuspecting warrior, burrowing his head into the man's stomach, and knocking him backward to the ground. Mustafa slowly opened his eyes, lifting his head from the man's midsection just in time to see Kamil withdraw the bloodied tip of his kilij from the man's chest.

Haris directed his arrow toward the flame, which burned less than a foot from the barrels. "Don't move!"

Kamil looked up to see Haris aiming an arrow in his direction, and spun to see the match cord's racing flame. Haris released his grip on the arrow, and the projectile flew across the channel, striking and severing the match cord inches from the barrel, extinguishing the flame. Kamil stood there with mouth gaped, staring at the singed cord.

Haris lowered his bow. "The sapper!" He peered down the tunnel to see a shadow scale the sapper's wall. "He's getting away!"

Mustafa retrieved his sword and gave chase.

Haris began to set his legs in motion when he looked over again at Kamil, who was bent over clutching his left arm. "Kamil!"

Kamil took a deep breath and revealed his hand covered in blood, forcing Haris to move toward his friend.

"It is only a flesh wound!" Kamil said.

Haris cut a piece of cloth from his garment and wrapped it tightly above the wound. "That should stop the bleeding! Come let's see what type of trouble Mustafa has gotten himself into!"

Haris grabbed a torch, and he and Kamil set off running through the aqueduct, calling for Mustafa. After some time had passed, they heard the sehzade yelling back in the darkness, and soon came upon his silhouette standing in the center of the tunnel. Moving closer, they could see Mustafa pointing the tip of his kilij at the sapper seated in the channel, near to the corpses of the two men Haris had slain with arrows.

Mustafa released a heavy sigh. "He fell over the bodies!"

Haris grinned. "Sehzade, should you not get yourself killed, I think you will make a fine sultan one day!"

CHAPTER THIRTY

December 26, 1535

After praying inside the al-Aqsa Mosque, the four Ottomans gathered their horses and departed Jerusalem for the Kidron Valley where they retrieved their arquebuses from beneath the towering sycamore. From there they travelled northwest to Jaffa, arriving late in the evening and procuring rooms at an inn. At daybreak, the four travelers boarded an Ottoman galley, compliments of Sanjak-bey Husrev, and began the journey home by sea.

* * *

When at last the coastline had vanished, Mustafa found Haris staring outward at the Mediterranean's dark blue horizon. "Do you miss her?"

Haris turned his head and smiled. "Yes—yes I do. I have thought about Badra much in recent days, especially while watching the fuse burn down in the aqueduct. I feared I might never see her again."

"I have come to the conclusion that staring death in the eyes is a sobering experience."

"I've stared down death before, but it didn't seem to make me feel as I do today." Haris glanced back out at the sea. "I imagine knowing someone else's heart beats for me accounts for this burden of guilt I feel, as it comes from placing myself in harm's way." He spun toward Mustafa. "Sezhade! Your child! Fatma was due to give birth this month!"

"My thoughts have been with her and my child for some time now. I pray to Allah both are safe."

"Did you select names before you left Manisa?"

Mustafa smiled. "Orhan if the child is a boy, Nergissah if a girl."

"Then our return home should have extra meaning for both of us." Haris shook his head. "How close we both came in the aqueduct to spoiling such an anticipated homecoming."

Mustafa rested his hand on Haris' shoulder. "Thanks to Husrev's kind offer to provide us passage aboard this galley, soon we shall be back in Manisa having lived to tell of our adventure."

"It is the least he could have done for the role we played in saving Jerusalem from disaster. You do realize today is Saint Stephen's Day?"

"Yes—the day the plot was to be hatched." Mustafa took in a breath of the salty sea air. "It did not take long for the sapper to reveal all. Remind me again of the plot's details?"

"The plot had its origins with a Jewish group from Safed, a town near the Sea of Galilee. These men believed that a messianic age was upon them. They made contact with a number of radical Europeans—most of them Frenchmen—who carried their own messianic yearning for the second coming of Christ. After locating the ancient aqueduct, the plan to blow up the mosque took hold. The sapper was whom I thought he was—a former Janissary who deserted after the siege of Vienna, and apparently had wandered about Eastern Europe for some time, until setting a course for Jerusalem. Fleas have a way of finding the rat, and the two sides joined forces. The sapper provided the skills of tunneling the group needed to carry out their plan."

"And we brought an abrupt ending to their nightmarish fantasy."

"Fortunately."

"Your marksmanship with the bow is unlike any other I have ever witnessed."

Haris grinned. "It is what brought the two of us together."

Suddenly, one of the crew members could be heard yelling, "Vessel off the starboard side!" Haris and Mustafa quickly moved to the opposite side of the vessel where they viewed a single mast sailboat, drifting aimlessly. An order was given to raise the oars and shorten the sails of the galley, just before the captain appeared alongside Mustafa at the railing. Dressed in a white turban and a long, golden kaftan, the tall, bearded commander gazed doggedly at the sailboat.

"What do you make of it, Captain?" Mustafa asked.

"It is a sloop adrift, Your Royal Highness," he said. "There appear to be three men lying on deck with no sign of movement. I've ordered a row boat lowered to inspect the vessel should any-one on board need assistance."

Mustafa and Haris watched as a row boat containing six sail-ors came into view just beneath the galley, setting a course for the mysterious drifting vessel. Within a quarter of an hour, the boat had reached the sloop, pulling up along its starboard side. The Ottoman crew used hooks and ropes to moor itself against the vessel, before wooden planks were set up to permit four of the sailors to cross over. After another quarter of an hour, the sloop's sail was shortened, while another rope was tied to its bow from the row boat. Three of the sailors returned to the row boat, and the small Ottoman craft began towing the sloop back in the direction of the galley.

When the two vessels came within a few rods of the galley, a crew member standing in the row boat addressed the captain. "Three crew members aboard, Captain!" he yelled. "Two are dead!

The surviving member lays in his vomit, and his skin is cold with blueish spots covering his body! It looks to be the cholera!"

The captain frowned. "Throw the dead overboard and bring the survivor aboard the galley! Set the sloop adrift!"

Shortly after, the crew of the row boat completed the captain's orders and when the survivor had been brought aboard, Haris and Mustafa took an interest in the captain's attempt to question him. They noticed how the sickened man with sunken eyes lay on the deck, barely conscious, his skin weathered by the sun and tightened by disease. After taking a few sips of water from a wooden ladle, the man coughed violently and his bloodshot eyes opened. With a strained voice, barely above a whisper, he began to utter incomprehensible jargon before someone recognized the foreign language. "Does anyone speak French?" the captain asked.

Mustafa rolled his eyes at Haris. "The damn French, they seem to be everywhere, like a bevy of pesky insects!" He yelled, "Yes, I speak it!"

The captain stepped aside, allowing Mustafa access to the sickened seafarer. He dropped down on one knee to bring himself closer to the man's lips and the two men shared a brief conversation. Haris watched as the discourse paused for a moment, while the man stared pensively at Mustafa, before slipping his unsteady hand inside his vest. Slowly the man withdrew an alabaster box, smaller than a man's palm, and passed the container to Mustafa, before closing his eyelids and falling silent.

Mustafa rose, stepping away from the crowd that had gathered around the dying man. He moved some distance from the group, before stopping and lifting the lid on the small box.

Suddenly, the captain stepped up from behind. "Your Royal Highness, may I ask what he gave you?"

Mustafa closed the lid of the box, turned and looked the captain in the eyes. "Only a final request from a dying man."

Haris could see how the captain waited for the sehzade to reveal more information, but Mustafa said nothing and only continued to stare. Finally, the captain bowed and turned away, as Mustafa strolled nonchalantly toward the stern of the vessel.

Haris approached his friend. "Something of value?"

Mustafa looked about to make sure they remained some distance from the crew, before holding the box up for Haris to view. Inside was a small glass vessel—only inches in length with a rounded base and thin neck—trapping an amber liquid which filled the bottle. The vessel featured a petrified clay seal, while a pea-sized, shriveled, leathery object could be seen suspended inside.

Haris peered at the bottle. "The liquid looks like oil, perhaps spikenard. There is something floating in it. What did the sailor say it was?"

Mustafa's eyes widened. "He said the object was the Holy Prepuce," he whispered. "Haris, it is the holy foreskin of the infant Jesus!"

Haris gawked. "Incredible! It is a fascinating claim! Surely you don't believe the lunatic ramblings of a dying man?"

"With religious relics, can any claimer be believed? How can such things be proven?" Mustafa grabbed hold of Haris' arm. "If it is true, just as my father's collection is seen as symbolic of his revered status as caliph, the fact this sacred object has found me could be a sign of my destiny!" He closed the lid to the box and squeezed it tightly in his hand. "What do you think?"

Haris cupped his bearded chin. "I think there are Christians who constantly feel the need to seek such reassurance of their faith . . . or maybe, it's just the French."

"Remember, you were once Christian."

"Yes." Haris frowned. "Then, what you hold within your hand is either a blessing or a curse. Let us hope it is not the latter."

CHAPTER THIRTY-ONE

Manisa - late February, 1536

Beneath the pavilion's central dome, Haris and Badra cuddled together within the shadow of the marble colonnade, when he noticed how her amorous demeanor gave way to an amusing look. "I'm so thankful you have shaved that hideous beard from your face," she said.

He chuckled. "This is the third time you have told me since my return."

"And I shall continue to remind you."

Haris caressed the fine silk of her canary yellow robe. "You look like a beautiful bird."

Badra laughed. "Are you saying my face protrudes like a beak?"

"Of course not." Haris smiled. "Only how the color of your robe reminds me of a bird. In my eyes, no creature on earth can compare to your beauty."

He could see her eyes light up like sparkling gems. "Those are the words which move me," Badra said. "How I've missed them so." She leaned into him, provoking a passionate kiss, before sighing as their lips parted. With her eyes still glued to his, she sat upright with a smirk. "It is the same robe I wore the night the Sehzade propositioned me."

Haris sneered. "Is that so?"

Her smirk transformed into a large grin. "Yes. In fact, he placed the scarf on my shoulder—right here, beneath this very pavilion."

Haris glanced around the pavilion. "Hmm . . . I have no scarf, but this is a fitting location to ask for your hand in marriage, my love."

Badra gaped, bringing her palm to her mouth. "You are proposing?"

"I think that is what it is called." Haris smiled as he took her hand. "Will you marry me?"

Tears welled up in Badra's eyes. "Of course, I will!" The two lovers embraced tightly for a few moments, before she pulled herself from his grasp. "When shall we marry?"

Haris shrugged his shoulders. "I was thinking May." He could see how Badra's excitement faded to a fretful glare. "What is it?"

"No, not May! May is unlucky, and not on a Saturday—also very unlucky!"

Haris laughed. "Then we shall marry in June, and not on a Saturday."

Badra relaxed as she melted into his arms. "I prayed for your safe return from Jerusalem, knowing that someday soon you would make me very happy!"

Suddenly, their tender moment was interrupted by a chamberlain who appeared from behind a colonnade. He stepped forward gingerly, bowing his head before addressing Haris. "My apologies, Vizier Haris, but the sehzade wishes for you to know that a messenger from Constantinople has arrived."

Badra sighed.

Haris smiled before kissing her. "I am needed, my love. We shall continue to plan later."

* * *

Haris entered the Audience Chamber to find Mustafa at the far end of the room, seated on the throne. Standing beside him was Mahidevran, while positioned before them stood the messenger—a uniformed Janissary. Haris quickened his pace and stepped up beside the Janissary, bowing before Mustafa. "Your Royal Highness," he said, before repeating the bow in the direction of Mahidevran. "Kadin."

Mustafa nodded toward Haris, before addressing the Janissary. "It was only last week I returned from my visit with the sultan in Constantinople. There, I was briefed on recent news from across the empire. This leaves me surprised by your sudden visit."

The Janissary bowed. "Your Royal Highness, the reason for my visit is to inform you there has been a fire in the Eski Saray."

Mustafa's posture stiffened. "Was anyone harmed inside the palace?"

"No, Your Royal Highness. However, there was considerable damage to the harem. It has forced Hurrem Sultan to relocate to the Yeni Saray."

Mahidevran scoffed. "How terribly convenient."

"Mother!" Mustafa glanced at her with scolding eyes.

"Well, everyone knows how the witch has been trying to convince the sultan to have her move in with him!" Mahidevran exclaimed. "I find it all deviously suspicious!"

The messenger bowed his head.

"Mother, show some respect, please!"

Mahidevran huffed.

"Is there anything else?" Mustafa asked of the messenger.

"No, Your Royal Highness. The sultan wished for you to hear the truth about recent events in Constantinople, before unfounded rumors surfaced."

"Very well. Please thank the sultan for me." Mustafa threw a coy glance in the direction of Mahidevran. "And please convey to the sultan *our* relief that Hurrem Sultan is unharmed. Praise, be to Allah."

The Janissary bowed.

"Messenger, beyond the Audience Chamber's door, you will find a chamberlain who will show you to your lodgings for this evening," Mustafa explained.

The Janissary bowed again and turned away, moving toward the door. The room remained quiet until the messenger had slipped through the doorway.

Mustafa rose from the chair and wasted little time in addressing Mahidevran. "Mother! No matter what ill feelings you may hold toward the sultan and his wife, it is important for you to remain composed when in my presence! Your temperamental outbursts in such situations are seen as a reflection of me!"

Mahidevran said nothing, only bowing and spinning away. As she left the room, Mustafa dropped back down into the throne. "Do you think the fire suspicious, Haris?"

"It does not matter what either of us may think, Sehzade."

Mustafa nodded. "Of course not."

"Sehzade, if I may ask, when you were in Constantinople, how did your father react to your gift of the Holy Prepuce?"

Mustafa took a deep breath and leaned back, folding his hands across his stomach. "I decided not to give it to him."

Haris was surprised.

"After I told him of our Jerusalem adventure, at first he berated me—calling it a reckless, juvenile decision," Mustafa said. "But then as suddenly as a hungry, crying infant who is quickly brought to his mother's breast, the sultan grew calm, desiring to know more about the condition of Jerusalem. I told him about its crumbling walls, and how we foiled the plot to bring damage to the al-Haram al-Sharif. He then began to question me about the mood of the city's inhabitants. It was as though, on one hand as a father he felt the need to reprimand his son, yet on the other, as a sultan he desired to acquire knowledge of the city from a loyal subject." He frowned. "The experience left me confused to which role I play in his eyes. As a subject loyal to the sultan, I wanted to present the gift to him . . . but as a son, my disappointment in my father, would not allow it."

Haris said nothing.

Mustafa's face wrinkled. "You have no opinion on the subject?"

"I—I think I would have reacted as you did," Haris stammered.

"Haris, you seem preoccupied."

"I'm sorry, Sehzade. Only moments before I was summoned, I had asked Badra for her hand in marriage."

Mustafa smiled as he rose from the throne. "I am elated for you, my friend! But I must tell you how this will place me in a difficult position with Fatma. First my father weds, and now you—she will be jealous." He laughed. "May Allah bless you both."

Constantinople - March 14th, 1536

With the shutters opened, from his bedroom chamber window Suleyman could feel the cool breeze rush through him, while viewing white-capped swells on the Bosporus. Clad in a royal kaftan and robe, his chamberlains had just finished dressing him and exited the chamber, when across the room the door swung open. Suleyman turned slowly to find Hurrem entering, dressed as though she were gift wrapped in a high collared, long, black robe accentuating her red locks.

As a Janissary guard pulled shut the door behind her, Hurrem gracefully crossed the room to greet the sultan with a tight embrace, followed by a soft kiss. "Good morning, Muhibbi."

"Good morning, my sweetheart. I trust you slept well."

Hurrem gently fell back from his grasp and gazed into his eyes. "Yes, for it appears I can only find peace when near to you."

Suleyman smiled. "Your new accommodations, they are comfortable?"

"I could be sleeping in a stable of this palace, and I would not complain of my accommodations, for I am here, near to my love." Hurrem reached down and took hold of Suleyman's hands. "Knowing my chamber is only at the end of the hall from your room—when at one time it was located on the other side of Constantinople—makes me feel as a pearl in your jewel box."

Suleyman pulled her into a firm embrace, which evolved into a long, soft kiss, before he released her and moved back toward the window.

Hurrem stepped toward him, wrapping her arms around his waist from behind, and leaning her head against his back. "What is it, my love? You seem . . . tired, this morning."

Suleyman continued to stare out at the ships in the harbor. "I've had the dream again."

Hurrem lifted her head from his back. "Dream?" she asked, releasing her grasp on him. "You mean the lions?"

He spun around to face her. "Yes. It is always the same. I am outside of Jerusalem's walls and the lions are tearing me to pieces."

Hurrem frowned. "It is only because of what Mustafa told you about his journey to Jerusalem—news from a trip he made without your permission."

Suleyman drew a long sigh. "Yes, I have spoken to him about his poor judgment, but I think it is more. I believe the Prophet spoke to me in a separate dream I had a few weeks ago." His expression grew more somber. "The dream was very detailed. Muhammad stood before me, although our Prophet was faceless.

But it was very clear that it was He whom spoke to me." Suleyman paused to choose his words carefully. "He told me I will live to make many gazas, and that my 'descendants will not be cut off until the end of time'." The sultan paused again, while beginning a slow pace across the room with his head drawn to the floor. "The Prophet continued, by saying 'my intercession will always extend to you. And that I 'should spend the spoils on Mecca and Medina, and for the fortification of Jerusalem, lest the infidels invade it during the reign of your followers'." I recall the voice as soft, soothing, but persuasive. He commanded that I 'install a water basin in Jerusalem's courtyard and embellish the Dome of the Rock, and offer annual gifts to the dervishes there and rebuild Jerusalem'."

Suleyman brought his pacing to a halt at the foot of the bed, and faced Hurrem. "I spoke to Ibrahim of this, and he knows of a talented architect among the Ottoman Royal Guard named Sinan. On Ibrahim's recommendation, I shall commission him to engineer the rebuilding of Jerusalem."

Hurrem sighed. "Ibrahim told you of the engineer?"

"Yes, he is my right arm."

Hurrem twisted away from Suleyman, marching toward the chamber door, and turned its lock. Slowly she spun around and paced back toward the sultan, who remained still, wearing a dumbfounded expression.

She stopped before Suleyman, facing him with a sober stare. "Muhibbi, perhaps it is time to cut off your right arm."

Suleyman noticed how the resolute expression on her face had stolen her perpetual smile. "What are you saying?"

She gathered in a breath. "Ibrahim has betrayed you."

The words cut like a dagger, as Suleyman's eyes widened with disbelief. "How so?"

"He executed your finance secretary, Iskender Celebi while on campaign in Azerbaijan."

Suleyman frowned. "I am the one who ordered Ibrahim to execute Iskender. His carelessness led my army into a trap, and he insulted me by showing little remorse for his poor judgment!"

"But then Ibrahim confiscated his property!"

Suleyman shook his head. "I am not concerned by this."

"But there is more!" Hurrem reached out and grabbed Suleyman's hand. "There are reports of Ibrahim's drunkenness on the campaign into Persia, and his disrespect for the Quran!"

Suleyman pulled his hand from her grasp. "Your words bring me great distress! Why are you trying to turn me against my grand vizier—my friend? Ibrahim is like a brother to me!" He paused and stared closely at Hurrem. "Who has put you up to this?"

Hurrem said nothing, breathing heavily.

"Tell me, my love! Who is filling you with such venom?"

She swallowed hard. "Rustem—he has contacts within the army."

Suleyman scoffed. "Is he your spy?"

"He is not my spy!" Hurrem shifted her body to fill his view once again. "My love, Rustem is not only a loyal servant, but he is your protector! His status within the Enderun allows him to see and hear what we cannot!"

Suleyman gazed inquisitively into her sympathetic eyes. "Ibrahim would never betray me," he uttered softly.

"My love, my sultan, my world—people change," Hurrem described, now with a delicate cadence. "It is true that Ibrahim has served you loyally for all of these years, but you, Muhibbi have grown." Never taking her eyes away from his, she took hold of both of his hands. "Today you are recognized as the most powerful man in the world! Ibrahim no longer knows you as you were, because he has grown too, alongside of you, and his aspirations have become clouded! How can he not desire your throne? How could any man, whose duties day in and day out place him orbiting so close to the axis of the empire, not desire to occupy the throne himself?"

Suleyman pulled his hands from her grasp. "My love for you is everlasting, Hurrem." He grimaced as though he were suddenly wounded, spinning away from her, and moving swiftly toward the window. "But Ibrahim is my brother!" He breathed heavily, with his view focused on the harbor, while his thoughts coveted the idea of being anywhere else at that moment. "The thought of Ibrahim betraying me sickens me like the plague. Yes, he is close to the throne, but despite these indiscretions you have raised about him, he has done nothing to dissuade my trust in him."

Hurrem slowly stepped closer to him. "Muhibbi, after you returned from your campaign against Tahmasp and left Ibrahim in charge of Baghdad for those few months, he had the audacity to refer to himself as Serasker Sultan! He dared call himself sultan, my love!"

Suleyman took a deep breath and turned around. "How do you know of this?"

"Rustem received correspondence from a commander." Hurrem hesitated as Suleyman writhed, before continuing. "I have seen it. It is Ibrahim's handwriting! There can be but only one sultan! It is you, and no one else has the right to wear that title!"

"This news disturbs me!" Suleyman vented. "If my throne were ever to be threatened, I thought the threat would originate from one of my sons, and not from my grand vizier!"

"*Our* sons respect and admire you Suleyman!" Hurrem proclaimed. "None would ever try to usurp the throne! Do not forget that I am their mother—they would have to kill me first!"

Suleyman pondered Mustafa and Mahidevran for a moment, before his thoughts returned to Ibrahim. "Have I been blind to my grand vizier all of this time?"

Hurrem flashed a slight smile. "No. Your only fault is that you have treated him as a brother," she said, although Suleyman could see her smile fade quickly. "Ibrahim's loyalty to you has evaporated as morning dew does before the noon hour. His disrespect mocks you, my love!" She moved closer to him. "No matter how painful the task, you must do what is right and bring an end to his treachery! If it harms you to act so boldly against your friend, then allow me to absorb your pain! I am here for you Muhibbi! Let me be the recipient of your tears! Permit me to mend your broken heart! The sooner the empire is cleansed of the stench from his betrayal, the sooner the eyes of the subjects who serve you will be thrown open to your resolve! Then none will dare lay challenge to your throne!"

Clenching both fists, Suleyman was emboldened by her words.

Hurrem quickly enveloped her arms around his waist. "I am sorry, my love."

Suleyman closed his eyes and dropped his head, delivering a soft kiss to her crown.

CHAPTER THIRTY-TWO

Constantinople - March 15, 1536

Dusk had painted the horizon orange, rapidly giving way to a clear black sky sparkling with a few of the brightest stars set against the rising of a crescent moon. The cool air was comfortable, absent of a breeze, as Suleyman and Ibrahim prepared to partake in the *iftar*—the traditional Muslim meal offered at sundown to break the daylight fast during Ramadan. They sat on European-styled chairs positioned at opposite ends of a wooden table, set beneath the shelter of a small outdoor pavilion inside the courtyard of the harem.

The two men broke the fast with dates and water, before pausing to pray after the muezzin could be heard in the distance, calling Muslims to prayer from his perch on a minaret. Chamberlains watched the men carefully, awaiting the conclusion of their invocation, before covering the table with a variety of food items, ranging from lentil soup, rice, and dolma, to kebabs and lamb.

They began their consumption of the meal without conversation, barely raising an eye to one another, before Ibrahim broke the silence. "Sultan, how is your foot?"

Suleyman lifted his head to Ibrahim and took a drink of juice. "It is better. The swelling has gone down. Moses, my doctor, says it is the gout, and has prescribed a concoction made from autumn crocus." He frowned. "It is the sultan's curse."

"Curse? How do you mean?"

"There is record of most of the previous nine sultan's having such an affliction," Suleyman described. "Beginning with our first, Osman, whose death it has been attributed to. It will probably kill me as well." Suleyman reached for a kebab, before pausing. "Unless of course, someone kills me first."

Ibrahim scoffed. "You will live a long life, Sultan."

Suleyman glanced around at the courtyard's long shadows, fading with nightfall. "Just as a man wears many faces to his personality, the courtyard reflects a different look with the passing of each hour."

Ibrahim chewed on a piece of bread. "Sultan, I have spoken to Barbarossa about the Sehzade Mustafa's concerns with pirating in Seferihisar." He washed down the bread with a gulp of juice. "Since the Kapudan Pasha shares a similar past with the brigands, I'm not sure how seriously he took the request to look into it."

"Barbarossa's leadership is the heartbeat that pumps blood to my navy. He knows as well as I, how the corsairs are an essential part of the navy's success. One man's pirate is another man's soldier on the high seas." Suleyman frowned. "I appreciate you speaking with him, but it was only to satisfy Mustafa. It would appear my son is bored with his duties in Manisa, and this pirate issue is a way for him to assert his governance."

"It was bold of the sehzade to go to Jerusalem accompanied by only three others," Ibrahim remarked.

"It was misguided. He is fortunate that he met with no harm."

Ibrahim grinned. "Allah must surely favor him."

Suleyman took a deep breath, before being distracted by chamberlains illuminating oil lanterns hanging from the pavilion's eaves. "Speaking of the holy city, I have thought much about my plans for Jerusalem since the Prophet appeared to me in my dreams."

"Very good, Sultan." Ibrahim leaned forward in his chair with an expression of eagerness.

"In addition to rebuilding Jerusalem's walls, and restoring the Dome of the Rock, I wish to make changes to the city's gates. I will give Sinan the honor of being my architect."

"Very wise choice," Ibrahim said. "What sort of changes?"

"I want to add more gates. Mustafa told me that at present, there are six gates in Jerusalem. There needs to be more, and I wish there to be a gate flanked by a pair of statues depicting lions to commemorate the lions of my recent dreams. I believe Allah is warning me to protect the holy city. This gate will be a reminder of Allah's warning." Suleyman bit into a piece of lamb. He raised his eyes to Ibrahim. "But most importantly, there is another gate—it is called the Golden Gate. Mustafa told me it is the same gate he passed through to gain entrance into the holy city. Apparently, it is the gate Jesus took to enter Jerusalem, and it is the gate upon which it is foretold the Jewish Messiah will enter." Suleyman paused to set his cup down. "I wish for this gate to be sealed."

"You believe in the Jewish Messiah?"

"I believe in God, and in the gullibility of men. I have seen how naivety can lead to rebellion." Suleyman stroked his thin mustache. "As long as I am the sultan, there will be no imposter arriving on my watch. Should a true Jewish Messiah come, then I am certain mortar and stones will not detain his entrance."

"It is a wise decision, Sultan."

Suleyman sat back in his chair and gazed across the table at Ibrahim. "Do you know that of all the sultans before me, only one died a peaceful death of natural causes? It was Orhan, the second sultan. His reign endured for thirty-six years. He holds the distinction of having the longest rule and the longest life of any sultan. I can only pray my reign may match his health and longevity."

Ibrahim raised his glass. "May God give you good reward!"

Suleyman slowly lifted his cup, before bringing it to his lips. "Ibrahim, my father forced my grandfather to abdicate the throne, and he died only a month after going into exile. If I were to learn that one of my sons plotted to commit treason against me, what would you advise my response to be?"

Suleyman could see a bewildered expression flash across his grand vizier's face, and waited patiently for his response.

Ibrahim cleared his throat. "Sultan, you are not your grandfather, and none of your sons are your father. Thus, you needn't fear such a scenario."

Suleyman sighed, before nodding toward Ibrahim just as a chamberlain made a cautious approach. The sultan coaxed the servant to move closer with a wave of his hand, and with head bowed, the chamberlain stepped beside Ibrahim carrying a violin and bow.

"What is this?" Ibrahim asked.

"Remember when first we met as boys in Edirne?" Suleyman smiled. "You were playing the violin. I am not embarrassed to say how I was in awe of your talent playing the instrument."

Ibrahim smiled. "I remember."

"The sweet music your hands produced forged the beginning of our friendship." Suleyman placed both hands on the table and leaned forward. "I wish that you play for me now, so I may cherish those memories."

Ibrahim took the violin and bow from the chamberlain's hands. "If you insist, Sultan." He lifted the instrument to his shoulder and with gifted dexterity, brought the instrument to life, engulfing the courtyard with haunting, melodic music.

Suleyman closed his eyes and harkened back to an earlier time—a simpler age when the wonderment of a young sehzade lacked the complexities of the sultanate. *Why could we not remain as boys?*

The night grew late and the moon rose higher, while in between Ibrahim's violin playing the men continued to dine, taking respite on occasion to share recollections of how two friends had conquered their world together—filled with tales of youthful pining, boastful administrative accomplishments, and glorified battle engagements. The reminiscing, music, and dining lasted for a few more hours before Ibrahim could no longer hide a sudden bout of yawning.

"This has been a pleasurable evening, Sultan. I cannot thank you enough for your gracious hospitality," Ibrahim said. "But the hour is late, and I think I should return to my residence."

Suleyman rose from his chair, as Ibrahim did the same. "I wish for you to stay here in the palace this evening," the Sultan said. "I have arranged for you to have a room in the harem."

Suleyman could see the surprised look on Ibrahim's face. "Thank you, Sultan," Ibrahim said. "Then I shall look forward to the *suhoor* tomorrow, when we may dine again together before sunrise."

The sultan approached Ibrahim and the two embraced, exchanging kisses on each cheek, just as two chamberlains appeared. "They will show you to your room," Suleyman explained, releasing his grip on Ibrahim.

Ibrahim bowed, turning away from the sultan.

"Do you know what is today's date in the Gregorian calendar?" Suleyman asked, stopping Ibrahim, who spun back toward the sultan.

"The European calendar? It is the month of March, this I am sure."

Suleyman gave him a quizzical stare. "*Et tu, Brute?*"

Ibrahim nodded. "Ah yes . . . the fifteenth of March—the Ides of March."

"A date that needs no explanation, would you not agree, my friend?"

Ibrahim lifted his eyebrows. "Well—the role of Brutus in Caesar's final act is well known."

Suleyman grinned. "Goodnight, Ibrahim."

Ibrahim hesitated, flashing a puzzled look. "Goodnight . . . Sultan."

* * *

Within the eleventh hour, Ibrahim rested comfortably upon the bed in the harem's guest room facing the ceiling with eyes shut, cast in a deep slumber. He did not hear the three barefoot assassins with black face coverings below their eyes, enter his room. Slowly the three men took up positions around Ibrahim—one placing himself at the head of the bed and two on either side of the mattress.

Suddenly, Ibrahim awakened to find each of his arms being held firmly to the bed, and looked up to see piercing dark brown eyes staring down at him. In his panic he raised his head just as a rope was flung around his neck. As the rope was tightened, Ibrahim gasped for air, and managed to pull his right arm away from the grasp of one of the assailants, swinging it violently at the man who was strangling him. Although he struck his executioner several times in the head, the tautness in the rope never lessened, and soon he found his right arm secured again. Helpless, Ibrahim continued to gasp until drifting into unconsciousness, before his eyelids closed and his heart ceased to beat.

In a sign of disrespect, the assassins stripped Ibrahim's lifeless body naked, and rolled it from off the bed.

* * *

Suleyman had been unable to sleep, but near the hour of midnight stood at his opened bedroom chamber window, staring out at the moon. Suddenly, a shooting star burst across a darkened corner of the skyline. Suleyman sighed deeply, and began to weep silently.

* * *

Down the hall from the sultan's chamber, Hurrem heard a soft knock on her door and slowly opened it. Standing before her was a man with cold, dark brown eyes, and a bushy mustache. She noticed a flesh wound near his right eye. The man bowed, crossing his arms, and bringing his hands up to both shoulders, forming an X pattern. Hurrem could see immediately how the little finger of his left hand was missing.

The man slowly raised his head. "It is done."

CHAPTER
THIRTY-THREE

Over the next several weeks, news of the execution of Pargali Ibrahim Pasha spread to every corner of the Ottoman Empire, reverberating like tremors in the wake of an earthquake. Many rumors abounded as to why the person with the greatest proximity to Suleyman, aside from Hurrem, might be murdered. Since the sultan made no statement regarding the matter, his subjects were left only to test their speculative theories with one another. Europeans condemned the nature of the grand vizier's death, using the event as propaganda to advance the image of Suleyman as a tyrannical madman, while administrative personnel from across the Ottoman Empire found themselves on notice that the same fate beheld any man who dared cross the sultan.

Haris, who had admired the grand vizier since their first meeting, was deeply shaken by Ibrahim's execution; yet surprised by how the same could not be said of Mustafa. The sehzade openly expressed his sadness over the matter, but did not appear to exhibit abhorrence with the murderous act. Haris reasoned that perhaps Mustafa was making a public effort to conceal his detest for Ibrahim's demise in an effort to avoid his father's ire.

Manisa - April, 1536

On a mid-April afternoon with the palace gardens in full bloom displaying the bright colors of spring, Haris found himself within the Audience Chamber alongside Mustafa and Mahidevran. They had received notice that a messenger from Constantinople had unexpectedly arrived. Mustafa sat regally on the jewel-studded throne, flanked on either side by the first vizier and kadin, who sat on chairs of a more modest design.

Mahidevran leaned forward to smile at Haris. "I understand Badra is excited to plan your wedding."

Haris returned the smile. "Yes, it has consumed her thoughts for weeks now. Her beauty is magnified when she is happy, so her preoccupation pleases me."

"Then it would be wise to keep her happy," Mahidevran said.

Suddenly, at the far end of the room, the chamber door was thrust open revealing five men, all clad in black kaftans and dark breeches, wearing sheepskin kalpaks atop their heads. The men paced quickly across the chamber floor with self-assured strides, stopping at the platform supporting the throne. Haris took notice of their severe expressions, and could see how each displayed an empty sheath hanging from the belts at their waist, as weapons were forbidden inside the palace. He observed how one of the five carried a cylindrical wicker basket, before casting his eyes upon the central figure, sensing something eerily familiar about the man. Haris scrutinized his long, angular nose with crooked bridge and high cheek bones, before suddenly remembering. He gasped under his breath. *Megara Ali! The martolos!*

In unison, all five men bowed toward Mustafa. "Your Royal Highness, it is an honor to behold you this day," Ali began. "I remember our first meeting within the Yeni Saray when you were very young. To see you now as the esteemed sehzade, whose name

Mustafa can be heard heralded from every corner of the empire, truly is the blessing of Allah! God's peace, be upon you!"

Mustafa nodded slightly. "And God's peace, be upon you." He raised his left hand. "I'm certain you remember my mother?"

Ali bowed. "Mahidevran Kadin."

Mahidevran did not respond, emitting little more than a scowl.

Mustafa raised his right hand. "And this is my First Vizier, Lezhe Haris."

Ali bowed and when his head lifted, Haris could see the wide grin stretching across his face. "I believe the vizier and I have met before."

Mustafa turned toward Haris with a look of surprise.

Haris frowned. "We stumbled upon one another sometime shortly after I became your teacher, Sehzade. It was a brief encounter."

Mustafa sat back, folding his hands. "What is it that brings us together again?"

Ali's grin disappeared. "I am sorry Your Royal Highness that I must inform you our presence here today is not the result of a journey made to bear pleasant news, but rather to reveal disturbing information."

"What sort of information?" Mustafa asked.

"We believe—"

"And *we* are who, exactly?" Mustafa interrupted.

"His Royal Majesty and those of us in special service to the sultan." Ali bowed. "If I may continue—"

Mustafa nodded.

"We believe the sultan's harem has been infiltrated by a spy. Our informants in Europe have reported how sensitive information from inside the palace is being passed to Austrian agents."

Mustafa leaned forward on the throne. "What is the nature of this information?"

Ali produced a smirk. "Forgive me, Your Royal Highness, but the information you seek is privy to a certain few—orders of the sultan."

"I'll wager Hurrem falls into the classification of *a certain few*!" Mahidevran snapped, quickly biting her lower lip, as Mustafa glared at her.

Mustafa sighed, returning his attention to Ali. "Well, it would appear there is a lapse of security within the Yeni Saray. What does this have to do with me?"

"We have reason to believe the spy we seek is among the harem slaves gifted to Your Royal Highness by the sultan, upon your appointment to Manisa."

Mustafa and Haris exchanged an anxious glimpse.

"Why do you believe this?" Mustafa asked.

Ali grinned. "We were able to acquire a confession."

"From whom?"

Ali nodded to the man holding the basket. The man responded by removing the lid and reaching inside the container. Slowly, he pulled out the severed head of an African, set within a small fishing net.

Mustafa gaped, rising from the throne, as Mahidevran screamed and turned away. Stunned, Haris could not move, frozen to the chair, dropping his eyes to the floor, while his stomach churned.

"He was the chief black eunuch of the sultan's harem," Ali described, before directing his attention toward Haris. "He was called Jaheem, and I believe he was a friend of the vizier's."

Haris lifted his head, rising slowly from his chair. "You bastard!"

Ali held out his arms. "I will admit how my duty to the sultan often requires the use of extreme methods, but I assure you the recipients of such measures are not without guilt." He brought his arms back in, clasping his hands at his groin. "As his friend, I understand the pain Vizier Haris must be feeling at this moment, but it is true the eunuch was the middle man in the passage of information. Without his participation, there would have been no breach of security."

"You understand nothing!" Haris growled.

"Return your grim handiwork to the basket!" Mustafa commanded. "Megara Ali, I do not question your loyalty to the sultan, but it is your methods that disturb me! And it is not only your brutality to which I refer, but also your shock theatrics which leave me disgusted! Such dark antics serve little purpose but to bring forth pain and anger!"

Ali bowed. "I apologize, Your Royal Highness, for it appears my *antics* have been ill-conceived. The purpose was only to show you the success of my methods."

"Do you have a name for the harem girl whom you claim is a spy?" Mustafa asked.

Ali sighed. "Not as of yet. The African was strong willed. He endured much pain, and would not reveal a name before he died. He only pointed us in the direction of Manisa."

"You call that success?" Haris folded his arms across his chest. "Do you not believe for a moment Jaheem purposely pointed you in the direction of Manisa?" He scoffed. "You are a larger fool than I thought, Megara Ali! I'm sure the so called spy you hunt remains in Constantinople, if indeed there is any spy at all!"

Haris noticed how his insult only worked to feed Ali's penchant for strife, as his wily grin grew wider. "The transfer of messages ceased after Your Royal Highness' departure from Constantinople,"

Ali revealed. "Except for one message. That message is believed to have originated from Manisa two years ago."

"Two years ago!" Mustafa exclaimed. "It has taken you two years to bring me this news?"

"Please understand, Your Royal Highness, word travels slowly," Ali explained. "The exchange of information between our European spies is a deliberate process because of the great danger involved, but our sources are very trustworthy. Consider also how at present the empire is on high alert for acts of betrayal, particularly in the wake of the Grand Vizier Ibrahim's treason."

Mustafa frowned, dropping back into the throne. "And now what?"

Ali adjusted the sleeves of his kaftan. "We must question each of the women within your harem. It is for your safety, Your Royal Highness, as well as for the security of the empire."

"How long will this interrogation of yours take?"

"One cannot say. It would help if Your Royal Highness, Mahidevran Kadin and Vizier Haris might suggest with whom we might begin our questioning." Ali panned each of their faces. "Is there any women among the harem who may conjure suspicion among you?"

Mustafa turned toward Haris, who dropped his head, shaking it quickly.

"There is none among the harem who is a spy!" Mahidevran exclaimed. "I've known these women for some time now, and they are good, loyal subjects, dedicated to the empire and obedient to the wishes of my son!"

Ali respectfully bowed his head.

Mustafa raised his hand as a signal to procure his mother's silence. "You have your answer, Megara Ali," he said. "We have no reason to suspect anyone among the harem."

"Very well, Your Royal Highness," Ali said. "With your permission we shall retire to our lodgings, and begin our investigation tomorrow at dawn. If your chamberlains may show us where we shall reside while in the palace, then we shall leave you for today."

Mustafa rose from the throne. "Let me say this to you, Megara Ali. I understand the seriousness of your accusations and I will not interfere with your investigation. However, let me be very clear when I say that you and your associates are not welcome here! I do not wish for any of you to be crawling around the palace after dark like blood hounds! You may come and go as you please from dawn to dusk, but you will not retire in lodgings within the palace grounds! Go and find lodging in the city of Manisa!"

Ali grimaced, bowing his head. "Your wish is noted, Your Royal Highness. We shall return tomorrow at dawn."

"And Ali!" Mustafa continued. "If I learn that your methods of inquisition become anything more than questioning, I will put a stop to this investigation immediately! No one is to be harmed before I am briefed of your findings!"

Ali bowed, before all five men turned away from Mustafa.

"Megara Ali!" Mustafa called out again, stopping the men's departure. "I have not yet dismissed you!"

Ali turned toward the sehzade, sighing.

Mustafa grinned. "Now, you are dismissed!"

All five men bowed once more, turning and marching toward the exit, quickly disappearing beyond the chamber door.

Mustafa waited until he was certain the martolos were gone, before turning toward Mahidevran. "Mother, leave us please."

"Mustafa, as the Kadin—"

"Mother!" Mustafa interrupted. "I wish to speak to my vizier alone! Now, leave us!"

Mahidevran huffed before throwing a suspicious glare at Haris. "Very well!" She spun away from the men and stomped across the platform, exiting through the doorway.

Mustafa gathered in a breath, before facing Haris. "Have you been honest with me about Badra?"

Haris looked deep into his friend's eyes. "She is not a spy, Mustafa."

"You have never told me how you managed to share correspondence with her in Constantinople?"

Haris cleared his throat. "We passed notes, using Jaheem as our middleman." Mustafa shook his head, and Haris could see the disgust in his expression. "But it was always innocent, flirtatious language!" Haris plead. "There was no sensitive information in our letters threatening the empire! Megara Ali is obsessed with his powerful position within the martolos! The way he keeps that position is by inventing threats to the sultan, and later acts the part of the savior by performing his dirty deeds, taking the lives of innocent victims!"

"Haris, if Jaheem could pass notes between you and Badra, who's to say he did not also pass notes between Badra and the Austrians?"

Haris swallowed hard, rubbing the back of his neck with his hand. "Perhaps it could be true. But I know her, and I trust her!"

Mustafa reached out and gripped Haris' arms. "Since the day we met, you have always been direct with me. I believe you, my friend, but if Megara Ali learns of your correspondence with Badra through the use of Jaheem, he will turn your romantic overture into something sinister. You, as the vizier, may be able to avoid suspicion, but I fear for her safety."

"As do I." Haris began to pace the platform, before suddenly stopping and casting a despondent glare in Mustafa's direction.

"She needs to leave the palace, and go somewhere far away, where the martolos cannot find her!"

"You would send her away, perhaps forever?" Mustafa asked with a contorted expression. "How could you do such a thing?"

Haris gazed at his friend with desperation. "Because . . . I love her."

CHAPTER

THIRTY-FOUR

As dawn broke the following day, Haris summoned Badra to his apartment, and waited for her anxiously, pacing the room until hearing the knock on his door. Upon seeing her smiling face in the hallway, he scanned both ends of the long corridor to be sure they were alone, before hurrying her inside.

"What is wrong, Haris?" Badra asked. "You do not seem yourself this morning?"

Haris locked the door behind them without uttering a word and grabbed her hand, leading her across the apartment into the bedroom chamber. Beyond the bed, they moved toward another door that opened into the hammam.

Standing within the steam filled tiled room Badra removed her hat and veil. "I have already bathed this morning, Haris." She produced a suggestive smirk. "Do you desire my love again? Only the other night did we last complete *la petite mort.*"

Haris ignored her, listening to the sound of water gushing from the fountain, cascading into the bath. "We are here because it offers more privacy than does my apartment."

"You are acting strange," Badra said. "And where were you last evening? I searched for you after the dinner hour, but could not find you?"

Haris stepped closer, looking deeper into her the eyes. "I was in Izmir."

"Izmir? Why?"

Haris frowned. "My love, there is a problem." With those words, he could see a look of dread replace her quizzical smile. "Badra, do you love me?"

She gaped. "Why . . . of course I love you! What is the matter?"

"I need your honesty." Haris lowered his voice to a whisper. "While in Constantinople, did you exchange messages with the Austrians?"

Badra hesitated.

"Jaheem is dead!" A dire expression blanketed Haris' face. "You and I may be next, if you don't tell me the truth!"

Badra brought her hand to her forehead. "Jaheem! Oh, my—what have I done?" She cast a woeful look at Haris. "It seemed to be only trivial information!" She dropped her head, sighing. "When I arrived in Constantinople, an Austrian made contact with me through Jaheem!" she exclaimed, before lifting her eyes to Haris. "I never saw his face! It was all done through letters!"

"What type of information?"

"Just mundane things, like describing daily life in the harem, and what the likes and dislikes of the sultan were! It did not seem to be dangerous information!" Tears welled up in her eyes. "In return, the anonymous letter writer promised to search for my brother!"

"What about the day I saw you speaking with the Austrian here in Manisa?"

Badra swallowed hard. "The man knew my name! He surprised me, for I had never seen him before! When he desired to speak to me, I thought immediately he had news of my brother, but he did not! He only asked if I could still be counted on to provide information! I did not reply and turned away!"

His expression wrinkled with irritation.

"Haris, please believe me! I'm telling you the truth!"

"Why didn't you tell me the truth when I asked you that day?" Haris asked with raised voice.

"I'm sorry, my love! I was frightened! I did not want you to think ill of me!" She reached out and grabbed his hands. "I have not communicated with anyone about such matters since! Please, believe me!"

His expression softened. "I need to get you away from here. The martolos will first seek to question any women of the harem who can speak German. Eventually they will discover the truth, or at least bend the facts to make you appear the villain."

"Now that poor Jaheem is dead, who else but us would know the truth?" she inquired.

"Who can say who knows what? You may have enemies among the harem. As for Mahidevran, Mustafa assured me he would deal with her if you suddenly became suspect. But should his mother learn the truth, she may not be so forgiving in her effort to protect her son."

"It was such trivial information!" Badra shook her head. "Why would they care? I was not detailing secrets of the sultan's military strength, or passing along invasion plans!"

Haris thought for a moment. "The Europeans are constantly seeking dirt on Suleyman, so as to portray him as a demon."

"But the information was not vilifying!"

"Perhaps, but skilled scribes wield the pen like a sword, and can turn the simplest of facts into ugliness!"

She shook her head and moaned. "Everything was so . . . was so blissful, and now—" Haris could see regret in her eyes. "You said I must leave the palace, but where will I go?" she asked.

Haris pulled her closer. "Last night in Izmir, I arranged for Duman to take you away from here by boat."

"Duman?"

"Remember the fisherman in Izmir and the pirates?"

She nodded. "Where will he take me?"

"To Nin."

"Nin? Is that not where you were born?"

"Yes. I believe you will be safer there. It is controlled by the Venetians, lying beyond the Ottoman border."

Haris read sudden panic in her eyes. "But who will help me in Nin?" she asked. "I cannot just step off of a vessel and find a place to live and work, while waiting for you!" She hesitated, glaring at him. "You will find me, and join me?"

He gently grabbed her chin so her attention was unwavering. "Yes, I will find you. I just cannot leave at the moment. There would be too much suspicion, and the effort to hunt us down would be intense. I am hopeful that my brother is still the priest in the village. His name is Mateo. Your first stop in Nin should be to the Catholic Church, no matter the hour. It is important for you to remember these names, for they will offer proof that you know me. Aside from Mateo, my father was Franjo, and my mother Mirna. My baby sister is named Dinora."

He released his hand from her chin, and she repeated the names twice.

"Haris, but what of our wedding?"

He frowned. "Your safety is what matters first. We will be married once this storm has passed."

"When will you join me in Nin?"

Haris studied her fretful stare. "As soon as possible, but it may take time—maybe a month or more," he guessed, although realizing his estimation was given only to comfort her; for he knew not what lay ahead. "The martolos will be inside the palace throughout the day, if they are not already here. Stay out of sight! You should avoid them at all cost! If you must, pretend that you are ill. We will leave for Izmir tonight, after dark. Pack only enough clothing that you can carry—simple items and not anything too elegant. I will bring you something to wear for this evening."

Badra gazed longingly into his eyes and embraced him tightly, before burying her head into his chest. "Haris, I am sorry—"

* * *

An hour after darkness had descended over the palace chasing the martolos from the royal grounds, the Janissary guards at the gate of the second courtyard could see three individuals approaching on foot, guiding each horse by a lead line.

As they stepped closer, the guards recognized the silahdar agha. "The vizier has business in Manisa!" Kamil announced.

The Janissaries bowed, although Haris could see how the attention of the guards was suddenly drawn to the Janissary pulling the third horse, whose uniform and bork hung sloppily from the small frame. As they began to question the Janissary, Haris yelled, "What is the delay? I have urgent business awaiting me! Do you not recognize me, or the silahdar agha?"

Immediately, the guards rushed to open the gates, allowing the three to pass through. When the three were well inside the first courtyard, Haris glanced at the Janissary walking beside him. "Are you all right?"

Badra nodded. "As long as you are with me, I know I have nothing to fear, my love."

"Can you ride a horse?"

"Yes, back home I began riding as a small girl," she said. "But it has been a while."

"Stay close to me."

Once they had passed through the unguarded Imperial Gate, Haris, Badra, and Kamil, mounted their horses and rode off into the night. The three continued uninterrupted in the direction of Izmir—a distance that took them nearly an hour to make.

About a mile outside of Izmir, the three riders stopped when they spotted the burning lanterns of the port city.

Haris turned toward Kamil. "Wait for us here. The less people I involve in this matter, the safer it will be for all."

Kamil nodded, as Haris and Badra rode off toward the port city.

* * *

Within Izmir, Duman and his son were waiting at the dock as Haris and Badra arrived. After dismounting, Haris had a brief conversation with the fisherman before embracing him, and stepping back to join Badra.

Haris placed his hands on her shoulders. "Duman is a good man, and a capable sailor. He says providing that the voyage is blessed with fair weather he will have you in Nin before dusk tomorrow. Remember, when in Nin you must go directly to the church and ask for Father Mateo." Haris reached into the pocket of his breeches and withdrew a small wooden crucifix. "Should you forget the names, show my brother this." He handed her the religious artifact, which could fit into the palm of her hand.

Badra studied the Christ-like image of a bearded man on the body of a fish, before turning the crucifix over, and reading aloud the inscription carved on the opposite side. "Jadran."

"It is the crucifix my mother gave me the day I was taken away by the devshirme," Haris described. "My father hand carved a crucifix for each of his children."

Badra nodded, as tears filled her eyes.

"Do not weep, my love," Haris said. "We shall be together again soon. This is best for both of us. You will be safe."

"I love you, Haris!"

The two lovers shared a long, passionate kiss, before Haris pulled slightly away and gazed deeply into her eyes. "Forever . . . I shall find you, my love!"

She smiled as tears streamed down both cheeks. "I believe you! And I shall be waiting!"

They kissed again, before Haris helped guide Badra from the dock onto the boat. Quickly, Duman untied the moorings and cast off, while Haris watched her standing statuesque at the stern of the vessel, akin to one of Neptune's angels bidding farewell with a heart-rending gaze.

"Forever . . . I shall find you!" Haris called out, working to commit her face to memory; for he knew not when he would see her again.

CHAPTER

THIRTY-FIVE

A week had passed since the departure of Badra, and to take his mind off of her absence, Haris rode Alabaster inside the imperial stable. From the back of the galloping mare, he practiced archery, firing arrows at a wooden post. After three successful strikes he gathered his arrows, suddenly surprised to see a figure leaning on the far fence. Upon closer inspection, he recognized Megara Ali. *I wonder how long he has been watching me. He sneaks around like a leopard on the prowl.*

Haris slowed Alabaster to a trot, steering the mare in the direction of Ali. As he approached, he set an arrow to the bow and drew on the string, pointing the weapon in Ali's direction. With a dreadful stare, the martolos rose from out of his leaning posture. Haris released his grip, sending the arrow whistling through the air before it struck the fence post with a loud thud, only a few feet from where Ali stood.

Haris brought his horse over to the embedded arrow, pulling it from the wood.

"You are very skillful with the bow and arrow, Vizier." Ali grinned. "For a moment, I thought you were aiming the weapon at me."

Haris glanced at him. "I'm not so skillful—for I missed."

Ali scoffed. "Well—you have a sense of humor, I see. Perhaps we may take pause from such wittiness. There is something I need to ask you."

"I am busy Ali, and since I am not a member of the harem, I have no interest in your investigation." Haris kicked the mare gently, sending Alabaster into a trot, moving away from the fence.

"Again, with the wit. The question is about the woman called Badra," Ali called out. The mention of her name stunned Haris, but he ignored the request. The martolos persisted. "If you will not answer this question, then I shall seek out the answer from someone else within the palace. You know how women are, Vizier. They can be very vindictive."

Haris pulled on the reins, bringing Alabaster to a stop. He turned the horse around, emitting a reluctant glower as he steered the animal back toward the fence post. "What is your question?"

Ali smiled. "I understand you and Badra were to be married?"

"*Are* to be married."

Ali nodded. "Yet, she has left the palace?"

Haris hesitated in his response, glaring at him with irritation. "The wedding is in June. My future bride returned home to visit her parents, with the intention of bringing them back with her for the ceremony. You could not question her, because she left the morning of your arrival."

Ali nodded unconvincingly. "Where is she from?"

"Rumelia."

"Rumelia is a very large place. I am familiar with most of it."

Haris smirked. "That's right. You're its *gardener*, aren't you?"

Ali snickered. "Where in Rumelia was your future bride born?"

Haris remembered Serkan's place of origin. "Monastir."

Ali's eyes widened. "She is Macedonian? Beautiful women from that area of Rumelia."

"Are we finished?"

Ali tapped the fence post, exposing the missing finger on his left hand. "Vizier Haris, it would be foolish to hide any information to protect a friend . . . or lover. No position in government is exempt from treason. The fate that befell the grand vizier is evidence of what I speak."

Haris guided his mare against the fence where Ali stood, leaning forward in the saddle.

"You have information?" Ali asked, looking up at him.

Haris plunged the blade of the arrow he held downward, piercing the edge of Ali's sleeve, pinning his clothing to the post. "Listen to me, Megara Ali! It would be foolish for any member of the martolos to execute a suspect without proof! You have not proven to me that what you did to Jaheem was anything but murder! Tread lightly when crossing my path, for I promise my arrow will not miss its target a second time!" He pulled the arrow from the wood, and led Alabaster in a gallop across the corral.

* * *

Another week had passed, when beneath a clear afternoon sky, Haris strolled through the first courtyard with Kamil by his side. They were enjoying the sights and sounds of people perusing the many shops when approached by a young boy, who handed Haris a tied scroll.

"Where are you from?" Haris asked the boy.

The boy stood with his eyes cast to the ground. "Manisa, my lord."

"Who sent you to me?"

"A man who said he was from Izmir." The boy continued to stand steadfast, bowing. "He said he was a fisherman."

Haris exchanged glances with Kamil, before handing the boy

several coins. With a bashful thank you, he darted away, as Haris untied the scroll's ribbon and began to read. When he finished, he gave Kamil a troubling look. "The author uses Badra's name and writes that he must speak to me soon about an urgent matter involving her journey."

"Does he sign the letter?" Kamil asked.

"Not with his name, only with the drawing of a fish. It may be from the fisherman."

Kamil became alarmed. "It could be a trap!"

Haris sighed. "He may not have written his name to conceal his identity, should this letter have fallen into the wrong hands."

"When does he want to meet with you?"

"During *Salat al-maghrib*—at dusk when the muezzin calls us to prayer."

"Then I will go with you. Where are you to meet?"

"No, Kamil." Haris looked about, as though he could trust no one within earshot. "It is better that I go alone. This is my problem, and as I told you the night we took Badra away, the less people I involve, the safer for everyone—especially her."

"Everyone that is, but you!"

Haris placed a hand on Kamil's shoulder, and smiled. "I will be fine, my friend." He returned his attention to the scroll, as his smile faded. "The letter says our meeting is urgent. Do we still find ourselves within the month of April?"

Kamil was surprised by the question. "According to the European calendar, today is the first of May, Vizier."

"Badra said it was unlucky to be married in May." Haris sighed. "I fear my love may be in trouble."

* * *

Haris could not remember the last time the sun took so long to set—of course it was only the aching anticipation of news

369

pertaining to Badra that lengthened each hour. With a burnt horizon ahead of him, he set off on Alabaster dressed in plain clothing and a turban, just as the muezzin could be heard beyond the palace walls calling the faithful to the day's fourth prayer. He hadn't told Kamil where the planned meeting with the fisherman would take place, but Haris knew the sight well. It was an area of ancient Greek ruins located five miles southwest of the palace, situated just off the main road running from Manisa to Izmir. Haris thought the location of the meeting to be strange, but he reasoned Duman may have felt the palace or port city would attract too much unwanted attention.

When he came upon the point where six tall marble columns could be seen from the road, Haris exited the highway and guided his mare along a narrow path that ascended gradually, winding in between boulders and brush. Within a quarter of an hour he had reached the site of the ruins—an area littered with large chunks of hand carved marble—entering the clearing before bringing Alabaster to a halt. He scanned the area, observing only the deliberate movement of shadows amid the fading daylight, before guiding his horse toward an area of large flat stone that once formed the floor of the temple.

Suddenly, at the edge of the hill behind the ruins, he detected movement among the shadows, and could see a dark horse tied to a tree branch. A figure appeared from behind the column set farthest from him. Distance and the waning sunlight prevented Haris from identifying the man, but he decided to dismount. From the saddle, he stepped onto the elevated ancient temple floor, running his hand across his waistline to feel the handle of the dagger he concealed beneath his kaftan.

Haris began pacing in the direction of the figure, before stopping halfway from him. "Fisherman?"

The man took a moment before responding. "Haris? I have news for you."

Haris grew skeptical. "My future wife calls me by name, but all others address me by my title." He waited for a response, but there was none. He thought of a random name. "What news do you bring me . . . Altan?"

"There was an accident at sea—your woman was killed."

Haris caught his breath for a moment. "I am stunned," he said, slowly reaching inside his kaftan to remove the dagger. "Come closer, so you may share the details."

Suddenly, the man turned, leaping from the stone floor and began to run. Haris gave chase before stopping when he heard a horse's whine, and spun around to see a second man guiding Alabaster away by the lead line.

"Stop, thief!" Haris set off running after Alabaster, watching as the mare disappeared into the dark wood. Upon entering the thicket, he stopped at the sight of the horse standing near to the trunk of a large tree. With no other person in sight, he decided to approach the animal with caution. Upon reaching the horse, Haris glanced around uneasily, before returning his knife inside his kaftan, and placing his foot in the stirrup.

Perched atop Alabaster, Haris reached for the reins, when suddenly a man dropped from out of the foliage above, landing on top of him. The collision forced both men to fall from the frightened mare, and tumble hard to the ground. Haris rolled over on top of his assailant and began pummeling his attacker with both fists; but he did not see the second man step up from behind him clutching a thick limb. The attacker used the branch to strike the back of his head, rendering Haris unconscious.

Megara Ali and another martolos appeared from behind the thick brush, unable to restrain Alabaster, which galloped off into the clearing.

"The mare will find its way back to the palace," Ali said. "The sehzade will think Haris has deserted him and gone off to be with the woman." He turned his attention to Haris lying still, before addressing the man holding the club. "I told you not to kill him! It defeats my purpose if the vizier should die here!"

The martolos checked for a pulse. "There is a heartbeat. He's alive."

Suddenly another man appeared from out of the brush, and bent forward with his hands on his knees, trying to catch his breath. Ali looked at him. "What name did he call you?"

"Altan."

"Three of us will take the vizier to Seferihisar tonight," Ali said. "The other two will search the seaport of Izmir for a fisherman named Altan. When we find him, we will learn where the vizier has sent his future bride."

CHAPTER

THIRTY-SIX

Haris shirked when feeling the cold water splash across his face. He opened his eyes to behold a tall, long bearded man standing above him clutching an empty pot in his hand. Slowly the man's cinnamon colored kaftan, and ash shaded turban came into focus.

"Hmm—you're alive," the man said in Turkish. "We've been at sea for a full day while you've slumbered. Any longer, and you would have been of no use to me. I would have had to toss you overboard."

Haris sat up, recognizing how he rested against the wooden wall of a small room, and began to pick dry blood from his ears while his head throbbed. At first he thought the swaying he felt was related to his thumping head, before realizing it to be the rhythmic rocking of a ship. He returned his eyes to the man standing above him. "Where am I? Who are you?"

The man grinned, resting his hand on the ivory handle of a *jambya*—the curved dagger tucked into a wooden sheath at his belt, symbolizing its owner as someone of importance. "I am Salih Rais, the captain of this vessel."

"I am Vizier Haris."

"I know who you are." Salih grinned. "You must have truly angered the wrong person or persons to find yourself on my vessel."

"What sort of vessel is this?"

"I am a corsair, in service to the Ottoman sultan." Salih moved his grip from the jambya to the handle of the sword sheathed at his side. "I have sailed with Hayreddin Barbarossa before he was honored by the sultan with the rank of kapudan pasha. Together, we've battled Genoese, Venetian, and Spanish ships across the Mediterranean."

Haris felt a surge of adrenaline. "Then I command you to take me back to Izmir!"

"Izmir?" Salih laughed. "We set sail from Seferihisar. And my dear Vizier, my orders are not to take you anywhere—only to kill you."

Haris gaped. "Whose orders are these?"

"The orders came from a martolos, but I am guessing he too may be in service to someone else."

Haris tried to pick himself from off the floor, only to find the captain had unsheathed his sword, and pressed its tip against his throat.

"Do not try anything foolish, Vizier, for I don't intend to kill you! But should I have to, I will!"

"What do you want with me?" Haris asked.

"Fortunately for you, your position as a vizier makes you very valuable to me." Salih lowered his sword. "I do business with a greedy European in Tripoli."

"Tripoli?"

Salih sneered. "Yes, Tripoli. A prisoner of your status will fetch a high price."

"But your allegiance is to the sultan!"

"My allegiance is to whoever I wish it to be!" Salih moved toward the cabin door and held it ajar, calling names. He turned back toward Haris. "Don't look so disheartened, Vizier. After all, you are still alive."

Haris rubbed the back of his head. "Why would the martolos hand me over to you, and not kill me?"

Salih flashed a wide grin. "Perhaps he did not want anyone to know you are dead—only that you have disappeared." Just then two more buccaneers entered the cabin and began shackling Haris' wrists and ankles. "Well Vizier, I hope you will enjoy your cruise." He belched a hearty laugh. "Take him below!"

* * *

Below deck, Haris was dragged into the dark, dank belly of the ship cramped with what he guessed were about five dozen prisoners chained to rows of wooden benches lining the galley. In the middle of the starboard side of the vessel, he was shoved into a sitting position in between two men, while his ankle shackles were fastened to iron rings attached to the floorboards. One half of a large wooden oar set stationary in front of all three men, with its paddle protruding from out of a square hole carved in the side of the ship.

At first, Haris thought he had been thrust in with a bevy of women, for everyone about him displayed unkempt hair extending to their shoulders or beyond; but he could see how all, save him, were shirtless—their thin, but muscular bodies a ghostly pale. Their faces were nondescript, hidden behind long, thick beards and mustaches, concealing identities that no longer seemed to matter. And then he noticed a strong putrid stench circulating about the galley, which made him sick to his stomach. Haris looked to his feet, becoming repulsed at the sight of feces on the floor around him, and pools of liquid he guessed was urine. He scanned the soiled breeches of the men on either side, as well as those sitting in front of him, and concluded that they were forced to labor in their own filth.

* * *

Time moved slowly for Haris, whose dire situation began to weigh heavily on him with the passage of each day. Even with three men shackled to a row, pulling the forty foot long, three hundred pound oar was difficult work. He learned quickly that when the boatswain appeared below deck, rowing would commence into a coordinated rhythm guided by the bosun's whistle. Two other pirates would parade up and down the center aisle carrying whips, beating those men who could not keep pace. The rowing would continue for hours at a time, tearing away at one's muscles, while challenging the strength and stamina of each rower. Adding to the misery was how the low-lying galley set three feet above the waterline, resulting in the constant spray of salt water eating away at the skin.

Haris tried on occasion to communicate with his fellow prisoners, but the grim atmosphere and sense of hopelessness reflected within their distant stares, seemed to render conversation fruitless. Even if he had found someone with whom to talk, the language barrier often discouraged it, as he realized most spoke either Spanish or Latin—two languages unfamiliar to him. Eventually, he concluded many of the men were prisoners of war from the Iberian or Apennine Peninsulas.

The prisoners received meager food rations on a daily basis, and every two or three days were herded outside onto the main deck to receive a quick soaking from buckets of water thrown at them. Haris began to look forward to such days, for it became a time to stretch, catch a refreshing breeze, and to feel the warmth of sunlight on his face; although he learned quickly how the slightest deviation from the pirate's commands—no matter how harmless—could result in severe beatings.

Days and nights turned into weeks and months. With no mirrors, Haris need only look to his left and right to gauge his own appearance—hairy men reduced to the level of wilderness animals. They had become dispensable possessions, and it was not uncommon to view a man suddenly slumped over in his galley seat, wearing the pall of death.

He began to lose count of how long he had been imprisoned aboard the ship, and by peering through the opening where the oar extended, could only discern when the sun rose and set, guessing they were sailing the length of the Mediterranean. There were no ports of call, only the endless sight of wine dark sea, reminding him of Homer's famous poem, as well as a conversation he once had with the sultan.

One early morning, the boatswain ceased his whistling and oars were raised. Moments later Haris could feel the ship stop with the dropping of the anchor, followed by the appearance of several pirates who unshackled and dragged him topside to the main deck. From the port side, under a burning sun, he viewed many vessels of all sizes moored to stone and wooden docks. Behind the harbor, set a walled section of a city featuring a square-shaped stone castle keep rising above the one and two story buildings spreading out for miles in either direction from the citadel.

Haris' wrists were shackled and he was shoved into a row boat along with four pirates and Salih. The boat was lowered into the sea and the pirates began rowing in the direction of the docks.

Haris sat in the center of the boat facing Salih. "Where are you taking me?"

Salih smiled. "I told you of my European friend with whom I do business."

"We are in Tripoli?"

"Very soon, Vizier—very soon. At the moment, we are on the Mediterranean."

"But Tripoli is controlled by the Spanish King Charles."

"He gave it to the Christian Knights of Malta some years back."

"They are the enemies of Turkish corsairs!"

Salih laughed. "We are enemies, this is true. But there is a time for war and a time for business. Today it is business." He ordered the rowing to cease, allowing the boat to drift halfway between the pirate vessel and the port of Tripoli.

"Why do we wait?" Haris asked.

Salih looked around and saw a fishing vessel approaching them. He pointed at the boat. "We wait for them."

Within a few minutes, the fishing boat dropped anchor near the row boat. Haris looked upward and could see a bearded man leaning over the boat's railing wearing a white tunic centered by a large red cross with eight points.

Salih looked at Haris. "If I were to go ashore, I would be arrested. Thus, we must conduct our business at sea."

"Salih! We saw your flag!" the man called out in Turkish. "What do you bring me today?"

"God's peace, be upon you, Pelliquen!" Salih exclaimed.

"Enough with your insincere salutations invoking God," Pelliquen replied. "You know as well as I, that God will have nothing to do with your Saracen bootlegging soul!"

Salih grinned. "Then we share something in common, for your soul is undoubtedly tainted by the countless number of Muslim slaves you peddle across the Mediterranean in the name of your Christ!"

Pelliquen scoffed, before staring at Haris. "Who is this piece of cow dung you bring to me? Is he Muslim or Christian?"

Salih laughed. "He is authority."

"Authority? What riddle do you speak of?"

"Behold the Vizier of Manisa."

"Vizier? Can you prove it?"

Salih looked at Haris. "Tell him who you are."

Haris produced a contemptible stare. "I am no one."

Salih pulled the jambya from its sheath and pressed the point of the blade to Haris' neck. "Tell them you are Vizier Haris!"

Haris lifted his head to Pelliquen. "He's lying!"

Salih growled.

"Salih!" Pelliquen called. "Withdraw your blade! Why would a prisoner not wish to gain his freedom from your death ship by playing the part of a government official?" He paused and glared at Haris with a grin. "I believe he is the vizier."

A rope ladder was dropped over the side of the fishing vessel, and after the shackles were removed from his wrists, Haris was prodded by the end of a sword to climb it. With each rung he climbed, he thought about jumping into the sea, but reasoned it would not take him far enough from the vessels.

Pelliquen tossed a bag of coins into the row boat, watching the corsair captain pore over the booty. "It is always a pleasure to do business with you Salih!" He turned away from the sea and gave a long look at Haris who had scaled the railing. "Welcome aboard, Vizier. I am Jacques Pelliquen, the Lieutenant Grand Master of the Order of Malta. I hope you will enjoy your new palace," he said, followed by a bout of laughter.

CHAPTER

THIRTY-SEVEN

The knights forced Haris—shackled at the hands and feet—to march barefoot to the Casbah of Tripoli where a large Spanish fortress dominated the citadel consisting of four bastions connecting its ruddy walls that were linked in a rectangular design rising three stories. As he passed through the large, horseshoe arch gate, Haris viewed a central courtyard centered by a tall keep attached to several two story buildings set beside a church. He appeared undaunted by the fortress layout; although he sensed dreadful conditions awaited him within the corridors, made evident by the barred windows running the length of the inner walls on three sides.

Once inside the citadel, Haris suffered a dizzy spell that brought him to his knees while climbing three flights of stone stairs. Two knights walking on either side of him grabbed hold of each arm, and pulled him into an unsteady standing position. When the dizziness had faded he resumed the climb, before being led down two long corridors toward the southern end of the fortress, passing large wooden doors with small square openings set with iron bars. Haris limped from the sores and cuts covering the soles of his feet, and could not escape the stale air stinging his eyes, or the moaning of unseen faces concealed behind the many locked doors.

Stopping before a cell, the jailer used a skeleton key to

unfasten the lock, pulling open the heavy squeaking door that dragged across the threshold. With not a word spoken, one of the knights shoved Haris into the stark twelve by twelve room, closing the door behind him. The cold, stone floor of the cell sloped gradually from each corner toward a small drain in the center, and the only light available, streamed through a barred window set in the wall opposite the door, but positioned some twenty feet above, as well as from a narrow barred opening cut from the high, flat ceiling overhead.

Haris noticed the lone object within the cell proved to be an iron pot which he assumed was for human waste. He sat on the floor with his back against the wall for what he guessed was an hour before the door to his cell opened, revealing Pelliquen accompanied by a guard who carried a wooden chair inside the room, before exiting.

Pelliquen strolled inside, and set the chair in the middle of the cell. *"Parlez-vous Francais?"*

Haris shook his head.

"Merhaba Vizier."

Haris nodded.

"You don't look like a Turk," Pelliquen said in Turkish. "Perhaps you are one of those former Christians from Rumelia who have sold their souls to the devil Suleyman?"

Haris said nothing.

Pelliquen smirked. "I apologize if you find the condition of your new home lacking the amenities of a palace. The best I can do is to offer you a chair." He pointed to the furniture. "Please."

Haris found the strength to speak. "I have been sitting in a hellish galley for two months. It pleases me to stand for a while."

Pelliquen scoffed. "As you wish, Vizier. Is there anything you desire to ask of me? I don't make a habit of visiting my prisoners very often. You may want to take advantage of this opportunity, for you never know when, or if it shall present itself again."

Haris gathered in a deep breath. "I have been taken against my will! I am a vizier of the Ottoman Empire! You are French! Our countries have a treaty!"

Pelliquen nodded. "My place of birth is France, but as a Knight of Malta, my allegiance is to God."

"Then Salih was correct! You are no better than a corsair! What do you want of me?"

Pelliquen took a deep breath. "I have been to the Levant—to Damascus and Jerusalem. In that corner of the world, I was introduced to a Persian card game called *As Nas*. I quickly learned how the player who holds the *As* card is in a very good position to win the game."

"I am familiar with this game."

"Then you know the value of the *As* card, for it can change the course of the game at any moment." Pelliquen grinned. "You, Vizier Haris, are my *As* card. There may be a time when I need to play you."

Haris grimaced. "From where I stand, the only game you seem to be playing involves a masquerade! As a dealer in human bondage, you are merely an imposter who claims to be a Christian! May you rot in hades, Pelliquen!"

Pelliquen sneered. "And may you rot in this cell, Vizier Haris." He turned away, stepping toward the door, before stopping. "You may keep the chair. I'm sure at one point in the length of your stay you will have the desire to sit in it."

Haris watched as the door was pulled shut. He could hear the echo of their footsteps fade down the corridor.

* * *

The consistent transition of the cell from daylight into darkness provided one of the few deviations that broke the loneliness of Haris' incarceration. Another such variation was the daily visit from a prison worker. The man would come by twice a day, once in the morning to retrieve the waste pot and deliver a breakfast of figs, dates, and olives, and then again before dusk to bring a dinner of gruel with flatbread. Haris learned quickly that the plate and pot fit through a slender opening carved at the bottom of the door, and when banging could be heard at the door, he was to move to the far wall of the cell and wait for his food to appear. If the man could not see him in the far corner, then no food was left, or no waste pot was emptied. Haris called him *mavi adam*—blue man—because of the indigo dye staining his copper toned wrists. He guessed the worker to be a member of the local people descended from the Berber tribe called the Tuareg, whose tradition of dying their clothing was well known. Despite countless attempts by Haris to make conversation with him, the blue man remained disinterested and silent.

One morning, Haris was surprised when two guards came to remove him from his cell, escorting him to the courtyard for what he guessed amounted to about thirty minutes of fresh air and sunshine. Under careful watch, the guards permitted him to walk, exercise, or sit in one corner of the courtyard. He quickly learned the supervised visits occurred once a month and that he was one of six prisoners taken to the courtyard on those days. Haris reasoned how it was therapeutic seeing others in his same predicament; although any attempt to interact with his fellow inmates was forbidden.

The long days of imprisonment became weeks, and then months. There seemed to be little or no variation in the meals, although once in a great many days, the plate would feature a concoction of cooked vegetables and minced lamb that reminded him of a Turkish dish called *saksuka*. Haris had no answer for those rare occasions when the menu changed, but welcomed it. For a long time, hunger pains racked his body until he learned to eat his meager meals slowly.

Haris discerned by the position of the sun the cell's window faced south, which explained the lack of an easterly or westerly breeze to bring relief from the day's sweltering heat. He began to spend the daylight naked, while donning his clothing at night in an attempt to keep warm, and he used the rare occasions of rainfall pouring through the opening in the ceiling to cleanse himself. On moonlit nights, positioned at the door of his cell, Haris sat and watched the moon rise across his small, barred window. It proved always to be a brief experience, but as the months passed his moon gazing enabled him to become proficient at determining the arrival of the celestial body's various phases.

At first, his physical health took precedence, as he developed an exercise routine to maintain his strength and flexibility. In addition, he began a habit of pacing back and forth daily within the small cell, counting his steps and making an effort to increase those steps by fifty every day.

However helpful his physical conditioning proved to be, the passage of time began to gnaw away at his mental state. There were those melancholy days in which he could do nothing but weep or scream for hours, belaboring himself with thoughts of past decisions made, and what could have been of his life. Nor did an hour slip by without thoughts of Badra. He wondered if she were safe, hopeful that the martolos did not have the name of Duman, making their attempt to discover the true nature of her destination unsuccessful. He questioned whether she had ever made it safely to Nin at all, and if she had, did she find his brother? But what tortured his thoughts most was not being able to share his fate with her. He pondered much about Mustafa too, wondering if his friend had organized a search party to investigate his disappearance, or if perhaps the sehzade felt abandoned as well. Haris' helpless predicament tormented him more than the thought of dying alone or being forgotten in his solitary confinement—a thousand miles and a lifetime away.

One day, Haris noticed a small crack in the corner of his cell and after working at it for hours with his fingers, was able to loosen a stone. He decided this would be his writing utensil and began to mark the passage of days with a slash on the wall. As the number of slashes mounted, he had forgotten the characteristics of his own appearance, only aware of the long length of his hair. In time, he could count his protruding ribs while his breeches had become so loose around the waist, that often when standing he needed to hold them up with one hand.

One evening, as he emerged from a deep slumber, Haris observed movement within his cell. It was a small rat that had entered through the narrow opening at the bottom of the door—the creature having found a leftover crumb from the dinner Haris had eaten hours before. He named the vermin Megara Ali, recognizing embellished similarities between his martolos nemesis and the beady-eyed rodent. Despite his detest for both the martolos and the rat, Haris began to leave a morsel of food for his sneaky visitor each night, always accompanied with a question: *Why did you do this to me?* Of course, Megara Ali would never answer, only scurry away to seek a bite to eat from some other unfortunate soul. The routine became so regular that when the rodent ceased making an appearance three years into his incarceration, Haris was sure it was dead. He could only wish the same fate had befallen Megara Ali.

And then there was the day Haris realized he had forgotten about God. Of course, from the first day of his confinement, the daily distant chants of muezzins calling the faithful to prayer, or the toll of church bells in the courtyard, provided a link to the religious life beyond the prison walls; but it took a while for him to realize the difference between hearing, and actually listening. When he discovered this, he sought God through a daily ritual of prayer. At first, the recitation of Islamic verses was limited to five times a day facing the southeastern corner of his cell, which he assumed was in the direction of Mecca. It wasn't long before such actions of piety evolved into sporadic moments of prayer that transcended his Muslim routine.

As time marched onward, from the recesses of his mind Biblical verses began to resurface. Soon he found himself unintentionally blending the varied invocations of Biblical and Quranic verses to a point where eventually he could no longer differentiate between the many passages of both holy books. Haris came to the realization that he had done for religion what centuries of civilization had failed to do—find commonality with the belief under one God. Armed with an abundance of litanies to call upon, Haris entrusted his dire situation to the Almighty, eventually inspiring him to carve the following verse from Job on the wall of his cell: *'Though He slay me, yet will I trust in him.'*

Haris' religious awakening made him realize that without repetition, time began to dissolve recollection. As a result, he began to recreate past conversations while generating imagined future dialogue with those individuals whose lives had crossed paths with his own. In this way, he would not allow himself to forget. Each day he would craft imaginary dialogue with a different person from his past, although making certain to speak with Badra every day. Haris thought the creative approach to be either a common method of dealing with isolation, or a stage of impending insanity.

On a warm summer afternoon near dusk, Haris had just finished prostrating himself in prayer toward the corner of his cell when dinner arrived. He watched the plate slide under the opening of the door as it had done a thousand times before, but this time he would not wait for the Tuareg to leave. Haris sprung from the floor and burst across the room, placing his face against the window bars. "I demand to see Pelliquen!"

The Tuareg, stunned by Haris' outburst, had only finished rising from the floor on the other side of the hallway.

"You are no better than the Europeans—all these years, torturing me with your silence!" Haris exclaimed. "I know you are not mute, for I've heard you speaking with the knights! Pelliquen—I demand to see Pelliquen!"

To his surprise, the Tuareg stopped, and turned toward Haris. "Pelliquen . . . Pelliquen *muerto*."

"*Muerto*? Dead? *Muerto*—dead?" Haris could not believe it. "How long?"

The Tuareg gave a look of confusion reflecting is unfamiliarity with Turkish.

Haris yelled, "When *muerto*? When?"

The Tuareg eventually held up two fingers. "*Dos ano*."

"Two? Two what—two years?" Haris watched the Tuareg walked away, as he turned slowly toward the wall etched with hundreds of slashes. *Could Pelliquen have been dead for two years?* He began to weep, when a streak of pain shot through his head and the room began to spin before his eyes. Wobbling back and forth, Haris could not make the room stop its whirling, and dropped to the floor.

CHAPTER

THIRTY-EIGHT

Tripoli – August 9, 1551

The day began with a sunrise no different than any other of the thousands of dawns that had painted the floor of his cell a rosy glow; but quickly the morning developed into something much more. As Haris opened his eyes, he heard a series of explosions in the distance, which continued throughout most of the day. He had been aware of such gun bursts before, believing them to be related to local street celebrations, but this time the consistency of the explosions surprised him. Over the next several days, the relentless daylight bombardment grew louder, as it became apparent the violent activity drew closer. He tried to gain an explanation from the blue man, but the dutiful worker continued his creepy vow of silence; although he suddenly began performing his daily task with unusually hurried feet. And when the blue man made no appearance on the fifth day of the explosions, Haris sensed the assault had arrived at the fortress.

August 15, 1551

Plagued by hunger and filled with anticipation, Haris found no rest throughout the night. When the sunlight again burst into his cell, the deafening sound of explosions commenced with the consistency of a rooster announcing daybreak. One after another the ferocious roar shook the prison cell, followed by terrifying screams convincing Haris that the northern side of the fortress was under siege. He covered his ears with his hands and recoiled into the far corner of the cell, hoping he may find a way out of his hellhole, before it became his tomb.

Shortly thereafter, the bombardment ceased, and was replaced by bursts of arquebus fire with distant voices yelling indistinguishably. Suddenly, Haris heard an iron key rattling inside the cell door lock. With great surprise, he watched as the door swung open, revealing a uniformed soldier stepping into the room with his sword drawn. "There is one in here! He is alive!"

Haris understood the language, lifting his eyes to the soldier, and recognized the uniform as Ottoman, just as a second soldier passed through the doorway. The man stopped to behold the many slashes carved into all four walls, before addressing him. "Do you speak Turkish?"

Haris studied the man's face closely with disbelief. *Is it him? Can it really be?*

The soldier questioned him again. "Do you speak Turkish?"

Haris parted his lips and began to form the syllables. "Serkan," he gasped faintly.

The soldier gave a stunned look. "What did you say?"

"Serkan . . . it is me—Haris!"

Serkan slowly approached him. "Haris? Lezhe Haris?"

Haris nodded.

"Allah, be praised!" He reached down and grabbed Haris' arms and pulled him into a standing position. Serkan gaped as he stared at his frail, bearded friend before giving him a firm embrace, glancing once again at the cell's walls. "You have been imprisoned here all of this time? What cruelty is this?"

Haris could not answer, but only wept uncontrollable tears of joy.

After three days of rest, warm food, and a cleansing Mediterranean swim, Haris emerged from below deck of the sailing warship to find a light, steady rainfall beneath darkened afternoon skies. He negotiated the deck of the rocking vessel until firmly grabbing hold of the railing at the starboard side, glancing upward at the three enormous masts with sails full of wind. He closed his eyes as the cool rain struck his face, drenching the change of clothing Serkan had provided him.

Haris opened his eyes upon hearing his name called, and watched as Serkan approached, placing a hand on his shoulder. "You're getting soaked, my friend," he said.

Haris smiled. "I do not mind. It is the first time beyond four walls that I have felt rain against my skin in a very long time. I will never again complain of such a gift from God."

"I must tell you, I am truly relieved how you no longer smell." Serkan laughed, before shaking his head. "I do not know many men who could have survived as long as you did alone in that cell."

"To be honest, Serkan, if I had the means, I would have taken my life a long time ago."

"Praise, be to God that you did not."

Haris looked Serkan directly in his eyes. "God sent you to me, Serkan. I trusted in Him and He didn't slay me." He pushed his long wet hair back from his forehead. "Can you imagine being forced to have a conversation with none but four walls, for as long as I have?"

Serkan shook his head. "It troubles me to think of such a thing."

Haris raised his head to view the masts. "What is this ship? There are no oars?"

"It is a *kaylon,* a new warship within the Ottoman navy, powered by sails. No oars. It is only one of a few, but the plan is to build more."

Haris expressed confusion. "How long has it been since we left Tripoli? I don't remember having met the captain of this vessel?"

"Three days. The captain is the Kapudan Dragut. We are in good hands."

"Dragut is the kapudan? What of Barbarossa?"

"He died five years ago."

Haris stared at Serkan inquisitively. "I have so much to ask, and so much to learn, Serkan."

"I know you do. But now is not that time. You need your rest. Tomorrow I shall answer all of your questions."

Haris placed his hands on Serkan's arms. "I am happy you are here with me, Serkan. You have saved me."

* * *

The following morning, as the ship sailed eastward, Haris leaned against a cannon barrel while on deck, gazing out at the clear horizon. With the excitement of a child, he watched the daylight slowly chase away the darkness.

As the sun cleared the horizon, Haris noticed Serkan approaching, carrying two oranges. He tossed one to Haris, before bringing his hand up to shield his eyes from the sun. "It's beautiful, is it not?"

"I'm sorry, Serkan, but I don't think you can appreciate the sunrise with the same enthusiasm that fills me."

"I believe you are correct. How long have you been outside?"

"Most of the night." Haris bit into the orange, spitting a chunk of the skin overboard. "My galley experience continues to haunt me. I know this ship is not powered by the blood and sweat of prisoners, nevertheless I find it hard to spend too much time within the hull."

Serkan stepped to the opposite side of the cannon, leaning his back against the ships railing. "You have questions. I shall do my best to answer them."

Haris worked at peeling the orange. "I remember you as a Janissary. What are you doing on this vessel?"

"I am still a Janissary." Serkan pointed to the symbol of a soup ladle sewn to the breast pocket of his uniform. "I was promoted to the rank of corbaci. My orta was assigned to join the naval mission, attacking the locations of the Knights of Malta. We provide the ground troops. Our forces captured the island of Gozo two weeks before we attacked Tripoli."

"Congratulations on your promotion." Haris removed the last piece of skin from the orange. "Tell me, who was the leader of the fortress where I was imprisoned?"

Serkan thought for a moment. "A Frenchman . . . Gaspard de Vallier."

Haris shook his head. "Never once did I hear that name. He never made an attempt to visit my cell. After Pelliquen's death, the Frenchman probably did not know or care to know I was a prisoner."

"How did you come to be imprisoned?"

Haris bit into the fruit. "The martolos attacked me and handed me over to an Ottoman corsair."

"Ottoman—one of our own?"

A smirk ran across Haris' face. "Yes. The traitor traded me for a bag of gold coins." He chuckled. "It is the second time in my life that I have been exchanged for coins. He had orders to kill me, but saw value in my official title."

"Who do you believe ordered your abduction and death?"

Haris stared out at the dark blue sea. "It had to be someone hoping Mustafa would believe I had abandoned my duties, and fled to join Badra."

"The martolos continued to question women of the harem and searched the port of Izmir for several weeks after your disappearance."

Haris spun toward Serkan. "Do you know if they found anything?"

Serkan shook his head. "I do not think so. They told the sehzade they believed you fled to join your woman. At first I do not think the sehzade believed them, but as weeks and months passed without any word from you, we all began to wonder if it was true." He reached out and grabbed Haris' arm. "Believe me when I tell you that had I, Mustafa, Kamil—had anyone of us known your fate we would have gone to the ends of the earth to rescue you!"

Haris gently lifted Serkan's hand from his arm. "I believe you, my friend."

"To realize now that the martolos were responsible for your ordeal makes me want to behead all of them!"

Haris grimaced, pounding the cannon softly with his fist. "I wished for their death many times." He relaxed his hand, and took another bite of the orange. "What of Kamil?"

"He remains the sehzade's silahdar agha."

"In Manisa?"

"No. The sehzade was reassigned to Amasya. It's been ten years now."

Haris expressed confusion. "Why was Mustafa moved?"

"The sultan replaced him in Manisa with his son, Selim."

"Selim? I would have thought Mehmed to be Suleyman's first choice after Mustafa?"

"He was. Mehmed died from smallpox shortly after arriving in Manisa."

"I see." Haris frowned. "I don't like it. It sounds as if Mustafa may have fallen out of favor with Suleyman."

"The sehzade's popularity among the Janissary continues to grow. Because of this and his military experience, his relocation to Amaysa may be a strategic one. The city is closer to the border with the Safavid."

Haris was unconvinced. "How is Mustafa?"

"I have not seen the sehzade in some time. I remember he was very saddened by the death of his first born son. The child died of illness about a year after your disappearance."

Haris frowned. "That is tragic."

"Yes—but Allah has blessed him with more children."

"Fatma is the mother of them all?"

"No. The sehzade has had several consorts with whom he has sired children. However, he did take a wife a few years ago. She is called Rumeysa."

Haris' eyebrows lifted with surprise. "Like father, like son," he said, biting into the fruit. "Any news of Badra?"

Serkan frowned and shook his head. "I am sorry, Haris."

Haris grew somber. "I only pray she is safe."

"May God have mercy on her."

The men fell silent for a few minutes until Haris had finished his orange. "I imagine Suleyman is still playing war games. Which country currently has his army's attention?"

Serkan grinned. "Be careful not to sound too callous about our sultan, Haris. The wrong people may be listening."

Haris chuckled. "What could they possibly do to me that they haven't already done, aside from kill me? I have died a thousand deaths in that Tripoli prison."

Serkan sighed. "The Ottoman military is stronger and more respected than ever. The sultan has a solid alliance with France and has established a treaty with Venice. Although I believe the Venetians cannot be trusted. Austria's Ferdinand continues to be little more than a nuisance to Suleyman, and the sultan scored a great victory at sea against Charles' navy at Preveza."

"It sounds as though not much has changed in fifteen years."

Serkan gazed out over the sea. "At present, it is Tahmasp and the Safavid threat to the eastern border of the empire that preoccupies the sultan."

"Then I am correct, when I say not much has changed." Haris raised both arms to stretch. "Who is Suleyman's new grand vizier?"

"There have been three since Ibrahim's death. Currently, it is Rustem Pasha."

Haris quickly lowered his arms. "Rustem?" He scoffed. "Then maybe Mahidevran has been right all along."

Serkan look puzzled. "How so?"

Haris grinned. "Jackals—all of them a pack of hungry jackals." He brought his attention back to the sea. "What is our destination?"

·"Constantinople."

Anxiety swept across Haris' face, as he turned toward Serkan. "No! Not Constantinople! I cannot!"

"Haris, the kapudan is excited. He will be praised by the sultan for rescuing and freeing a captive vizier."

"I am no longer a vizier. Nor do I have any desire to return to that role." Haris sighed. "Serkan, I tell you Megara Ali is a born killer. He could have done away with me easily fifteen years ago. Displaying his handiwork at performing executions is his forte. Yet, he passed me off to another to do what he does with precision. I think he only spared my life because someone of importance set him to the task. That someone did not want my corpse to be found, or my death traced back to whomever gave the order. That person could very well be in Constantinople."

Serkan cringed with frustration. "But what shall I tell the kapudan?"

Haris thought for a moment. "Tell him that I have suffered enough. Explain to him how I wish to forget about my ordeal and quietly disappear."

"He will question such a request."

"Then you must persuade him to believe that the last thing the kapudan needs at the moment is evidence of Ottoman corsairs who kidnap viziers. He and the navy will be disgraced—should I decide to tell my tale."

Serkan nodded. "You may be correct, my friend. Then where shall we take you?"

"Karatas. The port is only a few hours ride on horseback from Adana. I will seek out my ana and baba."

Serkan sighed, shaking his head. "Several hours on horseback may be too far for your weary body to travel just yet. I am thankful your mind is as sharp as I remember it, but after your lengthy ordeal in prison, I can see with my own eyes how physically you are not whom you once were."

Haris scoffed.

Serkan grew more animated. "You are skin and bones! I have watched you pace the deck, moving like an old man with a noticeable limp! You hobble along as if all your muscles have been eaten away!"

Haris directed an earnest stare in Serkan's direction. "Please, my friend. I ask of you only to convince the kapudan to take me to Karatas. From there, I am in God's hands."

CHAPTER

THIRTY-NINE

Ten days later, the Ottoman kaylon dropped anchor off the coast of Karatas. Tucked away in the northeastern corner of the Mediterranean Sea, the tiny port featured crystal clear surf, and white powdered beaches familiar to Haris. Seated within a row boat that had disembarked from the ship, he recalled days in his youth when his ana and baba would bring him there to admire the great many species of birds which congregate in the area, and to explore the numerous turtle nests pitting the beach.

"This is a beautiful location," Serkan said, seated across from Haris. "I have never been here."

Haris smiled beneath his thick, unkempt beard. "There are remains of an ancient Greek temple nearby. Ahmet showed me it on several occasions. He says it is where Alexander the Great offered a sacrifice to Athena, before leading his men against the Persians at the Battle of Issus."

Serkan nodded. "Greeks, Macedonians, Romans, and now Ottomans—I wonder who will be the caretakers of this land after we are gone."

"Caretaking is a good way to describe it," Haris said. "Empires are like renters who suddenly find how one day they can no longer afford the rent."

"If that is the case, then God is the landlord," Serkan added, with a smile.

When the boat had reached the crude, wooden pier, Serkan accompanied Haris to shore and purchased a donkey from a local stable. He handed the reins to Haris. "Well, my friend, this is farewell."

Haris petted the animal. "Thank you Serkan for convincing Dragut to deviate from his course."

"You were correct, Haris. I sensed the kapudan did not wish to broach the subject of Ottoman corsairs."

Haris nodded, emitting a long sigh. "It has been a long time since you and I battled one another at the behest of the sehzade." He grinned. "I was lucky that day."

"No—we were both lucky, for had I defeated you, our journey together would never have begun."

Both men embraced one another, kissing each other's cheeks.

Serkan patted him on the shoulder. "Be safe my friend, and tell your ana and baba I asked of them." He grinned. "And do not be surprised if they cringe at the sight of you, because you look and smell like death!" He chuckled before a look of earnestness returned to his face. "Here, you may need this." He unfastened the sheathed sword from around his waist, and handed Haris the weapon. "May God give you good reward," he added, beginning a pace toward the row boat.

As he mounted the donkey, Haris watched Serkan climb into the boat—both men's faces remaining expressionless, as they shared a nod.

* * *

Nearly two hours had passed before Haris came upon acres of symmetrical rows of shrubby plants sprouting cotton, with the familiar sun-dried brick home in the foreground. When he approached the dwelling, he realized how his ana and baba must have seen him coming up the long dirt road; for the unsuspecting couple greeted him as a stranger outside, before he could dismount the donkey. Haris understood how their delayed response in recognizing him was rooted in his gaunt, ashen appearance, set behind a long, ragged beard; but he did not know the severity of his looks until he could see tears flowing from both of their eyes. *Serkan's description of him had been too kind.*

Over the next several hours, Haris stuffed his mouth with fresh fruit and vegetables in between a recounting of the series of events that had led him to their door. In return, they revealed how they knew of his sudden disappearance months after it had happened, learning the news from their neighbor—Jucef's sister. Like Serkan, they believed he had deserted his post and gone after Badra. For the first time, Haris divulged how leaving to be with her had been his original plan; although he had wished to delay his departure until after the martolos had concluded their investigation, and when he felt certain Mustafa was comfortable with the decision.

When Haris had grown fatigued with his narration, he retired to his old bedroom. There he found a mirror and for the first time in many years, examined his emaciated physique, topped with gray hair at the temples merging with a salt and pepper beard. Wearing a forlorn expression, he covered his eyes with his hands, and wept tears of exhaustion. Over the course of the next three days, he did little more than sleep, leaving his bed only for meals.

Over the following weeks, Haris' prolonged bouts of rest and Zahra's home cooked food, combined to gradually nurse him back to health. Regular bathing softened his coarse skin, while a haircut and sunshine on his face worked to brighten his disposition. He decided not to shave the beard, although he cut the facial hair back and began grooming it. It was when Haris began to gain comfort with his hygienic transformation that he began to appreciate his ana and baba's battle with the passing of time. On the surface, Zahra's hair had become completely gray, and aside from gray at the temples, Ahmet had lost most of his. Lines of age had appeared beneath their eyes and traversed both of their foreheads, while the speed in which they moved about seemed to have diminished greatly in the fifteen years since last he saw them. However, the inner spirit, resilient work ethic, and nurturing tendencies, which had always characterized both of them, remained unchanged.

As the weeks turned into months, Haris began an exercise routine involving calisthenics and running, while the building of his muscles came naturally with his desire to help labor on the farm. In the evenings, he would spend an hour or two before bed reading from Ahmet's library—books he had read in his youth; although he found a sense of rebirth in their rediscovery. The growth of his mental and physical strength began to work like rain nurturing a flowerbed, with the prize rose of his garden being memories of Badra. Thoughts of her became more prevalent with each passing day, forcing the once fading mental apparition of her to resurrect itself.

September, 1552

The year had passed quickly for Haris, aided by work in the fields melding the days together seamlessly, until Ramadan graced the Muslim calendar for the second time since his return home. The three of them had just finished breaking the fast after dusk, seated outside in the small open courtyard of the home beneath a rising full moon, when Ahmet posed a question that caught Haris by surprise. "How old are you, Haris?"

Haris thought for a moment, with a confused look. "I don't know."

"You were forty-seven in July," Zahra blurted.

"How do you remember?" Ahmet asked.

Zahra shrugged her shoulders. "I remember such things. He was brought to us when he was eleven."

"Eleven?" Haris frowned, shaking his head. "I am forty-seven? Where has my life gone?"

"A large portion of it in prison, I would say," Ahmet remarked.

"Now, now Baba, don't discourage him." She tilted her head, smiling at Haris. "You became a ghazi of the Janissaries and served as a vizier for the sehzade. Those are remarkable achievements that should not be forgotten."

"Thank you, Ana."

Ahmet sat back in the chair. "Haris, you told me six months ago how your goal was to return to Badra. What is keeping you from this?"

Haris hesitated, choosing his words. "You need help here on the farm."

Ahmet's eyes widened as he shifted forward in his chair. "Your ana and I are most capable of running this farm without your help. We appreciate your hard work, but it is not a necessity. You have seen the field hands who I employ. The operation will not cease in your absence."

"I'm sure what you say is true. But you're older—"

"As are you!" Ahmet exclaimed. "You are wasting time here when you should be out seeking the woman you love! God did not bring you back here to spend the rest of your days working at planting and harvesting cotton!"

Haris did not know how to reply, before Zahra reached across the table, taking hold of his hand. "You are afraid of what you might find, are you not, Haris?"

Haris swallowed hard. "It's been sixteen years. How could she not have found a new life—if she is even alive at all?" He stood up and stepped away from the table, raising his head toward the moon. "She once told me how on moonlit nights she would gaze at the moon, wondering if those she loved were also gazing at the same moon, thinking of her."

Zahra smiled. "Haris," she said softly, breaking his moon trance and casting his eyes to her. "Badra is out there. Believe she is gazing at the moon tonight thinking of you as you are of her, and it will be true."

CHAPTER FORTY

May 1553

With Ahmet's and Zahra's encouragement, Haris concluded that his destiny lay in finding Badra, and decided that come Spring, he would set off for Nin. In this way, he felt comfortable knowing he would be able to assist Ahmet in sowing the cotton fields before leaving. With his spare time, he began training with the sword Serkan had gifted him—working tirelessly at polishing his dormant warrior skills, believing they might be necessary in his quest.

One day in late May, after a heavy rainfall, Zahra noticed a puddle of water on the kitchen floor, realizing the roof had leaked. Haris was afraid for Ahmet climbing to the rooftop to repair the problem, and volunteered to fix it himself. While on top of the roof, Haris located the damaged tile, but made the mistake of looking down. Suddenly, a bout of dizziness came over him, leaving him to lose his footing and tumble from off the roof. He smashed onto the solid ground, striking his head, as well as the left side of his body.

Several hours later, Haris regained consciousness, opening his eyes to behold a welcoming, but unexpected face. "Jucef?"

Jucef smiled. "Lezhe Haris. It would appear you have returned from the dead."

"It is a long story. I was imprisoned for fifteen years."

"I have just learned the tale. Ahmet and Zahra have brought me up to date on the facts of your ordeal."

Haris winced as a streak of pain shot through his left shoulder and arm. He glanced down to see how his arm from the wrist to above his elbow was wrapped tight in linen, supported by two hollowed elder branches below the bending elbow and two above it. The branches were tied tight with rope to form the splint.

"From what Ahmet tells me, you are lucky you didn't break your neck." Jucef folded his arms below his chest. "How did you fall from the roof?"

"I grew dizzy when I looked to the ground."

"Have you always had such a reaction to heights?"

Haris grimaced and shook his head. "No, but I do remember falling over in my cell many times, as if the prison was suddenly rocking at sea."

"Have you ever suffered a head injury?"

Haris took a moment to think. "Yes. When taken captive by the martolos, I was struck in the head from behind."

Jucef grimaced. "I think that may be the root of your problem. Unfortunately, such a reaction to heights may be something you will have to live with for the rest of your days."

Haris frowned, taking a moment to analyze Jucef's face, with its familiar benevolence undeterred by the signs of age he assumed afflicted the remainder of the doctor's body. Silver hair encircled the bottom half of his bald head, with a thin frame supporting a pot-bellied midsection, while he sat leaning forward clutching a walking stick. "What are you doing here, far from Manisa?"

Jucef smiled. "I am no longer in service to the sehzade, for age has caught up to me. As it so happens, I am in Adana visiting my sister. She is the only family I have remaining, and so I plan to make my home here."

Haris raised his head. "How severe is my arm and shoulder?"

Jucef grimaced. "Your shoulder should make a complete recovery, but your elbow was shattered severely. You may never fully be able to straighten your left arm."

Haris sighed. "My skill with the bow and arrow?"

Jucef frowned, shaking his head.

Haris plopped his head back onto the pillow. "How long until I am free of this splint?"

"In about ten or twelve weeks."

With a disappointed face, Haris turned away from the doctor. "You had other plans?"

"Yes, to seek out Badra," he replied, staring at the wall beside his bed.

"Ah, the lovely maiden." Jucef grinned. "I am told she is the reason for the misfortune you have endured."

Haris brought his attention back to the doctor. "No, Jucef. I am to blame. I allowed myself to be led into a trap many years ago."

"Well, the important thing is that you are alive. But can the same be true of her?" Jucef rose from the chair. "I will return in a week to change the dressing and apply a plaster to your arm made of linen soaked in wax and lard."

Haris nodded.

"It is very good to see you again, Lezhe Haris. The last two decades working with Mustafa's royal family have been the highlight of my career. I was fortunate our paths crossed in Vienna."

Haris forced a smile. "Tell me, how is Mustafa?"

Jucef grinned. "He has developed into a born leader, and it is said how the Janissary corps respect him above all of Suleyman's sons. As his tutor, he has you to thank for this." He stepped toward the doorway. "Although I will admit that he has not been the same since your departure. He is less tolerant—more distrusting now, and impulsive. The sehzade possesses all of the tools needed to be a great sultan, but he lacks one thing—"

"What is that?" Haris asked.

"It's you, Haris. He lacks you—his voice of reason."

CHAPTER

FORTY-ONE

With the passage of summer, Haris' arm and shoulder injury healed, and although he did not plan it, his extended stay in Adana gave him opportunity to assist Ahmet in harvesting the cotton they had sewn. Mentally and physically, he had convinced himself he was now prepared to seek out his lost love; but as an ocean's surf rhythmically casts debris to the shoreline, he lived with the fear that events would continue to delay the commencement of his quest.

October 3, 1553

The sun loomed low on the horizon chasing the field hands from Ahmet's farm, when Haris decided to take his daily run in between rows of cotton. At one point during his exercise, he glanced at the front of the house where his eyes caught a two-wheeled horse drawn carriage at rest, surrounded by a dozen soldiers on horseback. With hesitancy he ceased his running, and moved toward the carriage.

As Haris approached the vehicle, Ahmet stopped him. "It is a special visitor from Amaysa."

Haris wiped the sweat from his brow. "Mustafa?"

Ahmet shook his head just as two soldiers opened the carriage door and assisted a veiled woman from out of the vehicle, clad in a black robe. She stared at Haris before delicately removing her silk facial covering. In unison, Haris and Ahmet bowed at the sight of Mahidevran, while from behind the carriage, a soldier appeared holding the lead line to a white mare.

"Alabaster!" Haris exclaimed, rushing toward his old friend. The horse bobbed its head up and down, whining as Haris placed his head affectionately against the animal's long snout, petting its nose.

The woman paced slowly toward Haris, viewing him with a wide smile. "It really is you! Your beard hides the unmistakable contours of your face, but it is those blue eyes that give you away—beacons into your soul. The same light that once guided my son through the challenges of becoming a man."

Haris continued to give his attention to Alabaster.

"Your mare found its way back to the palace the night of your disappearance—the only eyewitness to your fate." Mahidevran shook her head. "If only the animal could speak."

Haris stepped away from the horse. "Mahidevran Kadin, I did not abandon Mustafa."

Mahidevran turned away from him, gazing out over acres of cotton. "It is beautiful country here, far removed from the city." She glanced back at him. "Haris, walk with me."

The two stepped away from the carriage, moving slowly, side by side along a dirt path in a direction away from the house. "I know you did not desert my son," Mahidevran said, turning toward him with a heartfelt stare. "As a mother knows when her son is in danger, I recognized immediately how your disappearance all those years ago was the result of something much more diabolical. When the story of what you had endured finally came to be, I felt your pain. You did not deserve what was done to you."

Haris kicked a stone as he shuffled his feet. "Kadin, why are you here in Adana?"

She stopped, turning toward him. "As I feared for you when suddenly you vanished, I now fear for my son. I sense soon he may be in danger, and will need your help."

Haris sighed. "My days of playing Ottoman politics are over, Kadin. From what I have heard, Mustafa has established himself as the clear successor to the sultan's throne. He has survived more than fifteen years without me at his side. I think he has proven his worth. Most importantly, it is said he has the support of the Janissaries in the matter of succession."

"What you say is true, and you are to be commended for your tutelage of my son. He owes his success to you, Haris. You have always been his armor." She reached out and grabbed his wrists. "But I fear even the Janissaries may not be able to protect him from what may lie ahead. He is a proud man, prone to making a point with dramatics rather than using prudence."

"Are you aware of something?"

"I have had dark dreams, Haris. I fear Hurrem and Rustem may be plotting against my son, just as I'm sure they plotted against Ibrahim." She looked deeply into his eyes. "As I also suspect it was the two of them who ordered your disappearance. They wished to separate Mustafa from his armor, and they succeeded."

Haris frowned, troubled by her words.

"Do you know that Rustem married Hurrem's daughter Mihrimah?" Mahidevran revealed, releasing hold of Haris' wrists. "The house of Suleyman is being converted into a den of thieves who are working hard at stealing the sultanate away from my son!"

"Does Mustafa know I am alive?"

"Yes, but he has been preoccupied with war, as Tahmasp and his Safavid army threaten the eastern border once again. The sultan has requested Mustafa lead his army to meet up with him at

Eregli. He marches in that direction as we speak. He misses you greatly, and if not for this war, would come to see you. My son is relieved you are alive, Haris. But he does not know I am here today."

Haris' gaze turned distant.

Mahidevran soured. "You do not trust my instincts?"

He sighed. "Hurrem and Rustem have had many years to plot Mustafa's demise, why do you have such fears now?"

"Because I have seen how the accusation of betrayal becomes more of a weapon in times when similar peoples are at war with one another. The Safavid and the Ottomans are of the same Islamic faith despite how one practices Shia and the other Sunni. They are akin in many ways, with related customs and origins. The wind of change can shift easily over a landscape that is difficult to tell apart. One need only to look to Europe to see who the Christians fear more—it is not the Muslims, but rather, one another. That is why Catholics and Protestants kill one another voraciously."

Mahidevran gathered in a breath. "Ibrahim lost his life while the Ottomans were at war with the Safavid. Now I sense with grave concern that the timing is ripe for another false indictment of betrayal!" She turned away from Haris and faced the carriage, clapping her hands. Immediately, a soldier retrieved two bulging sacks from inside the vehicle and marched toward her. The soldier stopped before Haris, handing him both sacks.

"Despite your extended absence, Mustafa insisted on continuing your payment as his first vizier," Mahidevran described. "These are your earnings. They are well deserved, and should provide you with comfort for the rest of your days." She looked deeply into Haris' eyes. "I am glad you are alive and in good health. I have loved you like a son. I know what risk you take should you go to Eregli, but Mustafa is my only son, and a mother must do whatever she can to protect her offspring. If it is not too late, you may be his only hope." She latched the veil over her face, turning away from Haris, before stepping toward the carriage.

"Mahidevran Kadin!" Haris called out. "I will leave for Eregli in the morning!"

Mahidevran stopped and turned. "Then I have something for you." She opened the small purse attached to the belt around her waist, as Haris drew closer.

Haris watched as she pulled a silver chain from the purse attached to a circular piece of jewelry made of glass, featuring concentric circles in dark blue, white, and light blue. Mahidevran handed him the necklace. "The evil eye," she described. "It will protect you, for if the person wearing it is filled with good, then the amulet will reflect the malicious gaze of the one wishing to do him harm."

"Forgive me, Mahidevran, but I do not believe in such superstitions."

She grinned. "Nor do I. But as a gift from me, I am hopeful that when you feel its presence around your neck, you will think of me, and my desire for you to protect my son."

* * *

When morning had broken, Haris shared a long, melancholy goodbye with his ana and baba, not knowing when or if he would ever see them again. He handed them one of the sacks of coins, which he insisted they accept after much persuasion.

Recognizing how his journey to seek out Mustafa could be wrought with the danger of someone still wishing for him to be dead, he realized the need for a disguise to accompany his beard-ed face. Zahra gathered a long cloth robe and a short rounded cap for him to wear, while Ahmet gave him his subha, so the clothing and prayer beads might allow him to pass for an imam. He carried a dagger inside the waistband of his breeches, while concealing his sword beneath a blanket set underneath Alabaster's saddle, and was sure to wear Mahidevran's amulet around his neck. Before mounting his mare, the three prayed together, sharing tearful hugs and kisses. Then as the sun made its appearance in the eastern horizon, Haris set out in a northerly direction toward Eregli.

CHAPTER

FORTY-TWO

Eregli – October 6, 1553

Dusk had transformed the skyline into a purple haze as Haris brought Alabaster to a halt on top of the hill overlooking the Eregli valley. There he beheld a large military encampment stretching across the basin's floor, reminiscent of his Janissary days on campaign. Colorful pointed tents, thousands of men in vibrant uniforms, hundreds of horses and camels, and a massive assemblage of artillery seemed to stretch endlessly from one end of the valley to the other.

Haris guided his mare down the hillside, eventually meandering about the vast camp asking the whereabouts of the Sehzade Mustafa. He was sure to conceal the amulet beneath his robe, as his attire and request were met with strange looks; although he appeared to garner little suspicion.

* * *

At the top of the opposite hill, the largest of all the tents had been erected, gracing the encampment like a castle keeping vigilance over its domain. Surrounding the main shelter, as does a castle's moat, set a vast grouping of smaller tents arranged in a circle. These were the lodgings of the sultan's Janissaries, with

413

their positioning set up to reflect their elite position in service to the sultan.

As the day's shadows grew longer, the figure of a man could be seen gaining entrance to the main tent where he found Suleyman seated quietly in a chair, stroking his long beard. The man stepped up to the sultan and bowed.

"Rustem Pasha, you have news?" Suleyman asked.

Rustem reached inside of his kaftan and withdrew a piece of folded parchment. "Yes, Your Royal Majesty. Its writer is Hurrem Sultan." He handed the letter to Suleyman.

Suleyman read it silently and when finished, slowly folded the letter with a sigh. He raised his eyes to Rustem. "Her informants claim that Mustafa has been in communication with the Venetians. They would support his rise to the Ottoman throne, and in response, Mustafa would return Morea to their control—an area the Ottomans have ruled for nearly one hundred years."

"It is sedition, Sultan!" Rustem clenched his fists. "I have also heard rumors that Mustafa has made it known to Aysa Pasha, the beylerbey of Erzurum, of his desire for the throne!"

Suleyman became enraged. "Send for Mustafa—tonight! I shall confront his betrayal!"

* * *

Deep within the congested valley camp, Haris finally located Mustafa's tent, but the sehzade's guards would not permit his entrance, and a shouting match ensued. The boisterous exchange forced the sehzade's silahdar agha to step outside, where Haris recognized Kamil.

"What is the reason for this outburst?" Kamil questioned.

Haris studied his friend with contained elation. The silahdar agha's gentle facial features had withered slightly from age, and the once thick dark mustache now shone silver, but the dark brown eyes had not lost their welcoming luster. "Kamil, do you not recognize an old friend?"

Kamil gaped. "Praise, be to God! Haris!" The two men shared a long embrace. "You did not listen to me when I warned you not to seek out the writer of that letter! I should have been by your side! I have never forgiven myself for not disobeying you!"

Haris smiled. "I wish I would have listened to you."

"I have heard many rumors about your years away. What is the truth?"

"Kamil, I will tell you everything, but now is not the time. I must see Mustafa. It is important."

Kamil nodded, leading Haris inside the tent. As they entered, both men paused to observe Mustafa standing with his back toward the entrance, adjusting his golden robe.

Mustafa spun around. "Well Kamil, what was all of the shouting about?" Before anyone could respond, the sehzade stood frozen, glaring at Haris.

Haris sensed Mustafa's reaction mirrored what it must be like to have seen a ghost. Although for Haris, it was the flesh and blood standing before him that warranted surprise. Mustafa had grown up—no longer a young man, but a dark, handsome, strapping figure, with a commanding persona that could be unleashed without the utterance of a word.

Mustafa rushed across the room and the two men embraced long, and forcefully. Fighting back the tears, the sehzade pulled away slightly, while maintaining a grip on Haris' shoulders. "My dear, dear friend! It has been much too long! I heard about your ordeal and I promise when this war with the Safavid is ended, and Tahmasp is defeated, you will join me in Amaysa as my vizier! We will not rest until together we hunt down those who have wronged you!"

Haris smiled. "It is good to see you, Sehzade."

Mustafa released his hold on Haris. "And you as well! We have much to talk about, but at the moment, the sultan has summoned me to his tent."

Haris' smile faded. "I am not here to be your vizier. That period of my life is passed."

"You speak nonsense. We were great together, and we shall be so once again."

"I am here because of Mahidevran. She fears for your life."

Mustafa sighed. "She has been afraid for me since I was a child. Nothing is new."

Haris reached out and grabbed Mustafa's arm. "Do not go to your father's tent tonight!"

A serious aura enveloped Mustafa's face. "My destiny has been cast. My army has been summoned here by the sultan and tonight we will plan our attack for tomorrow against Tahmasp. The next day will end with a great victory, and my path to the throne will be unchallenged."

"Your father may believe you want his throne now!"

Mustafa pulled his arm away from Haris and scoffed. "I do not have any intention of taking the throne from my father, which is why I must adhere to his request to see me this evening. I want to profess my loyalty to the sultan and assure him he need not fear me. Haris, remember the day when you and I discussed how should I become sultan I could change the barbaric traditions of the empire? I could bring an end to the fratricide and assassinations staining the legacy of the sultanate. The bloodletting stops with my ascension to the throne."

Haris studied the passion Mustafa portrayed, recognizing there would be no changing the sehzade's mind this night. "Then allow myself and Kamil to accompany you to the sultan's tent."

Mustafa smiled. "You are a good friend, Haris. I have loved you every day in your absence and Allah has brought you back to me." He turned away from both men and paced to the rear of the tent where a slender wooden cabinet stood. Opening its door, he pulled out the tiny bottle with round base and thin neck, carrying it over to Haris. "The Holy Prepuce. It is yours now," he offered, handing the item to Haris. "If it was my amulet for all of these years, I cannot be sure. Perhaps you were the one who needed its powers more than I."

Haris studied the bottle within his hand. "Take the Holy Prepuce with you to the sultan's tent!"

Mustafa shook his head. "I must believe it has been merit, and not superstition that has prepared me for my role as sehzade. You, as my greatest tutor, stand before me as evidence of what I say." He placed his hand on Haris' shoulder and smiled. "Wait for me here. God willing, I will see you within the hour. We shall celebrate your return."

As Mustafa exited the tent, Haris squeezed the bottle, dropping his head in exasperation.

Kamil frowned. "Allah challenges us this day—"

* * *

Darkness had descended over the camp as Mustafa dismounted his steed before the sultan's tent. While his personal *mirahur* held his horse's lead line, Mustafa glanced to the sky where he observed a crescent moon looming overhead. He handed his sword to one of the sultan's guards and entered the tent opening. The royal shelter was divided into four sections, with a long narrow carpet cutting a straight path through each segment separated by sheer curtain walls that appeared to breathe as a cool breeze whirled about. Mustafa could see the silhouette of his father seated on a chair, flanked on either side by the flickering glow of lamps situated where the carpet ended within the tent's fourth section. As he passed slowly through each quarter, the dark corners of the wide tent became more foreboding, and Mustafa began to sense that he and the sultan were not alone; but his pride would not allow him to display any semblance of fear in the presence of his father.

Mustafa stopped before Suleyman and bowed, before noticing how the sultan sat clutching an arrow within his hand.

Suleyman raised his eyes to Mustafa and with both hands, snapped the arrow in two. "Dog! You still dare to salute me?"

Mustafa expressed surprise. "Sultan Suleyman Khan?"

"You have betrayed me, Mustafa!"

"No, Sultan! I have not betrayed you! I have come to you as you have commanded! I am your loyal servant! I am your son!"

Suddenly from out of the dark corners of the tent, three assailants rushed Mustafa. The sehzade lowered his shoulder and flipped one of the attackers into the air, throwing him into a collision with another, while kicking a third man in the face who had charged forward with his head lowered. The attackers were slowed momentarily by Mustafa's athleticism, but regrouped, coming in waves. Swinging his fists, Mustafa fought his assailants bravely, working hard to keep all three attackers in front of him.

Suleyman rose from his chair. "Incompetence! Finish him!"

Continuing to punch and kick his attackers, Mustafa broke free and sprinted toward the tent entrance. Suddenly, an assailant dove from behind and grabbed Mustafa's ankles, tackling him to the ground on his stomach. Quickly another attacker pounced on his back, and wrapped a bow string around his neck, pulling tightly.

Mustafa writhed, struggling to breathe, as the string became

418

taut. He tried to lift himself from off the ground, but the weight of the two attackers made his effort futile. He could sense his head growing lighter—his thoughts cast within a dense fog. Suddenly, through a dream-like mist he beheld his wife and children smiling, sprinting toward him . . . he shared an embrace with Haris within the shadow of the castle at Berndorf . . . and he could see his mother weeping for him with outstretched arms. He gasped. "Father . . . Father!" His muscles tightened as his face turned blue, and his eyes rolled to the back of his head. *Mustafa was dead.*

* * *

Within an hour, a deep rumbling cascaded throughout the encampment, chasing every soldier from his shelter, as the rumor of Mustafa's death began to swell. Haris and Kamil raced up the hillside in the direction of the sultan's tent where they joined a great many stunned Janissaries, lingering about beneath a pall of confusion. It was when they reached the crest of the hill, less than fifty rods from the royal shelter, that they could see the naked body of Mustafa lying in the grass. Frozen with disbelief, hundreds of Janissaries stood silently, transfixed on the grisly sight. Throwing listless stares at the entrance to the sultan's tent, they held vigil until suddenly Suleyman appeared, accompanied by Rustem.

The sultan deliberately perused the mystified expressions of the faces of his Janissaries, and gathered in a breath. "I am Sultan Suleyman Khan! My Janissaries, lying before you bear witness to the punishment for betrayal! Behold what fate awaits anyone— anyone who dares betray your sultan!"

There was no immediate response to the sultan's threat, and Haris watched how Suleyman moved his head from side to side, seemingly unnerved by the silence.

Haris' Janissary training conjured the warrior spirit within him, beseeching a violent reaction to Mustafa's death; yet such aggression became tempered with an abysmal somberness numbing his body. Tears saturated his cheeks, as he turned toward Kamil to view the angst on his friend's face. Without uttering a word, he watched Kamil step away and begin a march through the crowd of Janissaries until stopping at a large cauldron suspended from an arc-shaped hanger, positioned above a pile of dying embers. As Kamil placed both hands on the pot, he was joined by other Janissaries and together they pulled the cauldron from the hanger and tossed it on the ground, where it rolled over, spilling its edible contents. Instantly, a chorus of cries began to resound up and down the lines of Janissaries, calling out repeatedly, "*Why Mustafa?!*"

Boldly, Kamil stepped forward. "Sultan, the Janissaries wish to know the nature of the sehzade's betrayal!"

Suleyman stood steadfast and silent, noticeably stunned by the request. He took a deep breath and held his head up. "Your sultan will address the crimes of Mustafa in the morning! For now, we must put aside our fury and our grief! Let us retire peacefully and offer our prayers to Allah for mercy on behalf of the sehzade's soul! It has been an unpleasant evening for all!"

Suleyman and Rustem turned away from the soldiers, disappearing inside the sultan's tent, as slowly the Janissaries began to disperse from the hill. Within the royal shelter, Suleyman stood near the entrance, observing judiciously the retreat of his troops. He turned toward Rustem. "Did you see how the Janissaries overturned the cauldron? I sense a mutiny brewing! In all my years of ruling this empire, I would never have imagined such a response! What have I done?"

"The Janissaries are wounded, Sultan."

420

"More than I would have guessed!" Suleyman slowly paced back and forth, consumed with deep thought. Suddenly the sultan paused, lifting his head to Rustem. "I decree that you, Rustem, are stripped of your title as grand vizier, and you should return to Constantinople in the morning!"

Rustem's eyes widened. "I am to blame for this, Sultan?"

Suleyman cast a long stare. "If not you, then who other? It was you that brought me the news of Mustafa's betrayal!" He sighed with exasperation. "You will continue to work within the Enderun, but you shall move about as a shadow until the impact of this unfortunate event passes."

* * *

The following morning within his tent, Rustem gathered his personal belongings, before being interrupted by a presence appearing at the tent's entrance. Haris stood with head bowed, wearing the woolen cap Zahra had made for him, while carrying Ahmet's subha wrapped around his left wrist. When Rustem noted that he had not requested an audience with an imam, Haris realized his disguise had worked.

Still with his eyes cast to the ground, Haris addressed Rustem. "It is the sultan's wish that you pray with an imam before your journey."

Rustem sighed. "You may enter," he said, turning and marching toward the tent's center. Haris followed him until both men dropped to the ground on all fours, resting side by side in prostration.

As Haris touched his forehead to the ground, Rustem noticed the amulet dangling from his neck. "The evil eye?"

Haris quickly stuffed the amulet back inside his robe and with head bowed began to pray. "'In the name of God, most merciful and most compassionate'—" he began, proceeding to recite Quranic verses which were repeated by Rustem. The reverent discourse continued unabated until Haris, remembering how both he and Rustem hailed from Croatia, lifted his head and uttered in their native tongue, "May the wrath of Allah follow you eternally, as punishment for the execution of Mustafa!" Rustem gawked, and began to raise his head just as Haris withdrew a dagger, pressing the blade against his throat.

"What is this?" Rustem huffed. "Lezhe Haris!"

"Do not look at me! Cast your eyes to the ground!" Haris commanded, still holding the blade against his neck. "The stench of yours and Hurrem's treachery reeks from Eregli to Constantinople! Your handiwork has resulted in extinguishing the one bright son who would have brought dignity to the imperial house!" he scoffed. "I recall a conversation I once had with the sultan over a Biblical passage: 'He that troubleth his own house shall inherit the wind'. With the murder of Mustafa, I have no doubt such a prophecy will be fulfilled! None of Hurrem's sons can compare to the man and leader that Mustafa had become!"

Rustem found the courage to speak. "It is not righteousness that sustains an empire, but an instinct for survival!" He breathed heavily. "Mustafa's fault was his carelessness! He underestimated his enemies!"

Haris growled, clubbing the back of Rustem's head with the handle of the dagger. Rustem moaned and dropped face down to the ground, closing his eyes as he fell into a daze.

* * *

An hour had passed before Rustem's aids found him alone and unconscious. After reviving him with water, he requested Megara Ali be brought to him.

Before long, Ali sauntered inside the tent's opening, wearing an impish grin. "I am at your service, Rustem Pasha."

Rustem grimaced. "Lezhe Haris is alive!"

The color faded from Ali's face. "Forgive me, Rustem Pasha, but it is impossible!"

"He attacked me here in the sanctity of my tent this morning! I tell you he is alive! I have a lump on the back of my head to prove it! I am fortunate he did not kill me—perhaps he is as foolish as you!" Rustem grimaced, rubbing the back of his head. "The sight of the evil eye around his neck should have told me he was not an imam!"

"The evil eye?"

"Yes—the amulet! He wore it around his neck!"

"Do you fear him?"

Rustem shook his head. "No, I do not fear him! I loathe him! I am the grand vizier—!"

"I have recently learned you are no longer grand vizier, Rustem Pasha."

"Do not test me, Ali! I will one day be restored to the rank of grand vizier! What is important now is not my temporary demotion, but rather the preservation of Suleyman's sultanate! If Haris can roam this encampment a free man, then who's to say what other traitors walk among us!"

Ali shook his head and snarled. "I should have killed him myself."

Rustem frowned. "Your orders are to escort me back to Constantinople. Once I am safely in the capitol, you will hunt down Haris, and you will kill him!"

CHAPTER FORTY-THREE

Over the course of the next week, Haris rode Alabaster hard in a southwesterly direction across the Anatolian landscape, moving with purpose as though he were a fugitive. The pounding ride across the rugged terrain made his journey physically difficult; although his thoughts tormented him more. The tragic, senseless loss of Mustafa weighed heavily on his conscience, allowing him to torture himself with imagined scenarios of what could have been. Repeatedly, he chastised himself for not having been more forceful in preventing Mustafa from going to the sultan's tent, often finding himself crying out in the middle of the night for his deceased friend. There was also the feeling of great empathy for Mahidevran—a protective, loving mother, whose only son had been stolen from her. She had always been privy to the warning signs threatening Mustafa, but as a powerless pawn within the perfidious game of empire, she stood little chance against the darker nature of imperial power plays.

Haris began to surprise himself with feelings of pity for Suleyman as well, speculating that perhaps the sultan had been deceived by the jackals surrounding him into believing Mustafa was a threat to his throne. And he questioned his decision to allow Rustem to live, when he could have claimed vengeance and spilled his blood.

All such thoughts haunted Haris for many days, but could not alter his reality. What had been done was done. There was no going back to the world he once knew. His destiny now shifted into a quest to find Badra. Whether she was alive or dead he could not be certain; but finding the answer became his obsession.

* * *

Izmir

Haris dismounted Alabaster, and pulled the mare's lead line as he walked along the pier, finding solace in how the port remained unchanged since last he was here. He examined the many fishing boats moored to the dock, with the hope he might stumble upon the fisherman Duman.

From inside the hull of a vessel, a young man stood up and addressed Haris. "That is a beautiful horse you possess!"

Haris nodded. "Maybe you could help me. I am looking for an old friend—a fisherman named Duman."

The young man's face wrinkled. "I'm sorry, but Duman is dead. He passed away several years ago."

Haris frowned. "That is very sad. He was a good man."

"How did you know him?"

"He once did a favor for me."

The young man stared at Haris. "What is your name?"

Haris hesitated, before uttering, "Lezhe Haris."

The young man's smirk erupted into a wide smile. "You are the vizier who vanished many years ago. I am Onur. Duman was my father. I remember the day you rescued me from the pirates."

Haris returned the smile. "It is good to see you again, Onur. I'm sorry about your father."

"Thank you. How is your lady friend?"

Haris was surprised by the question. "I . . . I don't know. That is why I am in Izmir. I seek answers to her fate." He stepped closer to the boat. "You sailed with Duman the day I asked him to take the woman Badra to Nin?"

Onur nodded. "Yes."

"Did she arrive safely?"

Onur continued to smile. "Yes. In fact, my father and I stayed in Nin for two days until we were certain she had found the priest."

A sense of deep relief enveloped Haris. "Thank you! Thank you! This is good news!"

"That was a long time ago. I hope she is at peace."

Haris turned away and glanced out over the coastline. "There is only one way to be sure."

"You wish to go to her?"

Haris brought his attention back to Onur. "I can pay you whatever you desire. Will you take me to her?"

Onur smiled. "You once saved my life. It will be an honor to sail the vizier to Nin!"

* * *

Nin

It was late afternoon the following day when Haris bid farewell to Onur after the fishing vessel pushed off from an ancient wooden pier on the small islet of Nin, situated in a crystal blue lagoon. He rode Alabaster along a white, sandy beach until finding a dirt road giving way to a stone bridge leading into a small Croatian town. Noticing how most of the houses were alike in their appearance, his curiosity was aroused while passing a building within the town's center featuring a plain eggshell façade and four roofs of different heights meshed together. A circular roof capped the tallest section of the structure, while angular roofs jutted outward at lower levels. A few narrow windows were carved into each side of the building, with a steep bell tower suspended above the entrance.

As Alabaster trotted closer to the building, Haris recognized a few pedestrians walking about the narrow streets, and brought the horse to a halt upon seeing an old man shuffling along with the aid of a cane. "I'm looking for the priest, Father Mateo," Haris said in Croatian. He turned toward the strange building. "Would this be the church?"

The man nodded. "It is the Church of the Holy Cross. Father Mateo is the priest."

"Thank you." Haris decided to press his luck. "One more question, do you know where I may be able to find a woman named Badra?"

The old man shook his head. "I have lived here in Nin all of my life, but I have never heard such a name."

Haris nodded with a frown. "Thank you."

He continued onto the church, where he dismounted and secured Alabaster's lead line, before finding the front door to the building open. Stepping inside the small, but lofty nave, Haris watched a thin man clad in a dark skirted robe light candles on the altar beneath a suspended crucifix.

Quietly, Haris stepped up to a row of wooden pews set closest to the altar and sat down, watching as the priest completed his task.

The priest illuminated the last of the candles before turning around, surprised to find Haris seated in the pew. "Forgive me, friend. I did not hear you enter the church."

Haris smiled, focusing on the large eyes and delicate bronze contours of the priest's face, set beneath a head of thick black hair.

"I did not realize it until now, how much you look like mother! You have her eyes!"

The priest's smile transcended into a look of confusion. "Mother? I'm sorry, but—" He paused, stepping closer to the pew as Haris rose to a standing position. "Jadran? My brother? Can it be? Is it really you?"

Haris stepped forward and both men embraced. "It is me, Mateo! I've come home." They embraced again, before Haris pulled away. "You look well!"

Mateo hesitated with his response. "Brother, I'm not sure I can say the same for you. You look haggard, as though you have been traveling for some time."

Haris scoffed. "If you only knew. Tell me, how is mother?"

Mateo shook his head. "She passed away nine years ago. I wrote to you about her."

Haris frowned. "I was imprisoned."

"Imprisoned?"

"It's a long story that I will share with you at another time." Haris sighed, dropping his head. "For most of my life our parents were like strangers to me, yet I find it odd how I am overcome with deep sadness to know I shall never again lay eyes on either of them."

"What you feel is only natural."

Haris lifted his head. "And our baby sister, Dinora?"

Mateo's expression grew somber. "She is dead as well. She died some years before mother."

Haris dropped his head, painfully conjuring up what images he could of both his mother and sister, before lifting his eyes to Mateo. "The news you bear is unexpected and tragic." He sighed, before forcing a smile. "But I am glad to still have you, my brother."

Both men embraced again.

"Before I forget, I have something for you." Beneath his soiled robe, Haris reached into the pocket of his breeches and pulled out the small glass bottle, handing it to his brother.

Mateo gave the item a curious look as he turned it over within his palm. "What is it?"

"The Holy Prepuce."

Mateo's eyes widened. "The foreskin of Jesus?" He scoffed. "I have heard of such a relic, but how can you be sure?"

"I am not sure. In fact, I have my doubts. However, if I have learned anything about religion in my lifetime, it is how faith is not the search for truth. Rather it is the pursuit of inner strength. If one can find God within that bottle or within a piece of wood or among a bone fragment—then one has found faith. I have witnessed more than I care to remember of religious warfare, and have concluded there is nothing faithful about it. It is only used as a weapon to justify power."

Mateo nodded. "Strange words coming from a warrior."

"We are all warriors, brother—you and me. I have wielded the sword, and you brandish the scripture."

Mateo looked over the bottle again with intriguing eyes. "Thank you, brother. I don't know what to say? If it is truly what you claim it to be, then I am blessed to be its steward. The relic will find a special home within our church."

Haris glanced around the nave. "I think such a humble building as this is a fitting home for such a relic."

Mateo stared at the bottle. "Why did you bring this sacred object to me?"

"Because, like me, it needs a home," Jadran said. "It is an object worthy to be set within the confines of a splendid palace, but I know it will be of more use in humble surroundings."

"It is not the size of the structure that determines the piety of the church, but the sincerity of the devotion expressed by those committed to worship here."

Haris smiled. "Exactly."

"Jadran, over the years I have heard so many rumors about you. I heard you were dead and later that you were alive, but sold into slavery. At one point, a story claimed you had murdered a pasha and were a fugitive. What is the truth?"

Haris chuckled. "The truth is none of that. We have much to discuss and I promise I will tell you everything, but at the moment, my thoughts are only with her."

"Her?" Mateo smiled. "Ah yes—the beautiful maiden who showed up at my church so many years ago carrying a wooden cross engraved with your name."

"Is she still here—here in Nin?"

"She has never left." Mateo paced down the middle aisle of the church, before stopping. "She sits right here in this pew every Sunday for mass."

Haris moved toward the pew, and delicately rubbed his hand over the smooth wooden surface as though it were a sacred object. "Can you take me to her?"

"Yes, of course," Mateo said, before sighing deeply. "But there is something I need to show you first." He began a pace down the aisle toward the entrance, followed closely by Haris.

The two men stepped out into the fading sunlight, crossing the road and stepping into a small cemetery. Mateo weaved in and out of the symmetrical rows of weathered headstones and crosses, appearing unsure of exactly what he sought, until stopping before a plain, stone cross protruding from out of the ground.

Haris bent forward to read the inscription. "Marko." He righted himself and turned toward Mateo. "Who was Marko?"

"Your lady friend's husband. She is a widow, Jadran."

Haris felt a sickening sensation rise from within his stomach. "She took a husband?"

"Can you not blame her, Jadran? How long has it been since last you saw her—sixteen, seventeen years? Marko was a good man—twice her age, but a good provider."

"Does she still ask about me?"

Mateo shook his head. "She stopped asking many years ago."

Haris paced away from the grave site and stood staring westward at the fiery horizon. The revelation of Badra's marriage had blindsided him. He felt confused, betrayed, empty, as though for a moment he had returned to the perpetual loneliness of his Tripoli prison cell.

"Jadran," Mateo called out, breaking Haris' trance. "You just spoke to me inside the church about the importance of faith. Find your inner strength, and go to her."

Haris sighed and turned toward Mateo. "Take me to her."

* * *

A few blocks from the church, Mateo and Haris stepped up to a small, two-story stone dwelling and knocked on the wooden door without a response.

"She is not home?" Haris asked.

"She may be at the beach," Mateo guessed. "She is known to walk the surf almost daily at dusk. We may find Verena there."

"Verena?" Haris asked, with a look of confusion. "Of course! She uses her Christian name!"

A short while later, Haris and Mateo crossed the old stone bridge above the lagoon, where they could see the figure of a woman strolling toward them with a carefree gait, enjoying the ocean surf rushing in and out over her bare feet. They watched her pause occasionally to explore a shell on the beach, or to face the setting sun, as the soft breeze lifted her long hair.

Mateo decided to wait on the bridge, while Haris made his way down to the beach and began a steady pace in her direction. Even after noticing his oncoming presence, she continued to move at a leisurely pace, but as the distance between them narrowed, she stopped. Haris' pace quickened, while the woman stood frozen with her eyes fixated on his approach. When he had reached a point where he could distinguish her facial features, he stopped and stood steadfast. The two figures stared at one another with disbelief, as if beholding specters standing in the sand.

"Badra!" Haris exclaimed.

She gasped, before setting her feet in motion, sprinting toward him, and jumping into his outstretched arms. He twirled her around, while their lips locked together passionately, transcending into a series of fervent kisses—their intensity bringing both of them to their knees in the sand.

Tears rushed from Badra's eyes. "You came back to me!"

Haris delicately wiped her tears away with his fingers. "Forever I shall find you my love, and I have!"

"Am I dreaming?" She ran her fingers through his hair. "I have dreamt of this moment a thousand times—here, on this beach, falling into your arms!"

"Neither one of us is dreaming!" Haris beamed, relieved and elated with her reaction to seeing him once again. "And now forever we shall be together!"

"Oh, Haris!" They kissed again. "I thought you were dead! I waited for over a year, but you didn't come!"

Haris sighed. "It is not because I didn't try! I have endured much in the years since we said goodbye! But it was my desire to find you that has kept me alive!"

Badra looked up at the bridge. "Is that Father Mateo?"

"Yes, he led me to you!"

Badra's smile vanished, as she gathered in a breath. "My love, there is something I must tell you . . . I took a husband."

Haris ran his fingers through her soft hair, only now dirty blonde with the passage of time. "I know of Marko. Mateo told me."

Badra swallowed hard. "Imagine my situation," she began with rapid speech. "Alone as a single woman in an unfamiliar land. Your brother was a godsend, but I needed a provider and protector. Marko was a widower and so we decided to help one another. He needed a woman—I needed a man. He acted always as the perfect gentleman, caring deeply for me, and I loved him for it."

As he listened to her pleasing voice, Haris was besieged with bliss; for in her presence, he knew he was home.

Badra took his hand. "But please understand. The love I shared with Marko was as two very good friends who respected one another living beneath the same roof. It is different for you and me, for my heart burns for you, Haris! It always has! What I shared with Marko resembled the safety and comfort of a perpetual lamp glowing in the darkness. With you Haris, my love is a boundless, raging volcano!"

Haris smiled. "I understand. You have no reason to feel guilt."

Their lips united once again, before Haris pulled away, and gazed into her eyes. "I love you—Verena!"

"I love you too, Haris! I hope you do not mind sharing my home. It is small and simple. It will not be like the days living in the spacious palace of Manisa."

Haris sighed. "If I had to, I would live inside an hourglass with you."

CHAPTER
FORTY-FOUR

After a month of cohabitation, it became clear to Haris and Badra how the passage of time had done little to erode the intensity of their love. They agreed to discard their past identities linking them to the Ottoman world, and henceforth would be known by their birth names, Jadran and Verena. Croatian would be the language they would use to converse with the population of Nin, but within their household they agreed to speak German.

It was within this new, idyllic world of theirs, that the two lovers found themselves seated on a grassy bluff overlooking the lagoon, enjoying the sunshine of a Sunday afternoon within the shadows of an ancient church.

Jadran turned around to gaze at the small, ancient stone building set atop the earthen mound. He studied its central, circular stone keep appearing as its most distinct feature, rising almost twenty feet, with rectangular gaps at its crest set at intervals, presenting the appearance of a medieval castle. At its base, a number of small, medium-sized evergreen trees were planted, surrounding the structure statuesquely as arboreal sentries.

"What is the building?" Jadran asked.

"Saint Nicholas Church," she replied.

"It doesn't look like a church," Jadran said. "Neither does the church in town. From a distance, the dark leaves on the trees surrounding it make it appear as though the lower half of the building is stained in green."

"The trees are yews and their leaves are indeed vibrant this time of year," Verena said. "But I wouldn't advise eating them, for they are poisonous."

Jadran smiled. "I remember my mother telling me about this very location as a child."

Verena smiled. "It is one of my favorite places in Nin. Supposedly, seven Croatian kings were crowned here. It is said the church is hundreds of years old. The keep was added within the last fifty years as a watch tower to keep vigilant against a Turkish invasion."

Jadran laughed. "Well, it has not kept this former Janissary from breaching the hill."

Verena released a soft sigh. "Remember the many times we spent discussing life and our future, lying beneath the Lady of Niobe in Manisa? This place reminds me of those moments."

He leaned into her. "Then we shall make new memories here." They shared a long, passionate kiss.

She brought her hand to his shaven face. "I am happy you have shaved your beard. This is how I always remembered you, clean shaven with strong cheekbones—no beard to hide your smile, or your wisdom."

"My beard was my disguise. I was a shallow version of myself after all those years in prison. But I must admit I feel full of youth and vigor again without it."

A breeze ruffled Verena's hair and she pulled the strands from her face. "It is very sad what happened to Mustafa. I have not had a chance to express my sorrow to you since your return. But more than anyone, I know how close the two of you were."

Jadran leaned back on his hands, staring out at the placid waters of the lagoon. "Mustafa's flame was snuffed out before its time. It is difficult for a burning ember to catch fire when too many feet work at stomping out its glow."

Verena traced her finger along Jadran's arm. "News from travelers who have recently been to Constantinople report there have been daily protests over Mustafa's death, with thousands marching in the streets."

"I have no doubt. The sultan was naïve to think that his son's memory would fade with the wind." The corner of Jadran's mouth curled. "But I am sure Mustafa would have been happy to know how you and I have found one another."

Verena frowned. "I feel sorry for his wife and children."

"I think those inside the Enderun have become accustomed to assassination. It would seem not many seeking the throne can avoid it." Jadran pulled out the amulet from inside his shirt, hanging from the chain around his neck.

"Your necklace, where did you get it?" Verena asked. "Since your return, you have hardly been without it."

Jadran cupped the amulet in his hand. "It was given to me by Mahidevran when she asked me to go to Mustafa and protect him." He sighed. "I failed her."

"How can you believe that, Jadran? You told me how you tried to warn him, but he would not listen," she said. "You and I have nothing to regret about our time in Constantinople or Manisa. Do not forget we were enslaved! Our freedom was stolen from us a long time ago! Mustafa was a victim of the merciless world in which the Ottoman sultanate nurtures! You and I were lucky to have escaped that world!"

Jadran looked deeply into Verena's eyes, before leaning in to kiss her lips. "You are correct, my love." He removed the chain from around his neck and slipped it over her head. "This is no longer a weight of guilt for me. It is a splendid object belonging around the neck of a beautiful woman—the neck of my future wife."

The two embraced with a long kiss, before Verena raised her head to see two figures crossing the stone bridge. "Is that your brother?"

Jadran followed her stare to see two men pacing on either side of a horse. "The man on the right is Mateo. I'm not sure about the other one."

Verena rose to her feet with a large smile. "Oh, my! I did not think he would be here so soon!" She looked at Jadran. "I have another surprise for you, my love! It is my brother! He found me here in Nin many years ago and makes an effort to visit me at least once a year! You will finally get to meet him!" She grabbed hold of Jadran's hand, pulling him to his feet. "Come, let's join them!"

Together, hand in hand, Jadran and Verena trudged down the hillside in the direction of the waving men. As they drew near, Jadran kept his eye on the stranger, noticing his shoulder length blonde hair falling beneath a wide-brimmed feathered hat. When his attire came into focus, Haris noted how the man wore a doublet, slashed so the vivid fabric beneath it could be pulled through. At the sight of such flamboyant dress, one word came to Jadran's mind—landsknecht.

Jadran and Verena stopped a few rods before the men. She released her grip on his hand and rushed toward the landsknecht, embracing him with a firm hug. She turned toward Jadran. "This is my brother!"

Jadran and the landsknecht's eyes met, causing both men's lips to gape simultaneously.

"You?" Jadran blurted. "You are the brother of my future wife?"

"Haris—the Ottoman? You are my sister's lover?"

"As I remember, your name is Ademir."

Jadran could see how Verena appeared stunned. "How do you know one another?" she asked.

Ademir grinned. "We met many years ago as adversaries on the battlefield."

Jadran scoffed. "It seems you are like the plague, for I cannot escape you."

"Jadran!" Verena exclaimed.

Jadran shook his head. "I'm sorry, Verena. But it is just as you described—an incredible surprise. We have history."

Verena looked confused. "How can it be?"

Ademir grinned. "We are both warriors, sister. We are drawn to each other by the sword."

"I am no longer that warrior," Jadran explained.

"It's in our blood, Haris. We cannot escape it."

"And I am no longer, Haris. My name is Jadran."

Ademir scoffed. "No longer a warrior? A new name? Is this all for the love of my sister? How long have the two of you known each other?"

Haris scowled. "Your sister and I met the very same day I first allowed you to live!"

Verena grew flustered. "Well, the past is the past! Soon we shall all be family!" she proclaimed. "Put aside your differences and act not like little boys, but as grown men!"

Jadran grimaced and sighed, before extending an arm toward Ademir, who reluctantly accepted it.

* * *

A few days later, Jadran and Verena entertained Ademir and Mateo with a dinner celebration in the small open courtyard set behind their home. The delectable fare featured fresh fish, squid, and mussels, accompanied by a variety of local vegetables sautéed in olive oil. Pitchers of red wine flowed throughout the evening, casting all inhibitions to the wind, as the discourse grew heartier with the consumption of each cup.

Ademir watched Jadran take a sip. "I am surprised to see a Muslim drinking wine."

Jadran grinned. "I am surprised not to see a landsknecht gulping the wine."

Ademir laughed. "But you are Muslim, right? And the Quran forbids the consumption of spirits."

Jadran sighed, sitting back in his chair. "I have had wine in my lifetime. As a Janissary, it is true drinking spirits was strictly prohibited. During that period in service to the sultan I was more obedient to the law. The Quran describes intoxication as unfavorable, for it may impair one's ability to think clearly about God. I like to think Christians would agree with such logic."

Ademir took a sip from his cup. "It must have been difficult for you to have been forced to switch your allegiance to God after having been cast to the devshirme."

Verena reached over Ademir's shoulder to clear a plate from the table. "Remember brother, like Jadran, I too was enslaved within the harem."

"But you did not switch your faith, and have remained Christian," Ademir explained. "Jadran was raised a Catholic, and became a Muslim."

"I never switched my allegiance to God, Ademir." Jadran sat forward in his chair. "I switched my allegiance to the empire and my conscience. My kidnapping by men in service to the sultan, and my love for your sister, convinced me a better life existed beyond the Ottoman borders."

Mateo poured more wine into his own cup. "Thank God you and Verena have found a home in Nin, since it is an area controlled by Venice, lying beyond the borders of the Turks."

Jadran held his cup up to toast Mateo. "I agree, brother." He turned toward Ademir. "Where is your landsknecht employment taking you now?"

Ademir brought the cup to his lips. "Tuscany. The French are mounting an invasion there against Charles' forces."

Verena placed her hand on her hips. "You need to stop playing war, and find a woman with whom to settle down."

"I assure you that I have no problem finding women with which to lay, my dear sister," Ademir jested.

Verena grimaced. "This landsknecht business will kill you one day!"

"Your sister is right," Jadran added. "With each new battle, you press your luck."

Ademir huffed. "Ha! Advice from a warrior of the Janissary corps—the greatest elite fighting force ever assembled! Yet, he discourages my desire to make a living at war! It would seem the Janissary has grown soft in his old age!"

"I am no longer a Janissary."

Ademir rose from his seat. "Once a warrior, always a warrior!"

Mateo took a deep breath. "I think we've all had a little too much wine with this wonderful meal."

Ademir stared at Jadran, flashing a snide grin. "Perhaps, the wine reveals the truth. Let me ask you Haris . . . or Jadran . . . or whatever you may choose to call yourself. Don't you feel the desire for vengeance against those who wronged you?"

Jadran sighed. "It is not worth carrying such a heavy heart.

I have all I desire here in Nin with your sister and my brother. I have no need to stir up old wounds."

Ademir grabbed hold of the back of the chair, peering at Jadran. "But how can you accept what was done to your sister?"

Jadran rose slowly from his chair. "What do you mean?"

"What was her name—Dinora?"

"What about her?" Jadran asked, throwing a glare at Mateo.

Mateo held his breath, before speaking. "I think it may be best for all of us to retire for the evening."

"What about Dinora?" Jadran pressed.

"The martolos," Ademir said. "They violated her, tortured her, and they killed her! Has no one told you of her fate?"

Jadran threw a bewildered look at Mateo. "Is this true?"

Mateo reached out with both his hands. "Now, brother—!"

"Is it true?! Was Dinora killed by the martolos?!"

Mateo sighed and nodded slowly. "Yes. It is true."

Jadran pounded his fist on the table, rattling the dishes. "How did it happen?!"

"Some years ago, the martolos came to the village of Lezhe as they often did," Mateo said. "I was here in Nin, but mother and Dinora still lived in the house where we were born. Apparently, the martolos followed Dinora home from the market. One of them violated and beat her, while the others held mother, forcing her to witness the attack. Dinora died a few days later from her injuries, and sadly, mother was never the same."

Verena dropped a plate that shattered against the tile floor.

"I have no doubt that with my mother's heart broken, they killed both women!" Jadran barked.

Mateo delivered a heavy sigh, bowing his head.

"Did she identify her attacker?!" Jadran asked.

Mateo threw a glance toward Verena, before turning back toward Jadran. "Before she passed, both she and mother described her attacker as missing a finger on his left hand."

Jadran moaned, slamming his fist down on the table. "Megara Ali!" With an agonizing grimace, he left the table and marched hastily across the courtyard, in the direction of the stable.

"Jadran!" Verena called out. "What are you doing?"

Jadran did not stop to answer, but entered the stable, where he began to saddle Alabaster, as Verena rushed in behind him. "What are you thinking?"

He did not look at her, but worked at fastening the saddle straps. "I'm going to kill Megara Ali!"

"Are you mad? Where will you look for him? You would leave us here?" Verena approached him, grabbing his arm. "Stop this!"

Jadran pulled his arm violently away from her, causing her to lose her balance and fall to the ground. Fearing she was hurt, he reached down to assist her, when he saw Ademir standing before them with a determined glower, pointing the tip of his flat sword at Jadran's midsection.

Jadran slowly lifted Verena to her feet, all the while keeping an eye on Ademir's blade. "What are you doing?" he bellowed.

Ademir breathed heavily. "Once a Janissary, always a Janissary! You will never part with the warrior in you!"

"Lower your sword!" Jadran demanded. "You do not wish a duel with me!"

"Ademir, lower your sword!" Verena exclaimed.

Ademir shouted. "You doubt that I can defeat you with the sword?"

Jadran growled. "Trust me, when I say you will die!"

"Stop this!" Verena screamed. "I love both of you! I will not stand idle and permit the men I love to harm one another! You will have to kill me first!"

442

Slowly, Ademir lowered his sword. Jadran paced toward him and with the speed of a striking serpent grabbed hold of the wrist which clutched the weapon, squeezing it, and keeping the sword pointed downward. He gripped Ademir's neck with his other hand, pushing his head back against a beam.

Jadran pressed his face against Ademir's. "That will be the last time you will ever pull a weapon in this house, and live to tell about it!" He shoved him aside. "I have had enough of this madness! I'm going for a walk!"

* * *

An hour had passed, bringing calm within the household, when Verena wrapped a shawl around her shoulders and set out toward the stone bridge, where she found Jadran leaning against its railing. She approached him, embracing his waist.

Jadran gave her a sober look. "I am sorry about tonight. I think it was the combination of wine and the revelation of Dinora's fate at the hands of the martolos. I allowed my temper to get the best of me."

Verena looked into his eyes. "You have every right to be angry at the martolos. They killed your sister, as well as Jaheem. They were probably involved in Mustafa's death, and they nearly killed you! What man could possibly hold back such anger?" She sighed. "But, we cannot change what is done, Jadran! We cannot bring the dead back from the grave! You must find peace with your past!"

Jadran sighed. "I promise you that I am committed to us. I shall no longer dwell in memories of yesterday." He embraced her. "I will apologize to Ademir in the morning."

"Let's go home, love," she said. "It's been a long day."

CHAPTER

FORTY-FIVE

The following morning, Jadran visited the stable behind Verena's home where he found Ademir saddling his horse. Unassumingly, he stepped up behind him, watching Ademir slip the arquebus strap over his shoulder. "It's been quite some time since I've used such a weapon," Jadran said.

Ademir looked over his shoulder, acknowledging Jadran's presence with a nod.

Jadran moved closer to the horse and began to pet its face. "They say the firearm is the future of warfare, but I have spent my years as a warrior vanquishing foes with the sword, as well as the bow and arrow. Perhaps I am a relic."

"Sometimes the old ways can be best," Ademir replied.

Jadran smiled. "What route will you take to Tuscany?"

Ademir looked at him. "I will journey south down the coast to Zadar, and find passage across the Adriatic to Pesaro. Tuscany lies due west of Pesaro."

"The Ottomans control the Zadar hinterland, so be careful."

Ademir nodded, continuing to tend to the saddle.

Jadran cleared his throat. "I am sorry about last night."

Ademir stopped dressing the horse, and looked at Jadran. "I am sorry, as well. I had too much wine to drink."

"You are a good man, Ademir. You saved the men of the

Ottoman orta I served outside of Berndorf. You saved me that day."

Ademir smiled. "And you spared my life outside of Vienna. For this I will be forever grateful."

"Perhaps God had a purpose for our meeting."

Ademir grinned. "I'm not as close to God as you appear to be, Jadran. But I know my sister is happy and very much in love. You are the right man for her."

Jadran smiled. "I have something for you." He paced over to where Alabaster was stabled, lifting an object resting in the corner. He held it up as he approached, sure now that Ademir could see it was a kilij, and presented it to him. "I no longer have a need for this weapon, but I would be honored if you would have it."

Jadran discerned a sense of reverence in Ademir's demeanor as he held the curved sword. "It is I who am honored," Ademir said. "Thank you, Jadran." He replaced the sword around his waist with the new blade.

"I think you will find it lighter than the straight European blade," Jadran described.

Ademir attached his old sword to the saddle, before resuming his admiration for the gifted one. "Yes, but the weapon is only as good as the man who wields it." He lifted his eyes to Jadran. "I watched you vanquish those men in the forest outside of Vienna. You are the best warrior I have ever seen. Do you have any warrior wisdom for me?"

Jadran scoffed.

"I am serious," Ademir pressed.

Jadran grinned. "Well, I suspect there are many aspiring heroes who took their last breaths on the battlefield because they tried to go it alone. Always remember, two swords are better than one."

Ademir smiled. "Good advice. I shall heed it."

Jadran chuckled. "Enough talk of yesterday. You need to be moving on."

"What are you plans on this beautiful day?" Ademir asked.

"Maybe I shall purchase a boat today. I sense the fishermen in this village are wondering what it is that I do for a living. It may be time to play the part."

Ademir laughed.

"But first—a morning walk with Verena."

"I'm afraid she already has a head start on you," Ademir said. "She said goodbye to me earlier, and described how she planned to take a walk on the bluff near the old St. Nicholas Church. She didn't want to wake you."

Jadran nodded and stepped forward, wrapping his arms around Ademir, as the two men embraced.

"Godspeed Ademir," Jadran offered. "When you have finished in Tuscany, we will welcome your return."

* * *

An hour after he set off on horseback, and about a mile south of Nin, Ademir noticed how a crescent moon, hanging low on the horizon of the bright, blue skyline, had not yet diminished with the sun's rays. Suddenly, his attention became diverted by an oncoming traveler riding a steed. The rider's black kaftan matched the shiny, ebony coat of his horse, as well as the sheepskin kalpak on his head. The stranger brought the animal to a halt, waiting for Ademir to bring his steed alongside of him.

Ademir stopped his horse and nodded.

The man pointed in the direction from whence Ademir came. "Nin?" he called out.

Ademir nodded again and the man raised his left hand in a

gesture of acknowledgment, before moving on. Ademir snapped the reins, returning his horse to a trot, guiding the animal for another fifty rods. Suddenly he brought the steed to a halt. He turned to look back at the stranger, taking a moment to revisit the image in his memory. *Am I mistaken, or was he missing his little finger?*

* * *

Verena had reached the other side of the bridge on the bluff supporting St. Nicholas Church, when she heard the clopping of hooves approaching from behind her. She turned to see a man riding a dark steed.

"*Dobro jutro,*" the man greeted in Croatian from atop the horse. "Pretty woman, I am looking for a friend of mine. His name is Haris. Can you help me?"

Verena's heart began to race, as a worried expression enveloped her face. She lifted her eyes to the dark stranger. "I do not know of anyone with that name."

The man sighed. "Hmm . . . would you know the woman Badra? I believe she may be your age?"

She shook her head, and then noticed how the rider's eyes dropped to her breasts. She looked down, grabbing the amulet hanging from the chain around her neck.

"The evil eye," he said, flashing a look of surprise.

Verena turned away and quickened her pace, moving in the direction of the path that led to the church.

The rider grinned.

* * *

Shortly thereafter, Jadran crossed the stone bridge and began a leisurely pace up the hillside beneath the tower keep of

St. Nicholas Church. When he reached the top of the hill, he scanned the bluff for any sign of Verena, but found none. Sighing disappointedly, he turned to face the front door of the church, when his eyes caught sight of a small object wrapped around the iron door handle. Upon closer inspection, he recognized it to be the necklace he had gifted to Verena.

Suddenly, he heard the name Haris being called out, and looked to the top of the church, seeing two figures positioned in between one of the gaps in the circular keep.

"Haris!" the voice called again.

Jadran could see a man standing beside the terrified Verena, grasping a crop of her hair in one hand, while holding a dagger to her throat with the other. It took all but a dreadful moment for him to recognize the man. "Megara Ali!"

"Haris, I've been searching for you!" Ali yelled out in Turkish. "Come join us here in the keep! It is a stunning view!"

Jadran took a deep breath. *My past has found me!* He sprinted toward the church door.

Inside the small church, Jadran ran to the altar and grabbed a cast iron candleholder that stood waist high. Knocking the wax candle from off it, he carried the object toward the narrow stone stairway set to the right of the altar. Hurriedly, he climbed the winding staircase, but in nearing the top, grew dizzy and lost his balance, dropping to his knees. *"Please God, not now!"*

Jadran shook the haziness from his head. *"Verena!"* Mustering to find energy, he pulled himself to his feet, arriving at the open doorway to the rooftop and rushed outside. There he beheld Ali standing on the opposite side of the keep, continuing to threaten Verena with the dagger.

Ali grinned. "Ah, the vizier has arrived! As you can see, I have finally met your lady!"

Jadran produced a fretful glare. "I am here, Ali! Let her go!"

"Did you think Haris that you could hide from me . . . that you could be safe even beyond the borders of the empire?"

"I am not hiding or running from anything—least of all you, Ali! Believe me, when I tell you I have recently prayed to God for Him to send you my way! We have a score to settle, and He has answered my prayers! Let her go, so that we may settle our differences here and now!"

Ali scoffed. "Very well!" Ali lowered the dagger from her neck, but tugged hard on her hair, pulling her head over the edge of the wall. With his free hand he reached down, lifting her legs, and tossed Verena over the side of the keep.

"Verena!" Jadran yelled, rushing to the wall. Casting his eyes to the ground, he could see her lying face down beside the evergreen trees at the base of the church. "Verena!" he called again, holding his breath until he watched her roll over on her side.

Ali withdrew his sword, before glancing over the side of the tower. "It seems fortunate the trees below have broken her fall! What a pity, for now I will have to kill her too—that is, once I've finished with you!"

"I'm going to kill you, Ali!" Jadran rushed him, extending the candleholder outward.

"You battle me with a candleholder?" Ali scoffed, swinging his sword. "You make this too easy for me, Haris!"

Jadran blocked Ali's sword strokes with the candleholder, but the object could do little more than offer a defense. With a relentless attack, the martolos backed Jadran to the top of the winding stone staircase, forcing him to retreat backward down the stairs. Halfway down the winding steps, he tossed the candleholder at Ali, whose advance was paused by the flying object. His attacker's hesitation allowed Jadran to turn, but once again, overcome with dizziness, he fell forward, tumbling until coming to rest at the bottom of the stairs.

Ali rushed down the stairs with sword drawn, but when he turned the corner of the stairwell, an explosion ensued as an object whistled past him, and he fell backward. Looking out into the church's nave, he could see a man clutching a smoking arquebus.

Disillusioned by his miss with the firearm, Ademir tossed the arquebus to the floor, as Jadran pulled himself into a kneeling position. "Jadran! Here!" Ademir tossed the kilij to Jadran, who snared its handle from out of midair, rising to his feet.

Jadran charged into the stairwell again as Ali, surprised that his opponent was now armed, turned and began running back up the stairs. Jadran pursued him until rushing outside at the top of the keep. Both men squared off against one another, breathing heavily with swords drawn.

Jadran grinned. "Now I have the advantage!"

Ali removed his kalpak and sneered. "What advantage? We both have swords!"

"You forget my past! A Janissary armed with one sword is as good as ten men!"

Jadran could see the arrogance within Ali's face quickly fade. With a move of desperation, the martolos charged Jadran. The clash of steel echoed about the keep from the collision of swords, as both men moved in a circular, warrior dance. Sprightly feet countered one another's steps, and with left arms outstretched, both men worked at maintaining their balance, challenged constantly by the jarring of the swords. The swordsmen battled with ferocity, working carefully at feinting, lunging to strike, and defending appendages from one another's blade.

Ali's situation became more troublesome by the appearance of Ademir, emerging at the top of the stairs.

"You seem to be tiring, Ali!" Jadran teased. "It is much easier to sneak up from behind a defenseless man with a bow string, is it not?"

Ali growled, jabbing his sword; but anticipating the move, Jadran swiftly stepped backward to avoid the blade, slicing Ali's arm above the elbow. The martolos winced and fell back to the wall, as Jadran rushed his wounded opponent; however, when he neared Ali, his vision was drawn to the height of the keep, which began to spin rapidly, forcing him to pause. The martolos sliced deep into Jadran's thigh, causing him to cry out and bend forward. Ali shifted closer, moving to thrust his blade down on him. Jadran shook away the lightheadedness in time to block the strike, and buried his head into Ali's stomach, driving him backward over the wall. The martolos grabbed hold of Jadran's vest, dragging him over the side of the keep. Together they plummeted downward, losing the grip on their weapons, and crashed hard onto the yew trees below.

After watching both men disappear, Ademir turned, rushing back down the stairwell and through the church, emerging at the front door. Outside he found Ali sluggishly rising to a standing position, before retrieving his sword. Ademir rushed to his horse, and removed his flat sword from its sheath. He spun to see Ali beginning an approach toward Jadran, who lie motionless a few rods away.

"Martolos!" Ademir exclaimed.

Ali turned to face Ademir and growled. "Run landsknecht! This is not your fight!" The agony in his face evolved into a wicked grin. "It would only make my day more gratifying if given the opportunity to kill you as well as them!"

Ali stood his ground, as Ademir charged him, swinging his flat sword at the martolos' waist, but Ali blocked the strike. The weight of his sword pulled Ademir forward and Ali clubbed him at the back of the head with his forearm. Ademir tumbled face down at Ali's feet and the martolos raised his sword vertically, blade down, clutching the handle with both hands.

Suddenly, the cry of "Dinora!" could be heard, and Ali spun to see Jadran wearing a determined glower, carrying his sword and dragging his bloodied leg in a march toward the martolos.

"Dinora?" Ali questioned.

"My sister—whom you killed! I seek vengeance for her death, as well as for the deaths of Jaheem, Mustafa—" Jadran clenched his teeth. "And my mother!"

Ali scowled, raising his sword, unaware that Ademir had pulled himself into a kneeling position behind him. As the martolos began to move toward Jadran, Ademir grabbed the flat sword and thrust the tip of the blade into Ali's lower back. The martolos' body stiffened just as Jadran stepped before him, raised his sword with both hands and swung, beheading Ali with a single blow. The soaring head plunged to the ground, rolling down the hillside, while the headless body fell forward to the ground.

Breathing heavily, Jadran assisted Ademir to his feet. "Verena!" Jadran remembered and turned to rush toward her, finding her in a sitting position.

"My love!" Jadran cried out, dropping down beside her.

"I am all right, Jadran!" She breathed heavily. "Cuts and bruises from the trees, but I am all right!"

The two lovers embraced, before Verena caught sight of Jadran's injury. "Your leg, Jadran! We must dress the wound!"

Jadran winced, before smiling as he gazed into her teary emerald eyes.

Ademir joined them and dropped to his knees. "You are my friend, Jadran—my future brother-in-law, and my hero!"

"You are the real hero, Ademir—for you came back. I could never have vanquished him without you!"

Ademir nodded. "Two swords are better than one!"

Jadran smiled. "Yes—two swords!" He grimaced from a shot of pain streaking through his body. "I do not envy you though, for now you must journey from this near bout with death, to the killing fields of Tuscany."

Ademir produced a forlorn gaze, resting a hand on Jadran's shoulder. "Hmm . . . I think it may be time to take your advice, and place my landsknecht days behind me. Have you the need for another fisherman in your boat?"

"Only should your use of a fishing rod prove more skillful than your accuracy with an arquebus."

Both men grinned.

Verena did not share in the levity. "Jadran, will other men follow in the footsteps of this vanquished monster, and try to hunt you down?"

Jadran leaned forward and embraced Verena. He gazed upward at the morning sky, barely able to discern the dwindling outline of the fading crescent moon. "No, my love. I believe my past is at peace."

THE END

GLOSSARY

Agha – honorable title for an Ottoman officer

Akces – silver coins that were the chief monetary unit of the Ottoman Empire

Allah Hu Akbar – Arabic phrase meaning: God is great.

Ana – Turkish word for mother

Arquebus – long gun of the sixteenth century

As-salaam Alaikum – Arabic phrase meaning: Peace be upon you.

Baba – Turkish word for father

Bedouin – a nomadic Arab of the desert

Beylerbey – high ranking Ottoman commander

Boluk – company of soldiers

Boluk-agha – commander of a *boluk* (company) equivalent to a lieutenant

Boluk-bashi – commander of a *boluk* (company) equivalent to a captain

Bork – headgear of Ottoman soldiers

Corbaci – commander of an *orta* (regiment) equivalent to a colonel

Devshirme – Ottoman prisoners of war, hostages, or slaves purchased by the state

Dobro jutro – Croatian phrase meaning: Good morning.

Doge – chief magistrate of Venice

Dolama – coats worn by Ottoman *Janissaries*

Druze – a member of a political and Islamic sect living in Lebanon and Syria

Enderun – Interior Service of the Ottoman Imperial Court

Eski Saray – Turkish terms meaning old palace

Et Maydani – meat market in Constantinople (Istanbul)

Eyalet – a province

Falaka - punishment

Gedliki – Ottoman maids in waiting

Ghazi – Ottoman warrior hero

Gulden – gold coin

Hammam – Turkish bath

Harem – group composed of wives, female servants, concubines, eunuchs, female relatives all in service to the sultan

Haseki – mother of a *sehzade* (prince)

Iftar – evening meal taken at sunset during Ramadan

Imam – a person who leads prayer within a mosque

Jambya – a specific dagger with a short, curved blade

Janissary – elite fighting force of Ottoman sultans

Kadin – title given to a woman of the Sultan's harem

Kaftan – a man's long, belted tunic

Kapikulu Sipahi – *Janissary* cavalry

Kapudan – grand admiral of the Ottoman navy

Kaylon – first Ottoman warship with sails

Khitan – Arabic term for circumcision

Kilij – a one-handed, single edged, curved saber used by the Ottomans

Kizlar agasi – head of the eunuchs that guarded the imperial *harem*

Landsknecht – a German mercenary of the sixteenth century

Mamluk – a state that ruled Egypt between the thirteenth and sixteenth centuries

Martolos – an internal security force of the Ottoman Empire located in Rumelia (Balkan Peninsula)

Merhaba – Turkish word for hello

Millet – independent court of law pertaining to provinces within the Ottoman Empire

Minaret – a type of tower built adjacent to mosques from which the faithful are called to pray

Mirahur-I ewel – the chief supervisor of the Ottoman Imperial stables

Muezzin – person who proclaims the call to daily prayer in Islam from a minaret

Orta – Ottoman commander of a regiment

Ossuary – a container in which bones of dead people are placed

Pasha – high rank or office of the Ottoman Empire

Salat al-maghrib – one of the five mandatory daily prayers of Islam

Sanjak - administrative divisions of the Ottoman Empire

Sanjak-bey – high ranking official of a *sanjak*

Sapper – a soldier who performs a variety of military engineering duties such as mining

Sasuka – popular Turkish dish prepared with fried vegetables and tomato sauce

Sehzade – Ottoman prince

Serasker – title given to a vizier who commands an Ottoman army

Silahdar – *Janissary* bodyguards of the sultan and his family

Silahdar Agha – commander of the *Janissary* bodyguards who protect the sultan's family

Sipahis – Ottoman cavalry

Subha – Islamic prayer beads

Suhoor – pre-dawn meal of Muslims before beginning the day's fast during Ramadan

Tallit – Jewish prayer shawl

Tercio – Spanish military unit during the sixteenth century

Timarli – Ottoman cavalry composed specifically of Turks

Valide Sultan – Queen mother of the sultan

Vizier – the second most powerful administrative position in the Ottoman Empire after the sultan

Yarmulkes – a skullcap worn in public by orthodox Jewish males

Yeniceri agasi – Ottoman commander-in-chief of the *Janissary*

Yeni Saray – Turkish terms meaning new palace

ACKNOWLEDGEMENTS

I would like to thank my publisher Suzanne Fyhrie Parrott for devoting her expertise, enthusiasm, and guidance into bringing this literary project of mine to life.

ABOUT THE AUTHOR

Mark Macedonia was a Social Studies teacher within the Seneca Valley School District of Western Pennsylvania, where he spent over three decades teaching AP World History and United States History to high school students.

He holds a Bachelor of Arts Degree in communication from St. Bonaventure University, and a Masters of Arts in Teaching Degree from the University of Pittsburgh.

He published his first novel, *The Soles of Cyrus Eblis,* in February 2019. *Beneath a Crescent Moon* is his second novel.

Mark resides in Pittsburgh with his wife, Sandy, and their golden retriever Thor.

More about Mark on FirstStepsPublishing.com
Follow Mark on Twitter: @Mark.Mace625

Printed in Great Britain
by Amazon